HUMAN FACTORS IN HIGHWAY TRAFFIC SAFETY RESEARCH

WILEY SERIES IN HUMAN FACTORS

Edited by David Meister

Human Factors in Quality Assurance

Douglas H. Harris and Frederick B. Chaney

Man-Machine Simulation Models

Arthur I. Siegel and J. Jay Wolf

Human Factors Applications in Teleoperator Design and Operation

Edwin G. Johnsen and William R. Corliss

Human Factors: Theory and Practice

David Meister

Human Factors in Highway Traffic Safety Research

T. W. Forbes, Editor

Human Factors in Highway Traffic Safety Research

Edited by

T. W. FORBES

Michigan State University
East Lansing

WILEY-INTERSCIENCE, a Division of John Wiley & Sons, Inc.

New York • London • Sydney • Toronto

Library of Congress Catalog Card Number: 77-37783

ISBN 0-471-26560-8

Printed in the United States of America.

10 9 8 7 6 5 4 3 2 1

SERIES PREFACE

Technology is effective to the extent that men can operate and maintain the machines they design. Equipment design which consciously takes advantage of human capabilities and constrains itself within human limitations amplifies and increases system output. If it does not, system performance is reduced and the purpose for which the equipment was designed is endangered. This consideration is even more significant today than in the past because the highly complex systems that we develop are pushing human functions more and more to their limits of efficient performance.

How can one ensure that machine and machine operations are actually designed for human use? Behavioral data, principles, and recommendations—in short, the Human Factors discipline—must be translated into meaningful design practices. Concepts like ease of operation or error-free performance must be interpretable in hardware and system terms.

Human Factors is one of the newer engineering disciplines. Perhaps because of this, engineering and human-factors specialists lack a common orientation with which their respective disciplines can communicate. The goal of the Wiley Human Factors Series is to help in the communication process by describing what behavioral principles mean for system design and by suggesting the behavioral research that must be performed to solve design problems. The premise on which the series is based and on which each book is written is that Human Factors has utility only to the degree that it supports engineering development; hence the Series emphasizes the *practical application* to design of human-factors concepts.

Because of the many talents on which Human Factors depends for its implementation (design and systems engineering, industrial and experimental psychology, anthropology, physiology, and operations research, to name only a few), the Series is directed to as wide an audience as possible. Each book is intended to illustrate the usefulness of Human

Factors to some significant aspect of system development, such as human factors in design or testing or simulation. Although cookbook answers are not provided, it is hoped that this pragmatic approach will enable the many specialists concerned with problems of equipment design to solve these problems more efficiently.

David Meister
Series Editor

PREFACE

The importance of human factors in highway safety has been recognized for many years. Concern about safety on the streets and highways led to the calling of a first national conference on that subject in 1924 by Herbert Hoover, then Secretary of Commerce. As a result the first research project on "Psychological Principles in Automotive Driving" was set up under the auspices of the National Academy of Sciences–National Research Council at Ohio State University in 1927.

Since then numerous private, university, and government organizations and individuals have carried on research and other activities in attempts to ameliorate the problem. Not until 1966, however, when Congress passed the National Highway Safety Act, was the full importance of highway safety and its significance to the nation as a whole officially recognized.

The human factors research that has been done during the past 40 years applies to all facets of driving behavior. It relates to the various phases of driver education and training, highway and traffic engineering, driver licensing, traffic enforcement, public safety education, and other fields.

The research often was carried on with very limited facilities and support and by many investigators working independently on small studies. Reports appeared in a variety of journals and other publications that were scattered and are often difficult to find. A number of recent literature reviews and state-of-the-art studies are more helpful. Nevertheless, those who have not followed the human factors research in these various fields need to have some of these wide-ranging research results brought together and summarized.

For these reasons it seemed timely to gather and present some of this information on human factors in highway traffic and safety research. Although it is not easy to present such a wide range of material in a brief and easily intelligible form, it seemed that investigators who had been working in this field for some years could do it to best advantage. Therefore, the contributing authors to this book represent some of the many people who have been engaged in this field of research and who are not only familiar with the work of others but also have made noteworthy contributions themselves.

The aim of this book is to present an overall view of work that has been done in human factors relating to highway traffic and safety research. It summarizes and gives highlights and essentials of the early work in the various areas. It also reviews more recent studies in the various fields of highway traffic and safety research represented by the chapter headings.

The terms "human factors approach" or "engineering psychology approach," as used here, indicate the designing of the man-machine-environment task and/or system to fit human capabilities whenever possible. In areas where research has been based largely on other psychological viewpoints, the work is summarized, "human factors" approaches noted, and other approaches suggested.

It is not always possible to specify human behavior quantitatively, although progress is being made in that direction. However, certain principles can often be formulated concerning general relationships applicable to certain types of human performance. Such principles are included wherever possible.

The book is intended for practitioners in the traffic field who desire to become acquainted with the human factors applications. It is also aimed at students in introductory courses in engineering psychology or human factors engineering and in continuing education courses dealing with highway safety research. Therefore, the attempt has been to summarize and give the essentials but at the same time not to do violence to the accuracy with which the results of key studies are presented. It is hoped that the material will be found to be technically accurate though expressed in language understandable to those becoming acquainted with the field for the first time and to practitioners in different aspects of the traffic safety field.

To achieve this aim it was necessary to select, from the very large amount of work in various areas, research that is representative or illustrative of the different approaches. The references list studies reviewed and other reports that are to be consulted by the reader who wishes to obtain further information on a particular subject.

The book attempts to present the essentials of this very wide field of human factors research applied to highway traffic and safety. Each contributor summarizes for his particular area some human factors studies and results, in some cases giving examples and in others indicating where further information and applications of the human factors approach are needed.

Chapter 1 notes the social importance of the problem and summarizes some of the early studies of human factors in highway traffic and safety. The methods of the human factors research approach are outlined in Chapter 2. Chapter 3 describes driving task simulators, thus treating one of the characteristic human factors methods in more detail because of its importance.

Following chapters summarize research on characteristics and abilities of drivers, factors in sign legibility, other methods of presenting information to drivers, and driver judgments and skills in operating vehicles in traffic.

Next come treatments of certain special areas. Research on driving problems in the military setting may be viewed as one area of driving with special characteristics. But results are also applicable to civilian driving.

Human factors information in vehicle design is of great importance if drivers are to use their vehicles most efficiently and with fewest misperceptions and errors.

Another phase of traffic involves the pedestrian, his characteristics, and the problems of providing for his necessary movements. Often overlooked is the fact that everyone is at times a pedestrian.

Human factors research for evaluating and improving driver education has received less attention than its importance warrants. Such research, contributing to improved methods, should yield high returns.

Several chapters discuss factors known to cause various degrees of driving performance impairment. Studies of driver fatigue, effects of alcohol and drugs, and psychosocial factors all affect driving behavior. These are complex fields where more of the human factors research approach is needed.

The last two chapters examine the procedures for influencing drivers. Research on driver improvement treats methods and problems of retraining drivers with high accident or violation records or other indications of unsafe driving. And, finally, a presentation of modification and control of driver behavior by the legal system compares two approaches, the more recent applying human factors techniques to the system.

Thus the various chapters describe human factors methods and research results of interest to those in traffic engineering, enforcement, licensing, and driver education. Applications to public traffic safety education are not treated separately. However, most of the information will be of interest to the driving public and to those engaged in educating the driving public in traffic operation and safety.

It is hoped that this presentation of "human factors" information will be of interest and assistance to all of those working toward more efficient and safe highway traffic.

T. W. FORBES

East Lansing, Michigan
November 1971

ACKNOWLEDGMENTS

Preparation of a book of this sort requires the efforts of a great many people. As coordinating author, it is my pleasure to express appreciation to all of the contributing authors. Without exception they took the time from very busy schedules to develop their contributions, mainly because of a desire to make the information available and to further the interest and usefulness of human factors research applications in highway and traffic safety areas.

On behalf of the contributing authors, I should like to express thanks for the assistance of the many people without whose efforts the preparation of manuscripts and other materials would have been impossible. I wish also to thank the various authors and organizations which granted permission to use certain previously published materials.

For the original suggestion that such a book might be timely, I am indebted to Dr. David Meister, the series editor, and for suggestions and advice in arranging of the book to Gerald Galbo of the publisher's staff.

Also, the advice, counsel, encouragement, and backing of individual contributors and of colleagues at Michigan State University and elsewhere have been of great assistance. Special thanks go to Professor Gordon Sheehe, Director of the MSU Highway Traffic Safety Center, for making possible assistance with communications, copying, and other facilities. And finally, my personal thanks go to Mrs. June Schover, Mrs. Nancy Evans, and Mrs. Linda O'Leary and others for assistance in preparing many drafts, copies, and correspondence and to my wife, Louise, for encouragement, assistance and forbearance during preparation, collection, and arrangement of materials for the book.

T. W. F.

CONTENTS

HUMAN FACTORS IN HIGHWAY TRAFFIC SAFETY RESEARCH

I

INTRODUCTION

T. W. Forbes

Theodore W. Forbes is professor of psychology and research adviser on the staff of the Highway Traffic Safety Center at Michigan State University, East Lansing, Michigan. He was previously assistant director for Research of the MSU Highway Traffic Safety Center; Program Director of Highway Research, American Institute for Research, Pittsburgh; Technical Director, Committee on Highway Safety Research, National Research Council; visiting professor, Institute of Transportation and Traffic Engineering, University of California, Los Angeles; associate professor and chairman of Psychology, University of Hawaii; research assistant professor at the Yale Bureau of Traffic Research, and the Harvard Bureau of Traffic Research; and lecturer at Columbia University. Additional research positions in National Defense Research were at the Harvard Psycho-Acoustic Laboratory, Stevens Institute of Technology, and the University of Pennsylvania.

His Ph.D. degree was obtained in applied experimental psychology at Ohio State University. He has published research reports on various human factors problems, applying psychological techniques to such problems as highway sign legibility and visibility, driver testing, accident proneness, psychological applications to traffic engineering, near-accident analysis, human factors engineering, and highway safety research.

Dr. Forbes is a fellow of the American Psychological Association, and two of its divisions, and of the Human Factors Society. He is a member of the Acoustical Society and associate member of the Institute of Traffic Engineers and of the Operations Research Society of America. He has served on several committees of the Highway Research Board of the National Academy of Sciences—National Research Council, and on panels for other organizations.

SAFE HIGHWAY TRANSPORTATION—A MAJOR SOCIAL PROBLEM

The amazing development of the automobile and adaptations of it to move people and goods has made it a very important method of transportation which touches every facet of American life. The automobile has become so familiar and so widely used by almost every citizen that we sometimes take it for granted. Basically the purpose of the highway transportation system as a whole is to move people and goods efficiently and safely. This purpose has been recognized specifically by the Institute of Traffic Engineers (1969) as well as by other organizations in the highway transportation field. Thus the economy of the United States and our general way of life has become highly dependent upon truck, bus, and individual automobile transportation.

Individual automobile transportation contributes not only to our economic well-being but also to enjoyment of life of the vast majority of Americans. If anyone doubts this, let him try going without his car for a short time. Shopping becomes inconvenient, members of the family find it difficult to meet their appointments, and weekend recreation is hampered. In large cities and between cities bus transportation and other types of mass transportation are of major importance. But even so the individual auto is a valued possession, and withdrawal of driving privileges meets strenuous objection.

From the opposite viewpoint, there are losses to society from the large-scale use of automobiles. Air pollution problems have been noted recently and represent a separate field. But over the years losses from crashes both in monetary value and in loss of life and injury have been widely documented. Motor vehicle "accidents" resulted in 56,400 deaths and two million injuries in 1969. The equivalent monetary loss for 1969 has been estimated as approximately $12.2 billion (National Safety Council, 1970). Thus the importance of highway transportation and safety to the social well-being of the people of the United States is clear. Increasingly, a somewhat similar situation exists in other countries of the world as well.

HUMAN FACTORS BASIC TO MOTOR VEHICLE POPULARITY

It is widely recognized by those who have worked for many years in the field of highway transportation and highway safety that human factors have been basic to the development and the popularity of the motor vehicle. Only in these terms can we explain why the automobile has replaced other modes of transportation to such a great degree. Even though automobile ownership is not cheap in comparison to riding mass transit (where this is still available), most families in the United States own at least one and often several motor vehicles, sometimes at a sacrifice in other areas.

Among human factors shown to be responsible, convenience and time saving are two which have been of great influence. Increased variety of trips available, greater choice of route, and one's departure time, all play their part. Also, especially for a large family, the automobile may furnish vacation travel economy.

Many other factors have been pointed to by various observers of our "nation on wheels." Among these are prestige factors of owning expensive cars, appeal of high-performance automobiles, and pride in the sleek appearance or the handling capabilities of our high-performance cars.

HUMAN FACTORS UNDERLYING SAFETY PROBLEMS

The wide range of human behaviors involved in motor vehicle driving leads to the critical importance of human factor problems in highway safety. It has been clear almost from the first studies that errors, lapses, and limitations of automobile drivers were involved in 75 to 90 percent and, at least in part, responsible for a vast majority of mishaps. For example, Baker (1930) reported nine out of 10 accidents attributable to "personal causes." But it has not proved easy to isolate combinations of causal factors and remedies for these human lapses.

Thus the very convenience and the resulting wide range of users and uses of the motor vehicle responsible for its great popularity also contribute major difficulties in solving problems of safe and efficient traffic operation.

COMPLEXITY OF THE FIELD

The variety of components of the driving task, and the wide range of people, conditions, and purposes of driving, lead to problems which often seem simple on the surface, but which prove on further examination to be highly complex. For instance, one of the early theories was that a few "accident-prone" drivers caused most of the trouble, and that if these could be found and eliminated, most of the highway safety problem could be solved. Unfortunately, this has not proved to be the case.

OPERATION OF THE MAN—VEHICLE—HIGHWAY SYSTEM

Studies of individual driver and vehicle behavior have yielded much basic information. More such studies are needed but the results can become really meaningful and useful only when the driver–vehicle–highway–environment system is analyzed to show interactions and interrelationships. Each component of the system may contribute either to efficiency of traffic operation or to blocking of flow and inefficiency, with which safety problems are often associated.

The rapidly increasing annual motor vehicle mileage is well known, and again reflects the popularity and usefulness of automotive transportation. Improvements in vehicles and in both secondary roads and interstate highways have made this increase possible. The result is not only greater utility of vehicles, but also much more complex driving tasks presented to the human operator. Although more attention is often given to the highways and the characteristics of vehicles, it should be recognized and stressed that the human operators of these vehicles are critical parts of the system.

THEORIES OF ACCIDENT CAUSATION

What might be called the "driver culpability theory" was and still is often accepted. In other words, there is a tendency to blame the driver for inefficiencies and breakdowns in the system, and especially for accident occurrence. Clearly the driver must do his part, must remain alert, must make proper judgments and responses to the increasingly complex situations which confront him in modern traffic. And for a small group of drivers, special characteristics may result in repeated accidents. However, this is not by any means the whole story.

A quite different point of view may be called the "driver overload" theory. An early formulation of a multiple-factor theory of accident causation pointed out that not only multiple factors of highway and vehicle but also errors, misjudgments, or lapses on the part of several different drivers simultaneously may be involved in the causation of motor vehicle accidents. Thus adequate judgment and response by one driver may prevent a crash that might have resulted from an error of another driver (Forbes, 1950). Only in these terms can one account for the fact that traffic accidents, although entirely too frequent, are very rare events as compared to the opportunities for accidents. This fact and the multiple activities and distractions required were emphasized in a driving task description by the National Research Council Committee on Highway Safety Research (1952).

More recently Ross (1960) analyzed the driver's task in relation to requirements presented by the vehicle and highway system; and, Blumenthal (1968) noted fluctuation of requirements imposed by the system which, at unpredictable times, may overload the capabilities of the driver.

THE "HUMAN FACTORS" APPROACH

Definition and Need

The fields now known as "human factors," "human factors engineering," and "engineering psychology" all designate an attempt to design man–machine–environment systems to fit the capabilities and limitations of the people who will use them (Chapanis, Garner, and Morgan, 1949; McCormick, 1957, 1964; Chapanis, 1965). Essentially, human factors engineering applies the basic information obtained by engineering psychology, applied physiology, and related sciences to practical problems. The objective is to describe and predict the human capabilities required by system-imposed tasks; and then to design or redesign tasks to accommodate the abilities of the majority of users. This approach developed rapidly during and after World War II in aviation and other military equipment design.

However, a decade earlier, psychological or "human engineering" data were developed to aid traffic engineers in providing traffic facilities better adapted to the motorist's needs and abilities (Lauer, 1932; Matson and Forbes, 1938; Forbes, 1939). The traffic engineer's need for human factors information was pointed out, and data then available were summarized on sign design, overtaking and passing distances, and studies of driver behavior on different highway designs. Two summaries of earlier studies reported "human engineering" data in practical form for use by traffic engineers. This human factors approach was presented as a "positive and promising approach to the problem of both traffic efficiency and traffic safety" (Forbes, 1941; National Research Council, 1952). Further, the importance of designing vehicle controls, work space and visibility to accommodate most operators was voiced by McFarland (1952). And again the important role of human factors engineering in highway safety was emphasized more recently (McFarland, 1963). Finally, Leisch (1968) effectively described many highway problems involving human factors which are of critical interest from the point of view of the traffic engineer, himself.

Broader Definition

The term "human factors" is sometimes used in a broader sense. As noted, the pertinent characteristics and abilities of groups of intended users must be known as a basis for "human engineering." To design or modify the task required of the operator by the system, a team of engineers and human factors people together with designers, pilots, or other users applies the results of research to the immediate problem. The human is a social being, and much of his operation in any system is, at least in part, a team operation. Therefore, various phases of ability, judgment, perception, personality, motivation in social behavior, as well as in the individual alone, must be considered if system tasks are to be designed so that people can successfully carry them out. Thus, all factors affecting behavior of the human in the transportation system can be considered broadly a part of the "human factors approach."

Although early traffic safety research was based largely on a "driver selection" point of view, much of the information acquired can be formulated to serve as a human factors guide for the improvement of traffic engineering and safety approaches (Forbes, 1941; Forbes and Katz, 1957). When thus formulated, the results of this early work should be included as a part of the human factors approach to highway and traffic safety research.

BEGINNINGS OF THE HUMAN FACTORS APPROACH IN HIGHWAY AND SAFETY RESEARCH

Early Research on the Driver

The first research program on driver behavior and traffic safety resulted from recommendations of a committee of the National Academy of Sciences—National Research Council in Washington. Later programs involved other sponsors and resulted in research at a number of different universities. Examples of research will be summarized by their location for the period from about 1927 to 1955 because the earliest research activities were restricted pretty much to certain universities. This summary should not be considered as complete coverage of such research, however.

Psychology of the Driver—Ohio State University

From 1927 to 1929 a series of studies of psychology of the driver at Ohio State University was sponsored by a committee of the National Research Council and backed by a grant of $2000 for equipment. Such was the modest start! Weiss and Lauer (1930) edited a preliminary report of 14 different subprojects by several investigators. The existence of a small group of drivers with more than their share of accidents was noted. The selection idea of identifying them for possible remedial treatment or restriction from driving was the objective.

Lauer (Chapter 4*) reported an accident study of three groups of students and others totaling 357 people using interview and written questions. He reported that about 7.5 percent sustained about 50 percent of the accidents. Burtt (Chapter 5) tested out a criterion for safe driving using a checklist and observational method. Lauer and Weiss (Chapters 6 and 7) reported a study of driving responses and coordination which used a pursuit (or "tracking") task with automotive controls. Other apparatus measured eye, hand, and foot coordination. A total of 450 drivers allowed comparison of "accident" and "nonaccident" groups. Burtt and Forbes (Chapter 9) studied laboratory estimation of velocity of a moving pointer target. Forbes (Chapter 10) developed a moving belt, "miniature highway," driving task simulator. Dennis (Chapter 17) analyzed social characteristics of 693 drivers with traffic convictions (accident, speeding, reckless) compared to a random sample (470) from police records and from the city directory of Lansing, Michigan. Some significant differences were found in the different studies, but various limitations of the accident record data were noted.

Lauer and others in remaining chapters studied head movements, foveal and peripheral reaction time, and vision in driving. Lauer and Forbes (Chapter 18) analyzed 538 accident records of a fleet of 400 commercial drivers. Low speeds and 22 percent "standing" accidents reflect city traffic conditions in those days.

The "miniature highway" driving task simulator used an endless canvas belt about 20 feet long, which provided visual motion of the roadway toward the driver and of same-direction and on-coming miniature cars (see Figure 1). Looking over a miniature car hood through an eyepiece (1 inch high by about 3 inches wide) the driver could steer, accelerate and decelerate to overtake and dodge two-direction traffic of miniature cars.

Performance on this simulator later was related to estimates of speed carried out experimentally on a 1-mile stretch of test road (Forbes, 1932). Subjects estimated the point of passing a target car approaching the observer's car at speeds unknown to the subject. The observer's car always operated at the same speed. Correlations in the range of .42 to .55 were found between certain simulator scores and the road test.

Perhaps the most striking result, however, was the occurrence in the full-scale road tests of very large errors in speed estimation (from 30 to 50 percent of the distance from the judgment point to the passing point of the two cars) (Forbes, 1931). Average error ranged between 8 and 12 yards, but individual errors ran as high as 50 out of 200 yards distance

* Chapters here refer to Weiss and Lauer (1930).

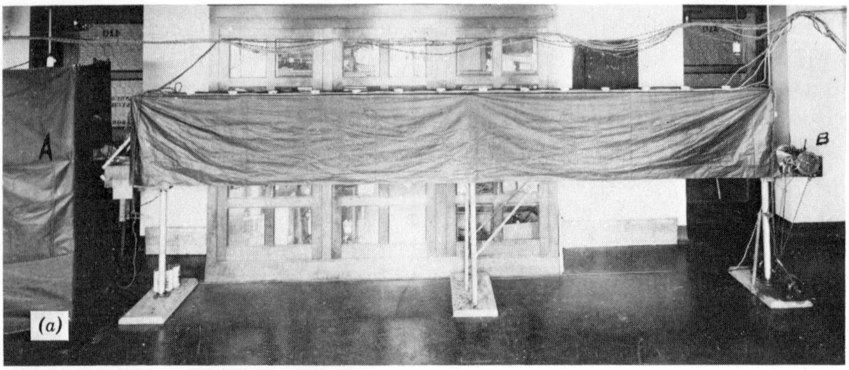

Figure 1. An early driving task simulator—the original "miniature highway." (*a*) Side view; (*b*) End view. A: driver's screen and eyepiece; B: planetary gearing control for canvas-belt roadway and miniature traffic traveling in opposite directions; C: canvas-belt roadway; D: steel tape carrying miniature cars toward eyepiece; E: simulated telephone pole; F: driver's eyepiece representing front of his car. (From T. W. Forbes, Chapter 10 in Weiss and Lauer, 1930, p. 74.)

between cars at the last point allowed for judgment. Expectancy apparently often outweighed the effect of actual on-coming velocity.

This study represents one of the first attempts to correlate driving task simulator scores with measurements of a similar driver ability in an experimentally isolated driving task on a highway.

Iowa State College Studies

In late 1930, Lauer transferred to Iowa State where he developed a "driver test clinic" approach. Vision tests, glare resistance, eye-hand-foot coordination, time to read signs, and license plate legibility studies were reported (Lauer, 1932; Lauer and Helwig, 1932).

Research in sign letter design and obstacle visibility and in various driver vision problems followed (e.g., Uhlaner, 1941; Stalder and Lauer, 1954). The driver laboratory conducted driver education and accident research. One of the earliest accident record studies analyzed a two-year sample of 7692 Iowa drivers' records (1948 and 1949) with 1806 total recorded accidents. Expected accidents by age group and reported mileage, when compared to actual accidents, showed 18 to 20, 21 to 23, and 54 to 56-year-old males significantly high. The need for care in making such comparisons was illustrated by plots of skewed distributions and variability around mean values (Lauer, 1952).

Massachusetts and Harvard Driver Studies

In 1933 DeSilva started work with driver testing equipment at Massachusetts State College, and later directed the "driver test clinic" program at the Harvard Bureau for Street Traffic Research from 1935 to 1938. A "steering," brake reaction time and "vigilance" test (simultaneous steering and braking) together with vision and glare tests and the Forbes "miniature highway" test were developed and made portable. Drivers were tested with this battery in various New England cities. Accident records of drivers called in because of poor driving records and of groups of volunteers were compared. A semiclinical approach was used in attempting to reeducate drivers.

A number of statistically significant differences were found in test scores of repeater and volunteer groups, but not consistently in the same scores for the different cities (DeSilva and Forbes, 1937).

In one city, a nine-month comparison of accident records before and after treatment showed a drop of about 68 percent in accidents for 98 repeaters given generalized safety education *only,* whereas 101 repeaters who *also* went through the test clinics showed a greater drop (87 percent) (Forbes, 1938).

Some of this reduction represented regression toward the mean to be expected since both groups had high accident records (two or more accidents in the previous nine months). Both groups may have been affected by the generalized safety campaign. But the 19 percent greater reduction in accident experience for the "clinic" group was thought to indicate greater learning and "compensation" by that group of drivers.

Perception Response Times—Harvard

Driver response times for differing complexity of task were measured in several of the programs studying psychology of the driver. These were shown to average about 0.5 second for simple response time to 0.75 second or more for complex response time. Driver responses were measured on devices using brake pedals and randomly presented signals while the driver was carrying on a tracking type of task (following a moving pointer or a simulated roadway scene) (DeSilva and Forbes, 1937).

Brake response time to an unexpected stimulus was demonstrated on the road by others in connection with driver education. A device attached to the bumper* fired two small cartridges of marker dye onto the pavement. The first shot fired by an instructor riding in the vehicle served as a signal to the driver to apply the brake. The second was triggered mechanically by vehicle deceleration. Measurement of distance to the point of actual stoppage then illustrated response time and stopping distance at a given speed.

DeSilva published a summary after moving to Yale and separating from the Bureau of Street Traffic Research titled *Why We Have Automobile Accidents* (1942).

Search for the Accident-Prone Driver

Bingham (1931) reported reduction of accidents of Boston bus lines and street railway operators by an accident record and clinical interview approach. He found that some drivers had two or three times as many accidents as the average driver—sometimes trivial but sometimes serious—often due to bad driving habits. He called for location of "accident-prone" drivers and remedial work by society.

Connecticut Accident Record and Test Research—Iowa State, Harvard, and National Research Council

A series of studies of traffic conditions was authorized in 1936 and carried out under the sponsorship of the U.S. Bureau of Public Roads. One of these studies, carried out under the National Academy of Sciences

* Developed and made available for driver education by the American Automobile Association.

—National Research Council, consisted of two parts: (1) an accident record study and (2) testing of 3600 drivers.

The first part analyzed accident records of almost 30,000 drivers in Connecticut from 1931 to 1936. In addition, accident records of certain Massachusetts drivers and several commercial fleets were studied. Analysis of accident records by age groups showed very high rates for drivers in the age group under 25 years, with a falling rate thereafter up to about age 60 or 65. These rates were not corrected for mileage driven, for which data were not available.

Drivers who had two or more accidents comprised 3.9 percent of the total and had 36.4 percent of the accidents of the total sample of 29,531 drivers. Accident records were available for a total of six years. When divided into two three-year periods, drivers having zero, one, two, three, and four accidents in the first three-year period were shown to have a rising ratio of accidents per driver for the second three-year period ranging from 0.1 to 0.7 accident per driver.

It was concluded that prediction of accident rate was possible on an "actuarial" basis for a large group but was not accurate enough for licensing individual drivers. These data were interpreted also as evidence for a small group of drivers who were "accident prone," and a larger group who were "accident free." Better training of young drivers was recommended because of their high accident record, and the need for teaching proper attitude and responsible judgment was suggested (Secretary of Agriculture, 1938).

The second part of this study involved the testing of over 3600 drivers.* Of this total, slightly over 3100 drivers had been continuously licensed in Connecticut which allowed psychophysical and interview test scores to be correlated with accident records. "Accidents per year of licensure" was the criterion used. The average period continuously licensed was 9.2 years. A multiple-correlation analysis was carried out using scores from both batteries of tests. The resulting maximum multiple-correlation coefficient using 22 test scores was +.350.

A sequential sorting method was also tried with cutting scores for best discrimination from 12 of the tests. It was noted that the overlap of "accident" and "free" groups was rather large even though significant multiple-correlation coefficients and sequential discrimination were obtained. Therefore, the selection of drivers by such means for licensing would not be practical (Cobb, 1938).

* Carried out in Hartford, Connecticut jointly by the Iowa State University Driving Laboratory under the direction of Dr. A. R. Lauer and the Harvard Traffic Bureau Driving Research Laboratory under the direction of Dr. H. R. DeSilva and Dr. T. W. Forbes. The project was directed for the National Research Council by Drs. H. M. Johnson and P. W. Cobb.

Accidents and the Normal Driver

Later to see what part the "normal" driver played as compared to accident repeaters, the accident data of Johnson and Cobb for the sample of 29,531 Connecticut drivers were analyzed further by Forbes (1939a). The accident frequency of operators in the first three-year period (1931 to 1933) was compared with the record of the same operators for the following three-year period. The resulting percentages indicated that of the 3.9 percent of operators who had two or more accidents in the six-year period, in the first three years only 1.33 percent had two or more accidents. If these drivers had been ruled off the road, only 3.7 percent of the accidents in the second period would have been eliminated. Thus, those consistently having more than one accident in the two three-year periods were only 1.3 percent instead of a total of 3.9 percent reported by Johnson, and in place of about 40 percent of the accidents they were responsible for only about 3.7 percent. Removing the 11 percent with one or more accidents would have eliminated only 20.7 percent of the accidents in the succeeding three years. This meant that the majority of the accidents were experienced by ordinary everyday drivers who were not consistently "accident makers."

This finding showed the "human factors" approach to be of greater importance. That is, the behavior and limitations of 80 to 90 percent of the drivers must be studied to determine what causes them to have one or possibly two accidents rather than concentrating on trying to identify a few consistently accident-prone people. This does not mean, of course, that special treatment for the small group of consistently high accident cases is not also needed.

Attitudes and Appreciation of Hazards—Cleveland Railway Co.

Attitudes and appreciation of hazards were reported to be important in accident causation in a study of Cleveland Railway Company streetcar operators. In addition to accident record analysis, case studies were made of motormen with higher than average records. Among factors indicated of most importance were faulty attitude, failure to recognize potential hazards, faulty speed or distance judgment, and impulsiveness. The 50 motormen with the highest accident records were interviewed (Cleveland Railway Co. et al., 1929).

Effects of Fatigue—U.S. Public Health Service

Several investigators studied the effects of long, continued driving. Among others, Moss in 1929 and Baker and Gunderson in 1935 reported on the effects of being "too long at the wheel."

An extensive study under the U.S. Public Health Service (Jones et al.,

1941) reviewed such studies and gave medical, physiological, and psychophysical tests to a total of 889 drivers in Baltimore, Nashville, and Chicago. The results indicated a general loss of psychophysiological effectiveness with increased hours of driving. The hours driven ranged up to over 10 hours during the day on which tests were made.

A "coefficient of scoring" was used as an index and plotted against the variables in question. This coefficient showed a consistent drop with hours of driving since major sleep as compared to measurements made with "zero hours." It was suggested that a "reasonable limitation of hours" of service of interstate truck drivers would reduce the number of drivers operating with low functional efficiency. New regulations of the Interstate Commerce Commission in 1937 were expected to have a desirable effect.

Michigan and Connecticut Driver Study—New York University

To overcome difficulties of previous research from uncontrolled and confounded variables, this study used matched samples. With the cooperation of state officials, an investigation of driver characteristics was carried on in both Michigan and Connecticut (Center for Safety Education, New York University, 1948). A criterion involving accidents and exposure was based on accident records and reports by drivers of miles driven. "Repeaters" were called in by state police or licensing officials and "accident-free" subjects were volunteers from cooperating industrial and other groups. Matching by sex, type of vehicle, and mileage was carried out. A total of 252 "repeaters" and 261 "free" were tested, for a grand total of 513 drivers.

Included were personal report data, vision tests, knowledge and information about traffic safety, a personality test, and interview questions. Some statistically significant differences between groups were found, but they were not consistently the same for the groups from the two states. Slightly poorer safe driving information, personality adjustment, motor control test scores, and the like were reported for the repeater groups. Again, the degree of overlap between the repeater and "free" groups was very great.

Thus on the whole many low correlations or barely statistically significant group differences were found by the various early studies measuring driver characteristics and comparing groups on an accident criterion.

Sign Visibility and Legibility—Bureau of Public Roads and National Bureau of Standards

A study to determine the best characteristics for highway signs by the U.S. Bureau of Public Roads and the National Bureau of Standards was reported in 1933. Test signs were set up outdoors and viewed through a shutter device which limited the time of observation. The observer tripped the shutter when he was ready. Observations were made in daylight and at night under headlights. Results were reported as percentage of letters seen correctly at a given distance. As a result, black letters on a yellow background were recommended for best daytime visibility and legibility.

Three different sizes of reflector buttons and seven different spacings of buttons in signs were tested for night legibility. An intermediate size and spacing proved best.

Six female and eleven male subjects made about 800 observations at the critical 350-foot distance under headlights for the night observations of reflectorized signs. Seventy observers made the observations of non-reflectorized signs to observe shape, color, and legends in daylight. Letters were transposed or different legends used for different trials (Mills, 1933).

Iowa State College Sign Studies

Research at Iowa State College recommended greens, yellows, blacks, whites, and metallic colored signs for both daylight and night, but not orange and red, which lost visibility at night. A spacing of 50 percent of letter width, dark letters on a lighter background, average reflection coefficient of 35 percent or slightly higher, letter width at least 33 percent of letter height and stroke width 25 percent of letter width were recommended (Lauer and Helwig, 1932).

Another paper reported that 9.7 seconds were required to read a sign including 12 destinations (Lauer, 1932).

A study of legibility (Uhlaner, 1941) used 16 subjects making three observations on each combination of letter and stroke widths under outdoor conditions. Daylight illumination was used, with the test letters parallel to the sun's rays and in the shade. Results indicated an optimum legibility distance for stroke width of 16 to 20 percent of letter height (for block letters). A second experiment with 15 subjects indicated 18 percent to be optimum.

Yale Traffic Bureau Sign Studies

Studies of sign visibility and legibility at the Yale Bureau for Street Traffic Research analyzed attention value into (1) target value (characteristics that make a sign stand out in competition with other signs and distractions) and (2) priority value (qualities that result in one sign being read first, given equal target value). An observer rode with drivers who were instructed to call out route, destination and warning signs as soon as they read them. Important factors for target value were color contrast, relative size, placement on sign posts and on the road, and reflectorization (for night observations).

Two types of legibility were studied: "pure legibility" (with unlimited time) and "glance legibility" (with limited time for observation). With wide Series D letters, legibility distance was 50 feet per inch of letter height. A viewing time of approximately 1 second produced by a shutter in front of the test signs simulated "glance legibility." This short viewing time of the test signs reduced legibility distance by 10 to 16 percent. Exposure times reduced to approximately 0.2 to 0.3 second gave no further reduction.

Short familiar and unfamiliar syllables were presented with the same 1-second exposure times. Fewer *unfamiliar* syllables were recognized and only three to four *familiar* syllables were recognized (Forbes, 1939c). Use of signs carrying no more than three or four familiar words was recommended so that a sign could be read in a single glance instead of requiring the 4 to 11 seconds reported for some signs by Lauer (Forbes, 1941). Similar glance legibility findings for rounded letters and 1-second exposure were reported by Hurd (1946).

A larger study by the Yale Traffic Bureau in cooperation with the Pennsylvania Turnpike Commission determined legibility distances for narrow Series B and wide Series D letters in daylight and at night. Six-letter words with one misspelling were used with letter heights from 6 to 24 inches. A total of 400 subjects made observations on foot. Eighty percentile daylight legibility distance (representing 20/20 acuity) was 50 feet per inch for Series D and 33 feet per inch for Series B. There was a 10 to 20 percent loss in legibility distance at night, which varied depending on whether floodlighting or headlighting was used (Forbes and Holmes, 1939).

Overtaking and Passing Distances—Yale Bureau for Street Traffic Research

Human factors research at the Yale Bureau for Street Traffic Research measured distances used by drivers in actual overtaking and passing on two-lane highways in several parts of the country. These were needed to guide designers of two-lane highway passing areas. A combination of stopwatch timing and photographic recording was utilized. Distributions of distances used by drivers were plotted and 80 percentile distances were suggested for design purposes, that is, the distance which would accommodate 80 percent of the drivers observed.

In order to analyze the data, it was found necessary to classify the observations into "flying passes" of forced return and voluntary return type, and "accelerative passes" of forced return and voluntary return types. When so classified, average distances and also 80 percentile distances showed a linear relationship to speed of the overtaken vehicle (see Figure 2). Median passing distances (similar to average values but less affected

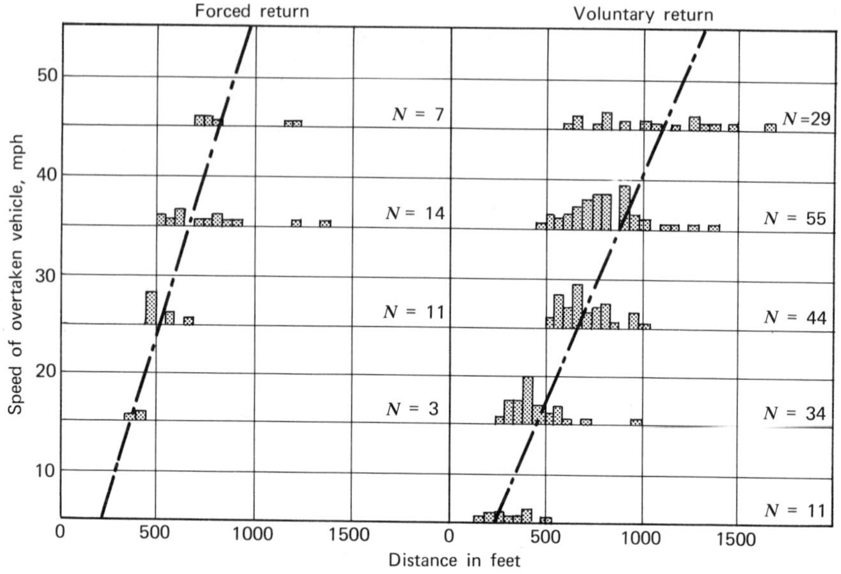

(a)

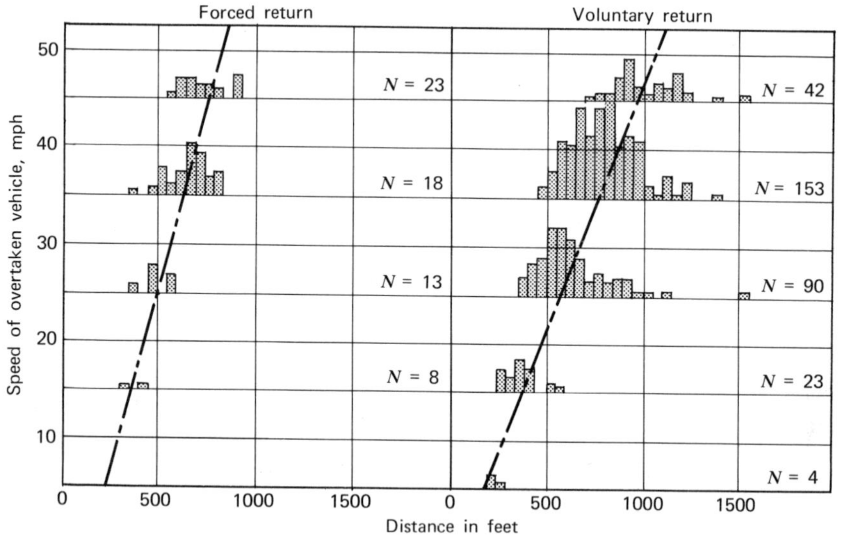

(b)

Figure 2. Distance to overtake and pass: (*a*) flying type; (*b*) accelerative type. (From Matson and Forbes, 1938, p. 105.)

by extreme cases) were consistently greater in the Mid- and Far West than in New England areas where hilly, curving roads restricted passing opportunities. Median distances were 100 to 400 feet greater at 50 miles an hour in the West for different types of passes (Matson and Forbes, 1938).

Clearance times at the end of a pass before the on-coming car arrived were also found to be shorter in New England than farther west. The 80 percentile distance and time values were compared. About 20 percent of the drivers returned to their own lane with 1-second clearance time or less (Forbes and Matson, 1939).

A method of measuring response time in pass initiation from air photos was described, but since facilities were not available for carrying it out, times were measured manually on the highway. An observer started a stopwatch as soon as visibility for the driver opened up ahead and then stopped the watch when the driver stepped down on his accelerator. Eighty percentile time values ranged from 2.8 to 3.5 seconds for straight highway passes and for curves and crest situations. These time values also were applicable to design of passing sight distances on highways (Forbes, 1939b).

A summary of these and other studies showed that perception–judgment–response time increases in proportion to complexity of the decision or judgment characteristic of the particular task. Both highway and aviation psychology studies were included since human factor problems have similar components in both fields (Forbes and Katz, 1957).

Purdue University Studies

As part of the Joint Highway Research Project (with the State Highway Commission), Lawshe (1939) reviewed psychological studies related to highway safety published after the Weiss and Lauer (1930) report. In the introduction, he noted that the accident-prone driver had been the concern of the psychologist but that traffic engineers had been forced to cope with human factor problems related to engineering. He reviewed publications on topics such as accident analysis and contributing causes; critical speeds and related topics; observations of speed, lateral position and behavior on curves; sign legibility and visibility studies; driver characteristics and accidents, fatigue, vision, perception, and attitudes.

Later studies included others by Lawshe, a study of legibility of numerals (Kuntz and Sleight, 1950), and others.

Psychological Factors in Safe Driving—U.S. Army Personnel Research Laboratory

Road tests for the selection of Army truck drivers were reported in 1943. Due to continuing costs of accidents, a program of research on psychological factors in safe motor vehicle operation was set up in 1949 under the Personnel Research Section of the Adjutant General's Office. A first study developed a criterion "more reliable and meaningful than a road test or accident rate by itself" (Uhlaner et al., 1952).

A separate chapter will present in more detail other important contributions from this laboratory.

Human Factors Research at U.C.L.A.

In 1949, the Institute of Transportation and Traffic Engineering was established at the University of California with a human factors research staff on the Los Angeles campus. A series of experimental crash analysis, driver test, and accident record studies started at that time.

As examples of separate studies, measurement of highway sign lowercase and capital-letter legibility* confirmed earlier results and showed the effect of familiarity of names on test signs. As compared to 50 to 60 feet per inch of letter height for scrambled letter signs, familiar names gave 80 to 90 feet per inch (85 percentile value representing 20/20 or "normal" vision). Four groups of 54 to 56 observers made 3939 total observations. Lower case, when measured by "loop height," gave about 10 percent greater legibility distances than capitals (Forbes, Moskowitz, and Morgan, 1950).

A photographic study of speed, volume, and center-to-center headways between vehicles showed minimum values of 0.5 to 1 second between cars within platoons. To obtain clear distance or time between cars, the equivalent of average car length must be subtracted. Therefore, minimum spacings were at or below minimum brake reaction time for the average driver (Forbes, 1951).

Continuing large-scale research in driving simulation, reactions to highway environment, effect of drugs, and fatigue are presented in later chapters.

Harvard School of Public Health Accident Prevention Research

A program of research in accident prevention was reported by McFarland (1952). A plea was made for vehicle design to suit the operator, selection to eliminate accident repeaters, and maintenance of physical fitness.

A report on "Human Factors in Highway Transport Safety" McFarland and Moseley, 1954) analyzed accident and human factors problems in truck and bus drivers, and design of truck and bus cabs and controls.

* In cooperation with the California Highway Department, Sacramento, California.

A study of vehicle evaluation with J. W. Dunlap and others was summarized.

Human Variables in Motor Vehicle Accidents (McFarland, Moore and Warren, 1955) reviewed many research reports organized in the epidemiological conceptual framework of "agent-host-environment" factors and relationships.

Many later reports have contributed human factors, vehicle evaluation and human body size data as well as aging, visibility, and carbon monoxide information.

SUMMARY

Automobile transportation on our streets and highways contributes greatly to convenience and enjoyment of life. At the same time, breakdown of the driver-vehicle-highway system operation in the form of congestion and of accidents is a major social problem. Early research on psychology of the driver showed consistent accident repeaters to be a small part of the problem (though special treatment for such groups is important). By far the largest share of traffic accidents is experienced by drivers who have one accident only. These mishaps involve misjudgments or lapses of the "normal" driver and a combination of causal factors which overload a driver's abilities.

The "driver testing" approach showed low correlations of a wide range of ability measurements with accident records. Such low correlations are consistent with the relatively low probability of accident occurrence and the theory of multiple causal factors that may overload drivers' capabilities at unpredictable times.

The need for "human factors" data on drivers' abilities to guide traffic engineers and highway system design became evident from early research. Development of human factors data was advocated as the more positive approach to improved traffic safety and efficiency.

Examples were given of early research which contributed data on human abilities and limitations. Numerous other studies could not be included in this historical review, but many will be referred to in later chapters. These and other research results contribute human factors information for guiding driver-vehicle-highway system design to improve safety and efficiency.

REFERENCES

Baker, J. S., Ch. 1 in Weiss and Lauer, *Psychological Principles in Automotive Driving*, Ohio State Univ. Contributions in Psychology, No. 11, Ohio State Univ., Columbus, Ohio, 1930, 1–6.

Bingham, Walter V., The Prone to Accident Driver, *Proceedings of the 17th Annual Conference on Highway Engineering*, Ann Arbor, Mich., 1931, 1–12.

Blumenthal, Murray, Dimensions of the Traffic Safety Problem, *Traffic Safety*, **12** (1968), 7–12.

Center for Safety Education, New York University, *Personal Characteristics of Traffic Accident Repeaters*, Eno Foundation for Highway Traffic Control, Saugatuck, Conn., 1948, 64 pp.

Chapanis, Alphonse, *Man-Machine Engineering*, Wadsworth, Belmont, Calif., 1965, 134 pp.

Chapanis, A., Garner, W. R., and Morgan, C. T., *Applied Experimental Psychology*, Wiley, New York, 1949, 434 pp.

Cleveland Railway Co. and Policy Holders Service Bureau of the Metropolitan Life Insurance Co., The Accident-Prone Employee, 1929, 27 pp.

Cobb, P. W., Selecting the Accident Prone Driver by Means of Tests, Paper at Annual Meeting of the Highway Research Board, Dec. 1938, mimeo., 24 pp.

DeSilva, Harry R., *Why We Have Automobile Accidents*, Wiley, New York, 1942, 394 pp.

DeSilva, Harry R. and Forbes, T. W., *Driver Testing Results*, WPA of Massachusetts, Boston, Mass., 1937, 98 pp.

Forbes, T. W., Visual Estimation of Velocity in Connection with Highway Safety, Abstract of Dissertation, Ohio State Univ. Press, 1931.

Forbes, T. W., Measuring Drivers' Reactions, *Personnel Journal*, **11** (1932), 111–119.

Forbes, T. W., Age Performance Relationship Among Accident Repeater Automobile Drivers, *Journal of Consulting Psychology*, **2** (1938), 143–148.

Forbes, T. W., The Normal Automobile Driver as a Traffic Problem, *Journal of General Psychology*, **20** (1939a), 471–474.

Forbes, T. W., Methods of Measuring Judgment and Perception Time in Passing on the Highway, *Proceedings of the Highway Research Board*, **19** (1939b), 218–231.

Forbes, T. W. A Method for Analysis of the Effectiveness of Highway Signs, *Journal of Applied Psychology*, **23** (1939c), 669–684.

Forbes, T. W., Psychological Applications to the New Field of Traffic Engineering, *Journal of Applied Psychology* **25** (1941), 52–58.

Forbes, T. W., Street and Highway Traffic, Ch. VII In Fryer and Henry, Eds., Sec. 50, Transportation, *Handbook of Applied Psychology*, Vol. I, Rinehart, New York, 1950, p. 325–335, and refs. end of Vol. II.

Forbes, T. W., Speed, Headway and Volume Relationships on a Freeway, *Proceedings of the Institute of Traffic Engineers*, 1951, 1–24.

Forbes, T. W. and Holmes, Robert S., Legibility Distances of Highway Destination Signs in Relation to Letter Height, *Proceedings of the Highway Research Board* **19** (1939), 321–335.

Forbes, T. W. and Katz, M. S., Summary of Human Engineering Research Data and Principles Related to Highway Design and Engineering Problems, American Institute for Research, Pittsburgh, Pa., 1957, 103 pp.

Forbes, T. W. and Matson, T. M., Driver Judgments in Passing on the Highway, *Journal of Psychology*, **8** (1939), 3–11.

Forbes, T. W., Moskowitz, Karl, and Morgan, Glen A., Comparison of Lower Case and Capital Letters for Highway Signs, *Proceedings of the Highway Research Board*, **30** (1950), 355–373.

Hurd, F., Glance Legibility, *Traffic Engineering*, **17** (1946), 161–162.

Institute of Traffic Engineers, *Constitution,* Art. I, Sec. 3, Yearbook, Institute Traffic Engineers, Washington, D.C., 1969, 3.

Jones, Benjamin F. et al., Fatigue and Hours of Service of Interstate Truck Drivers, *Public Health Bulletin #265,* U.S. Public Health Service, U.S. Government Printing Office, Washington, D.C., 1941, 286 pp.

Kuntz, J. E. and Sleight, R. B., Legibility of Numerals: The Optimum Ratio of Height to Strokewidth, *American Journal of Psychology,* **63** (1950), 567–575.

Lauer, A. R., Improvement in Highway Safety, *Proceedings of the Highway Research Board,* **12** (1932), 389–401.

Lauer, A. R., Age and Sex in Relation to Accidents, *Highway Research Board Bulletin* **60** (1952), 25–35.

Lauer, A. R. and Helwig, Donald, Improvement in Highway Signs, *American Highways,* **11** (1932), 14, 15, 19.

Lawshe, C., Jr., A Review of the Literature Related to the Various Psychological Aspects of Highway Safety, *Highway Research Bulletin No. 2,* Research Series #66, Engineering Experimental Station, Purdue University, Lafayette, Ind., 1939, 59 pp.

Leisch, Jack E., Highway Safety, Design and Operations Freeway Signing and Related Geometrics. Hearings—Special Subcommittee on the Federal-Aid Highway Program, Committee on Public Works, House of Representatives, U.S. Government Printing Office, Washington, D.C., 1968, pp. 349–399, see esp. pp. 360–363.

Matson, T. M. and Forbes, T. W., Overtaking and Passing Requirements as Determined from a Moving Vehicle, *Proceedings of the Highway Research Board,* **18** (1938), 100–112.

McCormick, Ernest J., *Human Factors Engineering,* 2nd ed., McGraw-Hill, New York, 1964.

McFarland, Ross A., Human Factors in Highway Transport Safety, *Highway Research Board Bulletin,* **60** (1952), 36–43.

McFarland, Ross A., The Role of Human Engineering in Highway Safety, Ch. 12 in Bennett, Degan, and Spiegel, *Human Factors in Technology,* McGraw-Hill, New York, 1963, pp. 207–229.

McFarland, Ross A., Moore, Roland C., and Warren, A. Bertrand, *Human Variables in Motor Vehicle Accidents,* Harvard School of Public Health, Boston, Mass., 1955, 203 pp.

McFarland, Ross A. and Moseley, Alfred L., *Human Factors in Highway Transport Safety,* Harvard School of Public Health, Boston, Mass., 1954, 295 pp.

Mills, F. W., The Comparative Visibility of Standard Luminous and Nonluminous Highway Signs, *Public Roads,* **14** (1933), 109–128.

National Research Council, Committee on Highway Safety Research, The Field of Highway Safety Research and Highway Safety Research Correlation Conference, 1952, reprinted 1956 as National Academy of Sciences National Research Council, Publ. 454, Wash., D.C.

National Safety Council, *Accident Facts,* National Safety Council, Chicago, Ill., 1970, 344 pp.

Ross, H. Laurence, Schematic Analysis of the Driving Situation, *Traffic Safety,* **4** (1960), 4–7.

Secretary of Agriculture, Motor Vehicle Traffic Conditions in the United States,

Part 6, The Accident-Prone Driver, House Document No. 462, Part 6, U.S. Government Printing Office, Washington, D.C., 1938, 52 pp.

Stalder, H. I. and Lauer, A. R., Effective Use of Reflectorized Materials on Railroad Boxcars, *Highway Research Board Bulletin,* **89** (1954), 70–75.

Uhlaner, J. E., The Effect of Thickness of Stroke on the Legibility of Letters, *Proceedings of the Iowa Academy of Sciences,* **48** (1941), 319–324.

Uhlaner, J. E., Goldstein, Leon G., and VanSteenberg, N.J., Development of Criteria of Safe Motor Vehicle Operation, *Highway Research Board Bulletin,* **60** (1952), 1–16.

Weiss, A. P. and Lauer, A. R., *Psychological Principles in Automotive Driving,* Ohio State Univ. Contributions in Psychology, No. 11, Ohio State Univ., Columbus, Ohio, 1930, 165 pp.

II

GENERAL APPROACH AND METHODS

T. W. Forbes

PURPOSE OF THE CHAPTER

The purpose of this chapter is to introduce the general research methods used in the human factors approach and thus lay a foundation for later chapters, in which the authors will treat special applications to their particular topic. The present description, therefore, will describe basic techniques and illustrate their use in certain studies to make the description more meaningful.

THE GENERAL APPROACH

The same sequence is not always followed in approaching a man-machine environment problem in highway safety or in other applications of the human factors approach. The method must be adapted to the particular situation and the requirements of the problem. However, for the purpose of discussion, a logical sequence can be suggested as follows for designing the system (in this case the driver-vehicle-highway system) to fit people. In the field of highway and safety research some of these procedures have been almost ignored because everyone assumed that driving was a simple and obvious task. This has proved not to be so.

ANALYSIS OF THE TASK REQUIRED BY THE SYSTEM

A task analysis is usually a first step in approaching a man-machine environment problem. Since the task of any operator depends upon system requirements and constraints, at least some degree of analysis of system-imposed requirements is necessary. Included may be a general description of the tasks of various people in the system and then a specific analysis of the operator's task. This task analysis may be very complete and specific if individual operators' abilities are to be investigated. On the other hand, in some cases a complete, specific task analysis may be so detailed and extensive that it becomes confusing and difficult to use. In that case, a less detailed one may serve better.

In many cases, people in the system must work together to assure that the system will operate in the desired way. Therefore, team behavior also must be analyzed and measured.

In highway transportation and safety research, analysis of the driver's task has often been an informal, almost incidental one, based on the experience and opinion of the particular investigator. Much better would be a careful analysis based on objective data if available or, if not, on carefully analyzed expert opinion.

MEASURE ABILITIES OF OPERATORS

Characteristic abilities and limitations of ability must be measured, observed or estimated for the majority of persons (drivers, pedestrians and others) who will form the human part of the system. In order to develop such a "population stereotype," research methods of experimental and applied psychology, physiology and related sciences are most applicable. In addition to the group characteristic, it is also important to know the range of variation among individuals.

ANALYZE THE MOST LIKELY ERRORS

On the basis of information about the task and the abilities of the type of people involved, some estimate of the most likely errors can be made. If the highway facility or vehicle has not been built, experimental methods using mock-ups and part- or full-task simulation may be of assistance. Such a procedure has been very effective for human factors problems in the aerospace field. For various reasons, it has been more difficult to obtain accurate simulation of driving tasks, but efforts to achieve it have been underway for many years and already indications are it will be of great value.

Where the particular highway facilities (such as interchanges or signalized intersections) already have been built, actual system breakdowns can be studied. Recorded or observed driver behavior carefully analyzed can show driver errors or failures. These in turn, when properly analyzed, may indicate features in the task presented to the driver by the design which need modification.

Accident record analysis is one method of studying system breakdowns but it is not the only method. If records are reliable and carefully treated, accident studies can be valuable. Unfortunately as often executed there are many possible shortcomings which will be discussed later. Other methods include observation or recording of driver-vehicle behavior in traffic and subsequent analysis of hazardous occurrences.

DESIGN OR MODIFY THE SYSTEM TO FIT ABILITIES AND LIMITATIONS

Knowing the ability and limitations of drivers, special equipment operators or others in the highway system, some of the system characteristics can be designed to fit people's abilities. If already built and in use, system characteristics may be modified. This approach has been very useful already in producing more efficient and safer highway traffic, as the following examples will illustrate.

In Relation to Highway Characteristics. As operating speeds of vehicles increased, highways were widened, made smoother and designed with straight enough alignment to fit the speeds of which the vehicles were capable. Such developments reduced time available for driver judgments and it became necessary to inform drivers about what lay ahead. This was done by making the highway alignment visible, by delineation with striping and markers, and by various kinds of signs.

To guide design of these highway characteristics, some driver characteristics that had to be known included vision and visibility factors, time to make decisions, and legibility distances of highway sign symbols and letters in terms of their size and background.

These types of human factor data from early studies influenced the design of highway alignment, ramps, traffic control devices, and other features and helped make them more usable by the motorist. Without such changes from earlier design, highways would be very difficult to drive. In fact, it would have been impossible to drive the older highways under the traffic loads and speeds now common.

In Relation to Vehicle Characteristics. With the first automobiles, the problem was to get equipment that would run reliably. Now, however, the development of the vehicle is such that the more critical question is how well the driver can handle it. He must be able to use the various controls correctly, obtain the proper information from speed and other indicators, judge environmental and operating conditions, and control the vehicle in relation to other vehicles and the highway itself.

To design vehicles for these objectives also, the necessary information on driver characteristics includes ability to reach controls, sensitivity to visual cues from the highway, remembering to turn switches on and off, ability to see and read dials such as the speedometer, and ability to see through the windshield and judge speeds of other vehicles ahead or to the rear.

In the history of automobile development, some driver limitations often were not appreciated until after failures occurred. But over the course of time, changes in vehicle controls were made because of experience with human lapses. For instance, drivers consistently forgot to reset the manual choke control so cars emitted black smoke, polluted the atmosphere, and burned too much fuel. The automatic choke was a design change to overcome this.

Similarly, gear shift controls were standardized because drivers became confused when different makes of cars had different kinds of shifts. Now the automatic drive carries this one step further so that drivers no longer have to learn the intricacies of engine speed-change and gear-shifting which used to confuse many.

Recognition of the importance of driver behavior factors resulted in experiments to guide various phases of vehicle design. Description of modern human factor experiments leading to other improvements in vehicle design are presented in Chapter 9.

In Relation to Operating Procedures, Laws, and Regulations. The earliest driving procedures, laws, and regulations were mainly those required by the physical characteristics of the highways and vehicles. It has become clear, however, that these features of highway systems operation must be related to convenient, acceptable, and safe human behavior factors. For example, a human factors study first recommended use of passing distance long enough to include 85 percent of those observed as a guide for passing distance design (Matson and Forbes, 1938). Measurement of speeds used by drivers and determination of the 85 percentile speed is now commonly used by traffic engineers for setting speed limits. Parking regulations are designed best when a background survey of parking needs and driver responses are used as a basis.

Whenever procedures or regulations run counter to the behavior of the majority of drivers or to their judgment of what is reasonable and safe, the regulation probably needs to be redesigned.

TRAIN PEOPLE TO OPERATE THE SYSTEM

After task requirements are determined and abilities of people are known, the human factors data, if properly analyzed, should serve as a guide for training. Training may be for operators or for designers. Valid human factors research results are of considerable importance for training of both.

PROBLEMS OF OBSERVING AND MEASURING BEHAVIOR

Obtaining Reliable and Repeatable Measurements

Anyone who has attempted to measure human behavior knows that it is quite variable. For instance, when measurement of sign legibility distances was first proposed, some doubted that reliable measurements could be obtained. It had been tried and "found to be impossible." This was quite correct when the method included only the physical factors and did not control certain psychological factors. One of these "human factors" was knowledge of the test signs from the first trial which resulted in much greater apparent legibility in a second trial. When this familiarity factor was controlled, and when certain other engineering psychology techniques of measuring human behavior were used, stable, reproducible, and predictable values resulted (Forbes and Holmes, 1939). In fact, these 1938 Pennsylvania data were confirmed surprisingly well by a California study 12 years later (Forbes, Moskowitz and Morgan, 1950).

This example illustrates problems that underlie all measurement of human behavior. The human responds to so many different variables in almost any task that special techniques are necessary to separate effects of desired factors and to measure interactions between several factors. These techniques have been worked out in experimental psychology and other behavioral and social sciences. They may combine experimental, observational, and statistical methods.

Constant and Variable Errors

Both constant and variable errors are characteristic of human behavior involving skilled judgments. Variable errors arise from variations of skilled performances in different trials by one person or by different people. As an example, judgments of speed by a group of skilled traffic observers may be expected to vary randomly around a certain correct value.

Constant errors, on the other hand, occur where judgments consistently vary around a value greater than or less than the true value. Returning to the example of estimates of speeds, a constant error also may be found under certain conditions. After driving continuously at a higher speed for some time, and then decelerating, drivers judged their speed on the average as lower than the actual. That is, when asked to estimate their speed without a speedometer to consult, drivers thought their speed was lower than it actually was (Barch, 1958). By the use of proper statistics, reliable estimates of such variable and constant errors can be obtained.

Control of Other Factors

Unknown or undesired variables may influence driver behavior. These must be eliminated or else controlled so that effects can be separated out. The very procedure used to observe or to measure driver behavior may change the behavior being measured. This can occur, for instance, if observers are stationed where drivers can see them or if some special equipment, markings or other conditions are visible to the drivers.

Care must be taken, therefore, to avoid such unintended influences on driver behavior. If possible, observers or measurement devices should be located where they will not be seen by the drivers. Special signs or markings that indicate to drivers some special condition or operation underway must be avoided if possible.

Laboratory simulation of part of the driving task may be used to control unwanted factors. In one study, effects of glare and of sign luminance on legibility were separated with such a method. Reduced-scale test signs were presented in a light controlled "tunnel." Observations were made by a large number of subjects to determine legibility distance at different luminances with and without glare (Allen and Straub, 1955).

In laboratory experiments, also, care must be taken that the instructions to the subject do not inadvertently suggest as desirable or undesirable a particular type of response. Any such unintended suggestion may change the response of the subject.

Analysis of Group Data

Where a wide range of reactions or abilities is involved, proper use of large group measurements and statistical analysis of variability can be employed to advantage. The size of the group required will depend upon the variability of the behavior involved. This variability in turn may depend upon the number of interacting variables and the range of subject characteristics. Proper statistical sampling methods must be employed.

Sometimes a simple plot of scores by subclasses may be very revealing. In visual performances, for example, it is known that age of the subjects usually makes a difference. A large group of subjects and data analyzed by five- or ten-year age groups may be required to show age trends. After that, comparisons between two different groups of drivers may show meaningful differences greater than chance expectancy which otherwise might have been hidden. Such a procedure was found necessary in obtaining baseline measurements of low contrast vision under simulated night driving conditions as compared to daylight conditions (Forbes et al., 1969). Average loss in vision scores between simulated day and night conditions increased somewhat with age. However, greater than the age trend was the range of extreme scores from the average value within each ten-year age group.

Where relationships between behavior measures of groups of people must be analyzed, accepted psychological statistical analysis and experimental design principles are applicable. A well-presented, understandable description of psychological statistical methods is given by Chapanis (1959). Included are the usual methods of correlation between two sets of scores, calculating group mean and median values to obtain a stable measure, determining group variability, and determining the probability that mean differences are greater than chance.

Most of these statistical methods are based on assumptions that distributions of scores are "normal," that is, of symmetrical bell-shape form around the average. For most ability measurements this assumption holds.

However, for some traffic variables distributions are notably skewed. The frequency distribution of drivers experiencing different numbers of accidents in a given time period is a good example. The number of drivers following at different time headways in traffic is another (see Figure 1).

Use of average values or of Pearsonian correlation is questionable with highly skewed data, but nonparametric methods can be used. The chi-squared technique is one of the best known of these. Because of certain pitfalls, care should be taken that such techniques are properly applied and conclusions properly drawn. For a good presentation of nonparametric methods see Siegel (1956).

Even though single variable statistical approaches do not show significant traffic behavior effects or relationships, there may be a logical reason to suspect influences from multiple interrelated variables. For example, static and dynamic visual acuity, glare vision, driver age, driving at different times of night and day, familiarity with signs, signals and regulations, fatigue, and other factors might in different combina-

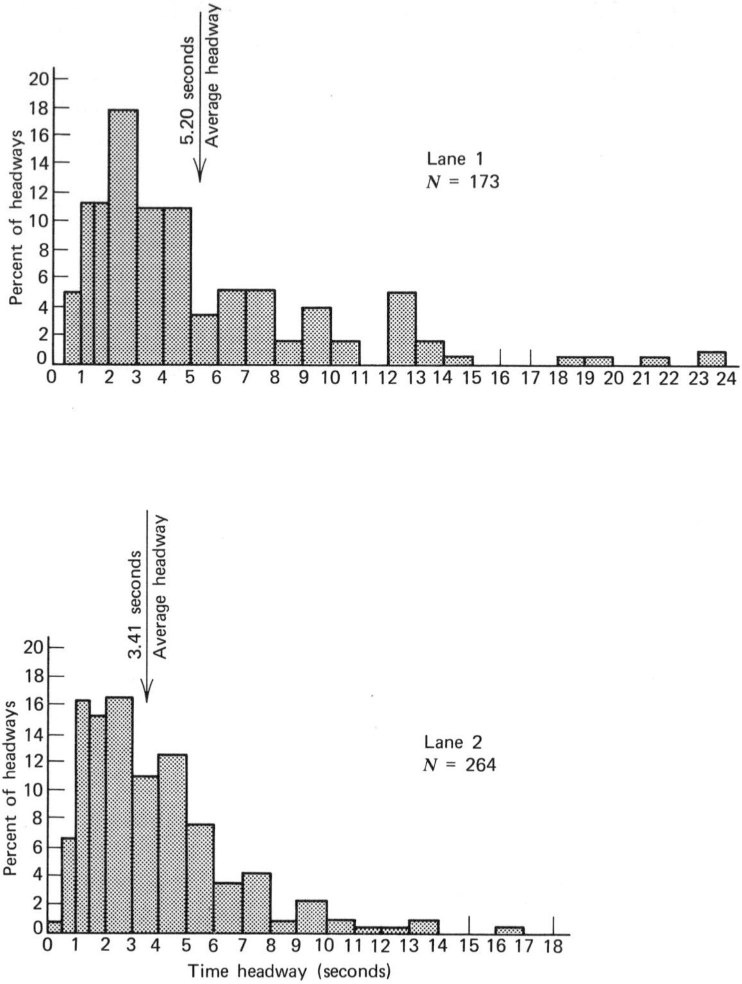

Figure 1. Distribution of individual time headways at night, Ford Expressway, Detroit; 7:15 to 7:30 p.m., February 14, 1958, lighted. (From Forbes 1960.)

tions and proportions affect safe driving behavior. If measures of each variable can be obtained on a group of drivers, statistical evaluation of combined interrelationships with a criterion can be calculated by several multiple-factor techniques. These techniques now have been made easier by electronic computers.

Multiple correlation may be used with a large number of variables, to determine the combination giving best predictive relationship to some criterion. A case in point is the multiple correlation of test scores with accidents-per-year in the early Hartford, Connecticut research (see Chapter 1). A multiple correlation of 0.35 was obtained, indicating that best weighting of the 22 scores accounted for about 12 percent of the variance.

Factor analysis is applicable when a large number of first-order correlations with a criterion are available. It may show groupings or "factors," conclusions from which can illuminate possible causal relationships. Conclusions as to the meaning of "factors," however, depend greatly on interpretation of the investigator.

Another multivariate technique that has been used in driver behavior research is discriminant analysis. This procedure develops the best weighting of several variables to discriminate between two criterion factors or between several criterion factors.

Each of the multivariate analysis methods has strengths and limitations. A good technical description of multivariate methods will be found in Anderson (1966) and other chapters of Cattell (1966).

Need for Cross-Validation

In designing an experiment, it is accepted that an hypothesis should be set up first, independent of results of the experiment, and then tested by the experiment. Otherwise, the experimental results may be interpreted into both an hypothesis and proof of it at the same time. It is axiomatic that such circular reasoning must be avoided.

In problems as complex as traffic safety, there has often been a tendency to set up very general hypotheses. Sometimes it is necessary to do a pilot experiment to make a very general hypothesis specific enough to be tested. In the pilot study when certain variables show a statistically significant relation to a criterion, this becomes a specific hypothesis to be tested by a repetition of the experiment on another group of subjects. This is the general process known as "cross-validation." For confirmation, the same combination of statistically significant differences or correlations must result from *the same experiment with a second group of subjects.*

As an example, in the early driver test work at Harvard, a very general hypothesis was that abilities tested would show a relation to accident records. Significant differences between high accident and volunteer groups on certain tests resulted in City A. The same tests and comparisions were used on other groups of drivers in Cities B and C. There were some significant differences *but not in the same test scores and combinations.* Therefore, cross-validation did not confirm a given combination of test scores as differentiating high accident and volunteer groups (DeSilva and Forbes, 1937).

Cross-validation is even more important when the experiment uses multivariate techniques such as multiple regression and discriminant function analysis. These techniques are designed to develop the best possible combination of scores for discriminating between criterion measures or groupings. When numerous scores (different variables) are available, it is almost always possible to develop a combination that will give statistically significant relationships. But unless the same combination gives significant discrimination again with a different group of subjects, the results obtained in the first experiment cannot be considered confirmed. They may have been the best combination to discriminate only for that particular experiment or comparison of subjects.

In early studies the need for cross-validation was often overlooked until repetition by other investigators failed to confirm the reported findings by a first investigator. An example showing the importance of cross-validation is that reported by Rainey and Conger (1959). Accident-repeater and accident-free military personnel were differentiated by certain test scores in a first group. But on repetition with a second group of subjects, except for one test, the same combination of scores did not differentiate.

Case Studies

In contrast to the group data method, individual case methods may be necessary to investigate reactions and causal factor combinations which may differ for each individual. Interview and questionnaire methods must be carefully designed to obtain particular types of information and to avoid suggesting what answers are desirable.

Questioning of drivers and others involved may give details of what happened. This method has been useful in accident studies to get at background information about causes of driver behavior. It may be necessary to interview relatives, friends, and others.

Human Errors and System Effectiveness

As noted earlier, the behavior of the people involved in the operation of the system must be studied in relation to the task, the kinds of judgments, and decisions and responses required of them by the highway transportation system. Although knowledge of human abilities and limitations furnishes a general background for guidance of system design, data on human errors give an indication of some specific breakdown of system operation. In the highway system, therefore, the study of causal factor combinations in accidents and near accidents may yield valuable information.

The analysis of accidents at given highway intersections or other locations has proved valuable to traffic engineers for remedying special highway location conditions which pose hazards. Accident records over several years reflect the behavior and the errors of a large group of drivers under various highway conditions. Thus, a large number of occurrences may be studied even though accidents are very infrequent for any one driver or any short time.

Here the concept of "normal human error" is of importance. Studies in the experimental psychology laboratory have shown that under certain conditions the majority of a group of people will make errors in perceiving certain features of the situation.

Normal Errors

Such "normal errors" of perception differ from the variable and constant errors of judgment mentioned above. If many drivers consistently misinterpret a situation because of a visual pattern presented by the design layout, for instance, this represents a different kind of error than variable errors in estimating speeds and distances on a familiar highway.

Studies of accident location characteristics from a human factors approach (analyzing the perceptual factors presented to the driver) may uncover such "normal errors." A good example is an off ramp that looks like the main highway. In some locations, the off ramp design gives it the appearance of the through highway, whereas the through lanes turn and disappear, giving the appearance of an off ramp. Not all, but many drivers may be observed to take the wrong turn in such a situation.

Normal perceptual errors may possibly have been involved in some accidents such as confusion of headlight switch and cigarette lighter in night off-the-road accidents. Normal perceptual errors in the interpretation of destination and arrow direction on highway signs may be indicated by last-minute changes of path of drivers (Forbes, 1953).

Elimination of "Designed-In Errors"

It may be possible to modify stimulus conditions in the highway situation or in operation characteristics of the system to eliminate such "normal errors." Experimental use of colored delineation lines and markers to avoid the misinterpretation of several left-hand off ramps is being tried in Michigan.

Again, Hulbert and Burg (1957) showed that errors in interpreting destination signs can be reduced by adding a line separating two destinations and their respective arrows. In this way, the relation of the arrow to the place name and the perceptual organization of the sign are made clear to the driver.

Designed-in errors may influence some but not other drivers, possibly explaining why some drivers have only one accident over a period of years as shown by accident records. Significantly the largest proportion of total "accidents" happen to one-accident drivers.

To reduce the system breakdowns represented by single accident occurrence, the elimination of designed-in errors in the highway situation is vital. Toward this objective, detection and analysis of normal perceptual errors of all kinds, and even more important, their prediction in the design stage of the interchange or other highway features are of primary importance.

The Good Driving Criterion Problem

A widely used method of relating behavior factors to their practical effects is to compare "good" and "bad" groups on the factor being measured. Another is to obtain an index of "goodness" and relate this by mathematical correlation or graphic analysis to the factor being measured. For either technique, some measurable criterion of "goodness" must be available.

The ultimate objective of highway and safety research is to contribute to safer and more efficient motor vehicle transportation, as noted in Chapter 1. For safety the ultimate objective is reduction of fatalities, injuries and property damage crashes. Therefore, records of traffic accidents and their results seem the most direct and natural criterion of success. For evaluating state, national and other large-scale highway safety programs, accident record data on large groups for long time periods can be useful and valid.

However, problems arise with regard to accident records as a criterion for evaluating behavior of individual drivers. In earlier studies one difficulty with accident records as a criterion arose from lack of completeness and accuracy of records. Another basic lack was some reliable index of amount of driving or exposure. Even in the improved accident record systems today, these shortcomings still are found.

Finally, drivers who have accidents in a second three-year period are for the most part different people from those who had accidents in the preceding three-year period. A study of over 29,000 drivers' accident records in Connecticut showed that three-quarters of the drivers having multiple accidents in the second period were different people from those having multiple accidents in the first three-year period (Forbes, 1939).

A very recent study (Burg, 1970) showed higher numbers and percentages of accidents for California drivers, which probably reflects more driving and better reporting. But again, the majority of those experiencing multiple accidents were different people in the second time period, suggesting chance factors and learning.

Therefore, "accident groups" become accident-free and vice versa, and a large proportion of any group of subjects will have zero scores on an accident criterion in any given time period. A careful review of research on human variables in traffic accidents by Goldstein (1962) discusses the problem in detail and shows that very low correlations have been found in most studies.

Substitute Criterion Needed

Therefore, a more usable substitute criterion would be of great value. One approach was a criterion based on ratings of an observer who rode with drivers as noted in Chapter 1 (see Burtt, Chapter 5 in Weiss and Lauer et al., 1930).

A much more sophisticated approach was part of a broad research program on psychological factors of military driving established in 1949. The instrument developed for measuring military drivers included four rating scales and a checklist that resulted from the use of 11 experimental scales by supervisors and associates. The results were submitted to extensive statistical analysis including (1) reliabilities, (2) correlations with an accident responsibility index, (3) intercorrelations among the scales, and (4) results of a factor analysis (Uhlaner et al., 1952). For later work and further discussion see Chapter 8 on military drivers.

Development of a valid substitute criterion is needed in many areas of highway safety. One recent review of research specifically called for development of an intermediate criterion for evaluating driver education (Lybrand et al., 1968), and a second pointed to similar problems in developing better driver licensing methods (Miller et al., 1969). For further discussion, see Chapter 11 on driver education and Chapter 15 on driver improvement.

Malfetti et al. (1962, 1965) asked experts to rate "critical incidents" in research to improve driver education. This procedure uses expert opinion as a yardstick but ties it to specific behaviors (Flanagan, 1949). Without a substitute criterion, such research may require measuring driving behavior of a large group, and then waiting to follow their later accident record over a period of three or four years. This is usually impractical, and even then only a relatively small number of subjects will have accidents.

As an intermediate criterion of safe driving, it is possible that certain items of unsafe behavior can be developed into a more useful criterion. Hopefully, such a criterion can be useful immediately, but can be related on a long-run basis to safe driving in modern traffic conditions.

Other Types of Criterion

Another type of criterion can often be used for the evaluation of factors affecting driver behavior. For instance, legibility distance, or the distance at which signs can be read, may be used to evaluate various factors of sign design and to improve sign effectiveness.

Still other yardsticks are effects on efficient traffic flow. Criteria for some studies are the occurrence of "slowdowns" in the traffic stream, behavior of drivers indicating a change of mind at intersections, delay in starting at a signal, and the like. Obviously, a suitable criterion must be selected by the investigator for each research problem.

SUMMARY OF BASIC HUMAN FACTORS METHODS

Thus, basically, human factors methods are those developed by experimental and applied psychology and related disciplines and applied to practical problems in the highway and traffic safety research area. A very good description of human factors research methods will be found in Chapanis (1959) and will not be repeated here.

The purpose of these methods is objective measurement or observations of driver behavior related to efficient and safe traffic. The behaviors to be measured are those of drivers, pedestrians, and other people such as police, traffic engineers, and those who regulate, react to, and influence driver behavior on the highways.

With the proviso that any of the methods will be used in a variety of ways and applied to a variety of problems, the human factors methods applied to highway and traffic research may be summarized as follows.

Laboratory Experiments

Experimental laboratory methods may be used to measure many types of behavior required in driving. Laboratory methods allow control of other variables so as to measure only effects of factors being investigated. Laboratory tasks usually include some degree of simulation, often on a reduced scale and involving a part of the driving task only. Therefore, a full-scale check of results in the traffic situation itself is desirable if at all possible.

For example, Allen and Straub (1955) determined legibility distances for reflectorized signs with reduced-scale laboratory measurements where light conditions were controlled. Forbes et al. (1964) studied factors in sign visibility by means of projected signs in a light proof laboratory. Both also carried out limited, full-scale outdoor observations to check applicability of the laboratory results.

Psychophysical Methods

One type of laboratory study measures senory and motor abilities by the psychophysical methods of experimental psychology. Informal analysis of the driving task has led to "driver tests" involving laboratory measurements of perception, judgment, and responses required. Included have been such abilities as visual acuity, field of vision, color vision, dynamic visual acuity, "steering" accuracy (now called tracking), perception-response time to signals while using automobile controls, estimation of speed and others. Abilities required in night driving may include vision against glaring lights, low contrast vision, and vision of obstacles, pedestrians, and similar targets at night.

The procedure has been to set up a task involving visual and other stimuli which can be varied in a systematic experimental design. Individual subjects then respond with control devices according to certain instructions. After a large enough representative group has been measured, results are analyzed by accepted statistical methods.

Laboratory Experiments and Task Simulation

As noted above, components of driving behavior to be measured have been derived from analysis of the driving task. Artificiality of separated task components has led to invalid results from measuring oversimplified behavior. Therefore, experiments on very simple behavior (e.g., simple reaction time) gave way to studies of more complex behavior (e.g., vigilance tracking and perception response time) and still further to definite simulation of the driving task. In fact, driving task simulation is involved to some extent in most driving behavior experiments.

More complete simulation of the driving task is required to investigate interactions between different part tasks in driving such as reading and interpreting signs, while changing lanes in traffic, or braking and then accelerating. Because of its importance, a complete chapter is devoted to a discussion of driving task simulation methods (see Chapter 3).

Simulation of traffic flow, another type of simulation, reproduces the behavior of cars in the traffic stream on the basis of physical highway characteristics, traffic flow and calculations by electronic computer. Such flow simulation typically uses an estimate of average driver response. The problems involved are of special interest to the traffic engineer for understanding and predicting traffic flow.

Vehicle characteristics have been simulated in comparable fashion to investigate effects of vehicle design changes. Here measuring variations of driver behavior is not the primary objective but rather studying effects of vehicle design on driver comfort and driver reaction to controls, lighting, visibility and other features (see Chapter 9).

To some extent each of these types of physical simulation must depend on driver behavior measures or estimates of some sort. Therefore, determinations from *driving task simulation* or other human factors research may contribute to other types of simulation.

Field Observations of Driver-and-Vehicle Behavior

Photographic measurements or observations in traffic may be used to study actual driver and vehicle behavior. Photographic recording, air photos, visual checks and ratings, and recording of driver control of vehicle behavior all have been used. Selection of proper environmental conditions, a large enough sample and consideration of daily, monthly and yearly cycles which influence traffic are of importance. In addition, care is needed to avoid influencing the results unintentionally by the measurement or observation process itself. If drivers see unusual procedures, their behavior is usually affected.

For example, two studies recorded car-following spacing in peak hour traffic by spaced serial photos taken from bridges over the highway and photographing traffic from the rear. This allowed the camera to be placed on the edge of the bridge away from and out of view of drivers in the direction of the traffic stream photographed (Forbes and Fairman, 1951; Forbes and Wagner, 1962).

An airphoto analysis of deceleration waves in peak freeway traffic showed different following behavior under conditions inducing a "caution mode" of driving (Forbes and Simpson, 1968).

Full-Scale Outdoor Experiments

A combination of the experimental method with outdoor full-scale conditions is often of advantage. Experimental observations may be set up under full-scale conditions on an untraveled or lightly traveled highway where traffic will not interfere. As always, the experimental design should equate or balance out undesired variables as much as possible to obtain clearly analyzable results.

Full-scale measurement of sign legibility distances was employed successfully in sign studies (see Chapter 1) and passing experiments on the highway by several investigators (see review by Franklin Institute, 1967).

Experiments Involving Driver Loading

Experiments which oversimplify the task have been mentioned. Whether in the laboratory or on the highway, if the subject has only to look for signs, for example, he will probably see many more than he would if driving. To avoid this type of effect, use of an auxiliary task to "load" the subject (the driver) has proved useful.

To provide a "time-sharing" laboratory task, Forbes (1964) required the subject to relight one, two, three, or four small red lights with correspondingly numbered buttons with one hand. With the other he indicated which of four simulated signs he saw first when presented without warning in the light sequence.

To measure "spare capacity" in information processing by drivers in actual driving, Brown (1965) used repetition of digits presented aurally.

This technique can be varied in a number of ways to increase sensitivity or to measure effects of interacting factors which are otherwise difficult to obtain.

Large-Scale Analysis of Accident Reports

States and cities, and private organizations such as truck fleets, maintain systems for continuous collection of accident records. Where a sufficiently large number of accurate records over a period of several years is available, study of records makes possible investigation of physical causal factors in accidents.

Such an approach condenses the reactions of a large number of people and allows investigation of particular highway locations or of traffic control or vehicle equipment in relation to accidents. Evaluation of hazards from human reactions typical of many drivers under special conditions is possible. The large proportion of drinking drivers in fatal accidents is a well-known example. However, questions of data reliability, changes in recording, in enforcement and in other procedures during the time required to obtain enough accident data, make it necessary to be extremely careful in analysis and in the kinds of conclusions which can be drawn.

The inapplicability of accident record studies to analysis of individual driver characteristics has been noted earlier.

Special Accident Investigation Studies

To obtain more accurate and reliable data, in-depth accident investigations have been used. These are of value for investigating personal and background social factors in accidents which cannot be obtained well from accident records. A multidisciplinary investigation team with additional special training is desirable. Such studies usually must be limited to a relatively small number of cases because of time requirements and high expense. An in-depth study of accidents by Northwestern University (Baker, 1960) sent an accident investigation team to the accident site. The team included a social scientist, an engineer, and a medical physician. Follow-up interviews and laboratory tests resulted in a wealth of data on 68 cases which added to but were not identical with items from official accident records of the same people.

An extensive series of studies by Cornell Aeronautical Laboratory enlisted the assistance of state and local police and medical people to obtain intensive data on crashes in different areas of the country.

Near-Accident Analysis

Near-accident reports are obtained from drivers who were almost but not actually involved in accidents. One advantage is that participating drivers can report their experiences or observations without legal complications of testimony concerning actual crashes. Another is that a great many more occurrences are available for analysis, some involving hazardous behavior that probably would have led to a crash except for quick action by another driver. Further, some drivers can also contribute information on emotional background conditions which would be unobtainable otherwise.

Such reports, of course, also have limitations because they depend on the particular experience and judgment of those reporting. But important information may be obtained in this way.

One near-accident study, carried out through the cooperation of 122 contributing drivers, indicated factors of "hurry" and "pushing through" to be of importance (Committee on Road User Characteristics, 1957). Of a total of 179 incidents reported, 109 involved at least one driver "in a hurry." A multiplicity of other factors were also reported.

Another study analyzed observations by one researcher who rode with 20 professional truck drivers. A total of 48 near-accidents were observed. Among other results, 86 percent involved passing or "following too closely." Of a total of 66 near-accidents by buses, about 75 percent were following too closely in passing (McFarland and Mosely, 1954).

Other Psychological Methods

Differences in knowledge of driving procedures, of emergency behavior, of laws and regulations and other items of knowledge such as trip planning have been studied by psychological test procedures and questionnaire or interview methods. Also, attitudes of drivers toward laws, regulations, enforcement and courts have been investigated by such methods.

Properly made questionnaires and carefully designed survey procedures must be employed. These procedures have limitations which are well known but they can be very useful for certain kinds of studies.

Specialized methods such as the "critical incident technique" may be used to sample expert opinion of commercial drivers, test drivers, driver education instructors or other special groups. A previously quoted study, for example, used the critical incident technique to develop driver education curriculum material from incidents solicited from a wide range of "experts" (Fine et al., 1965).

SUMMARY

Typically, the human factors approach analyzes tasks required by the man-vehicle-highway system, measures abilities and limitations of people, analyzes errors and system breakdowns and, from these sources, develops information for designing, redesigning or modifying driving tasks to fit people. Further, the resulting information furnishes a guide for education and training of those using the system.

Some of the methods of measuring abilities, analyzing group behaviors, relating behavior to a criterion and problems in accident criteria are discussed. Studies of near-accidents, use of various laboratory and full-scale experimental and observational methods are described briefly and illustrative reports are mentioned. Certain pitfalls are noted for some methods.

As would be expected, variations and combinations of these basic methods have also proved useful. Details of applications to various areas and problems will be described by other authors. The brief discussion in this chapter, hopefully, will give an introduction to some of the essential techniques included in later chapters.

REFERENCES

Allen, T. M. and Straub, A. L., Sign Brightness and Legibility, *Highway Research Board Bulletin,* **127** (1955), 1–14.

Anderson, Harry E., Regression, Discriminant Analysis and a Standard Notation for Basic Statistics, Chap. 5 in Cattell, *Handbook of Multivariate Experimental Psychology,* Rand McNally, Chicago, Ill., 1966, pp. 153–173.

Baker, J. Stannard, *Experimental Case Studies of Traffic Accidents: A General Discussion of Procedures and Conclusions,* Northwestern University Traffic Institute, Evanston, Ill., 1960.

Barch, A. M., Judgment of Speed on the Open Highway, *Journal of Applied Psychology,* **42** (1958), 362–366.

Brown, I. D., Measuring the Spare Mental Capacity of Car Drivers by a Subsidiary Auditory Task, *Ergonomics,* **5** (1962), 247–250.

Burg, Albert, The Stability of Driving Record Over Time, *Accident Analysis and Prevention,* **2** (1970), 57–65.

Burtt, Harold E., Development of a Criterion for Automotive Driving, Ch. 5, in Weiss and Lauer, *Psychological Principles in Automotive Driving,* Ohio State Univ. Contributions in Psychology, No. 11, Ohio State Univ., Columbus, Ohio, 1930, pp. 20–28.

Cattell, Raymond B., *Handbook of Multivariate Experimental Psychology,* Rand McNally, Chicago, Ill., 1966, 959 pp.

Chapanis, Alphonse, *Research Techniques in Human Engineering,* Johns Hopkins Press, Baltimore, Md., 1959, 316 pp.

Committee on Road User Characteristics, Analysis of "Near Accident" Reports, *Highway Research Bulletin,* **159** (1957), 23–27.

DeSilva, Harry R. and Forbes, T. W., Driver Testing Results, WPA of Massachusetts, Boston, Mass., 1937, 98 pp., see Tables 1–4.

Fine, J. L., Malfetti, J. L., and Shoben, E. J., *The Development of a Criterion for Driver Behavior,* Teachers College, Columbia University, 1965, 119 pp.

Flanagan, J. C., Critical Requirements: A New Approach to Employee Evaluation, *Personnel Psychology,* **2** (1949), 419–425.

Forbes, T. W., The Normal Automobile Driver as a Traffic Problem, *Journal of General Psychology,* **20** (1939), 471–474.

Forbes, T. W., Driver Characteristics and Highway Operation, *Traffic Engineering,* **24** (1953), 49–51.

Forbes, T. W., Some Factors Affecting Driver Efficiency at Night, *Highway Research Board Bulletin,* **255** (1960), 61–71.

Forbes, T. W., Predicting Attention-Gaining Characteristics of Highway Traffic Signs-Measurement Technique, *Human Factors,* **6** (1964), 371–374.

Forbes, T. W. and Fairman, G. W., An Improved Method for Determining Vehicle Speeds from Spaced Serial Photos, Research Report 9-2, Institute of Transportation and Traffic Engineering, University of California, Los Angeles, Cal., 1951, 21 pp.

Forbes, T. W. and Holmes, Robert S., Legibility Distances of Highway Destination Signs in Relation to Letter Height, *Proceedings of the Highway Research Board,* **19** (1939), 321–335.

Forbes, T. W., Moskowitz, Karl, and Morgan, Glen A., Comparison of Lower Case and Capital Letters for Highway Signs, *Proceedings of the Highway Research Board,* **30** (1950), 355–373.

Forbes, T. W., Pain, R. F., Bloomquist, D. W., and Vanosdall, F. E., Low Contrast and Standard Visual Acuity Under Mesopic and Photopic Illumination, *Journal of Safety Research,* **1** (1969), 5–12.

Forbes, T. W. and Simpson, Miles E., Driver and Vehicle Responses in Freeway Deceleration Waves, *Transportation Science,* **2** (1968), 77–104.

Forbes, T. W. and Wagner, F. A., The Effect of "Small" and "Compact" cars on Traffic Flow and Safety, *Highway Research Board Bulletin,* **351** (1962), 1–17.

Franklin Institute Research Laboratories, Overtaking and Passing on Two-Lane Rural Highways—A Literature Review, Contract CPR 11-2770, U.S. Department of Transportation, U.S. Government Printing Office, Washington, D.C., 1967, 44 pp.

Goldstein, Leon G., Human Variables in Traffic Accidents: A Digest of Research, *Highway Research Board Bibliography* **31** (1962), also *Traffic Safety* (March 1964), 26–31.

Hulbert, S. F. and Burg, A., The Effectiveness of Underlining on the Readability of Highway Destination Signs, *Highway Research Board Bulletin,* **36** (1957), 561–574.

Lybrand, William A., Carlson, Glenn H., Cleary, Patricia A., and Bauer, Boyd H., American University Development Education and Training Research Institute, Washington, D.C., 1968, 210 pp., Report PB-180-471 of Contract FH-11-6594 to U.S. Department of Transportation, National Highway Safety Bureau, see p. iii to xi for summary.

Malfetti, James L., Critical Incidents in Behind-the-Wheel Instruction in Driver Education, *Highway Research Board Bulletin,* **330** (1962), 69–86. Also see Fine, Malfetti, and Shoben.

Matson, T. M. and Forbes, T. W., Overtaking and Passing Requirements as Determined from a Moving Vehicle, *Proceedings of the Highway Research Board,* **18** (1938), 100–112.

McFarland, Ross A. and Moseley, Alfred L., *Human Factors in Highway Transport Safety,* Harvard School of Public Health, Boston, Mass., 1954, p. 225–255.

Miller, Louis and Dimling, John A., Driver Licensing and Performance, Vol. I, *Research Review and Recommendations,* Report PB-183527 of Contract FH-11-6533 of the U.S. Department of Transportation, National Highway Safety Bureau, by Spindletop Research, 1969, 341 pp.

Rainey, Robert V. et al., An Investigation of the Role of Psychological Factors in Motor Vehicle Accidents, *Highway Research Board Bulletin,* **212** (1959), 11–15.

Siegel, Sidney, *Nonparametric Statistics for the Behavioral Sciences,* McGraw-Hill, New York, 1956, 312 pp.

Uhlaner, J. E., Goldstein, Leon G., and Van Steenbert, N.J., Development of Criteria of Safe Motor Vehicle Operation, *Highway Research Board Bulletin,* **60** (1952), 1–16.

Weiss, A. P. and Lauer, A. R., *Psychological Principles in Automotive Driving,* Ohio State Univ. Contributions in Psychology, No. 11, Ohio State Univ., Columbus, Ohio, 1930, 165 pp.

III

DRIVING TASK SIMULATION

Slade Hulbert and Charles Wojcik

Slade F. Hulbert is lecturer in the School of Engineering and Applied Science and research psychologist at the Institute of Transportation and Traffic Engineering, University of California, Los Angeles. He obtained his Ph.D. in psychology from the University of California, Los Angeles.

Dr. Hulbert's major interests include human factors research in transportation systems, engineering education, and psychological behavior theories. Foremost among his research activities is development of the concept of simulation laboratories and his contribution to the improvement of traffic control devices and related engineering theory and practice. His many research publications are in this area and on the topics of age, alcohol, and fatigue effects on driving.

Dr. Hulbert is a fellow of the Human Factors Society, a member of the American Psychological Association and its Division of Engineering Psychologists, the Institute of Traffic Engineers, and the Training Committee to Review Safety Research Activities of the Highway Research Board (National Academy of Sciences—National Research Council); is now on the Group 3 Council of the HRB; is research adviser to the National Joint Committee for Uniform Traffic Control Devices and also to the California Traffic Control Devices Committee; and consultant to the National Highway Safety Administration, U.S. Department of Transportation.

Charles K. Wojcik is lecturer in the School of Engineering and Applied Science and research engineer at the Institute of Transportation and Traffic Engineering, University of California, Los Angeles. He obtained his Ph.D. in engineering from the University of California, Los Angeles.

Dr. Wojcik has been affiliated with the University since 1957, where his major fields of interest are engineering dynamics, control systems, and mechanics of vehicles. He is equipment design engineer for the U.C.L.A. Driving

Simulation Facility, and his other research interests include transportation systems in general. Dr. Wojcik's teaching background at the University includes experimental engineering, dynamics, strength of materials, advanced kinematics, and machine design. Before his association with the University, Dr. Wojcik was design and project engineer with various industrial concerns in the United States and Europe. He has authored and coauthored numerous research papers and reports.

Dr. Wojcik is a member of the Society of Sigma Xi and the American Society of Mechanical Engineers.

Simulation is used in highway and traffic safety research for the following reasons:

1. It is safer.
2. It is more economical.
3. It may be the only practicable way to create conditions that are controlled enough for research purposes.

The most intriguing and important aspect of driving simulation is the capability of studying research variables in a systematic fashion and thus determining their effects on driving behavior. For example, in a simulator it is possible to change road configuration, reduce perceptual cues, alter steering-gear ratio, vary steering-force gradient, induce mechanical failures, introduce a talkative passenger and observe their effects on the driver's performance. These variables—the road, the vehicle, and the social situation—can be manipulated either as single elements or as patterns. Such research is needed to understand the total driving process and especially to understand what contributes to successful driving and accident-involved driving.

DEFINITION

A driving simulator is a device that creates the illusion of driving when, in fact, the driver is not actually driving in the real and unrestricted environment. Two major aspects of driving are the visual environment and the motion (or physical forces) environment. Several national conferences and many reports clearly state that regardless of cost, there has not yet been developed a truly satisfactory method for creating a visual display of the driving environment that is unprogrammed enough to allow the driver realistic freedom of movement and yet has characteristics necessary for research control, manipulation, and safety for the driver in the test situation. This holds true even for real vehicles moving on public roadways or on proving grounds because even a "real world," total, 360-degree view from an actually moving vehicle is not a satisfactory visual display for all research purposes because the elements in that total view are not completely under control of the researcher nor can all (or even most) of these elements be adequately measured.

TYPES OF VISUAL DISPLAY

Motion picture devices are visually quite realistic, but severely limited in the degree of freedom of choice they can afford the driver. Motion pictures also greatly limit the researcher as to the type of driving scene he can experiment with.

Television systems and other model landscape types of display are far less realistic visually due to the poor image quality. Picture sharpness is three or four times less than motion pictures and depth of focus problems make it difficult to show a scene of uniform and maximum clarity.

Other systems, such as point light source, direct optical enlargement systems, and analog computer image generators, while they all have something to offer researchers, are more limited in potential than television or motion pictures. Computer-generated images do, however, offer promise of solving this most difficult aspect of driving simulation.

A SURVEY OF PROGRESS

A survey paper has (Hulbert and Wojcik, 1964) listed the sequence of events starting from 1948 when the UCLA Institute of Transportation and Traffic Engineering prepared a statement of the need for a research laboratory that would simulate the driving experience (Conference on Mathematical Models, 1967). In 1952 development of such a laboratory was initiated at UCLA where it has been in continual use and is still undergoing further development.

The feasibility of producing a simulation laboratory was first argued for in 1957 (Mathewson, 1957) and thoroughly documented in "Automobile Driving Simulation Feasibility Study," a PHS report (Cornell Aeronautical Laboratories, 1958). This study marked the official interest by the then newly created Accident Prevention Division of the U.S. Public Health Service, at that time under the direction of Dr. James Goddard. This interest has continued and was manifest in two development contracts: one with Goodyear Corporation at Columbus to produce a working prototype of a simulator with an unprogrammed visual display (in this case, closed-circuit television) (Anon., 1963a); and a second contract with RCA at Bethesda to produce a simulator with semiprogrammed display for research into driving behavior (Anon., 1963b).

The need for driving simulation research facilities was pointed out in the Williamsburg Conference (1958). Again, in a publication of the Special Committee on Highway Research Priorities of the Highway Research Board of the National Research Council (1959), driving simulation was included among the "19 broad areas of highway research, each of which is adjudged to rate A-1 in importance and urgency."

Early in 1961, a National Conference on Driving Simulation (1961) was jointly sponsored by the Automotive Safety Foundation, U.S. Bureau of Public Roads, and the U.S. Public Health Service. A report of this conference entitled, "New Horizons for Highway Safety Through Driving Simulation," states on page 8 that:

"Driving simulation offers important long-range benefits to traffic safety through research, training, and driver testing. Some authorities believe that stepped-up research, aided by simulation techniques, eventually will lead to a breakthrough in the reduction of accident rate. All are agreed that research can produce substantial benefits, and that the critical importance of highway safety in our social and economic life justifies the employment of all available techniques where applicable."

On page 16 the report continues:

"Ultimately, a step-by-step development of increasingly complex simulators offers promise of new and urgently needed information on the functioning of the vehicle-driver-road system. This could lead to a major breakthrough in the program to increase traffic safety."

Among the advantages of the simulation technique are:

1. opportunity to experiment without danger to life and property as might be the case in real-life situations;
2. ability to isolate variables in design and operation and to study each singly or in desired combination;
3. ability to establish and maintain experimental controls necessary for valid results;
4. use in predicting effect of proposed designs or control measures;
5. opportunity to simulate an accident as against the necessity of waiting for an actual accident to occur;
6. opportunity to measure scientifically, with laboratory instrumentation, driver performance in specific situations.

This 1961 conference further agreed that this avenue should be pursued and suggested that the Highway Research Board (HRB) of the

National Research Council of the National Academy of Sciences become the vehicle for further action. Accordingly in the January 1962 meeting of the HRB, a Special Committee on Driving Simulation was created under whose sponsorship more than 20 research papers have since been presented. This committee sponsored a seminar on Research Applications of Driving Simulation (1963) in February 1963.

The 1964 paper (Hulbert and Wojcik, 1964) listed the following simulator devices:

"A. Training Devices

1. The American Automobile Association as early as 1938 reported a single place trainer consisting of a mock-up of the driver's compartment in front of which is a model landscape. A moving belt loop representing the highway passes under a model vehicle. The speed of the belt loop highway and the lateral placement of the model vehicle are controlled by the trainee's accelerator pedal and steering wheel, respectively.

2. Aetna Drivotrainer, developed in 1953 by the Aetna Casualty and Surety Company, is a classroom trainer using motion picture display that is shared by the trainees, each of whom operates an individual mock-up of a vehicle. The driver's responses do not alter the visual display.

3. All State Good Driver Trainer produced in 1962 is a classroom device similar in concept to the Aetna Drivotrainer. Improvements were made in the visual display including wide-angle photography and error indicators.

4. Miles Motor Driving Trainer, developed from R. A. F. World War II equipment, as early as 1948, comprises a car mock-up facing a translucent screen onto which is rear-projected an image of a model landscape which moves in response to the handling of the vehicle mock-up. In this way the driver is able to control his apparent movement along the roadways and past the models of trees and buildings placed on the plexiglass landscape. Actually, the driver is moving the landscape relative to a fixed position light bulb which in turn causes a shadow picture to appear on the translucent screen. To the extent that the tiny bulb approximates a point of light, the shadow pictures are sharp and have realistic perspective. This type of visual display has become known as 'point light source' and is in use on other devices. The area over which the driver may operate the simulator is limited to a model landscape approximately 3 feet in diameter.

5. Sim-L-Car produced in 1961 by General Precision Ltd. is similar in

concept to the Miles Trainer. Provision was made to operate either a real vehicle or a vehicle mock-up.

B. Testing Devices

1. Aetna Drivotron developed by Rockwell Manufacturing Company and introduced in 1961, comprises a motion picture in front of a vehicle mock-up for evaluating an individual driver. Speed and lateral placement illusions are under control of the driver.

2. U.S. Armed Forces have developed several devices for operators of heavy equipment. Early work of this sort was accomplished at the Detroit Arsenal and the Navy Special Devices Center at Sands Point, N.Y.

C. Research Devices

1. An Analog Driving Simulator developed in 1960 by General Motors Research Laboratories uses an automobile cab with a visual display on an oscilloscope tube facing the driver through the windshield area in line with the steering wheel. The visual display consists of a series of five horizontal bars located one above the other. Each bar, from top to bottom, represents the width of the road at successively closer locations to the front of the car. By making the top bars shorter than the bottom, the display is not unlike a much simplified perspective view of the road. Lateral displacement of the bars relative to one another indicates curvature, and displacement of the car on the road. Thus the driver can determine both his present lateral error and the future course of the road. The display is generated by a continuous loop transport with five reading heads which may be spaced at desired increments. The road curvature is recorded on the tape. Tape speed which is controlled by the driver is then analogous to car speed. The lateral placement illusion is dependent on the vertical alignment of the 'stack' of bars which is controlled by the steering wheel position in relation to road curvature signal.

2. Liberty Mutual Insurance Company has developed a simulator in which the driver operates a mock-up of a vehicle in response to a rear-projected scene produced by the same device used in the Sim-L-Car. In addition, there is being developed the capability of displaying moving vehicles to which the driver can react and interact.

3. In 1964 there was developed at George Washington University, Washington, D.C., a device that could be called a 'surface vehicle simulator.' Using a point light source display and computer-linked servo mechanism, the driver will be studied as a variable in the design of

control systems for novel vehicles as well as for conventional. Significant advances have been made in the design of this point light source display system by extending the size of the model landscape and the field of view available to the driver.

4. At Ohio State University has been developed a device in which a driver may be studied as he operates a vehicle mock-up in response to a closed circuit T.V. picture of a moving roadway on which a model vehicle appears to be traveling. This picture appears on a T.V. picture tube. A computer link provides feedback to the display so that the driver may vary his apparent lateral placement, speed, and following distance behind the model vehicle. Speed is the belt speed and following distance is distance of the model vehicle from the T.V. camera lens. The model vehicle moves independent of the belt, but appears to be riding on the roadway. On a separate belt mounted at a right angle to the roadway, there appears a representation of telephone poles. Both belts move at the same speed.

5. In Japan, a simulator has been produced that is similar to the one at UCLA in that a real vehicle operates on rollers in response to a motion picture display. Some provision has been made for simulation of inertial forces.

6. At Harvard University, a vehicle mock-up can be operated in response to an oscilloscope display (Neuberger, 1963). A two variable 'pursuit' display is used, one variable of which represents the input (or desired output) and the other variable represents the actual output of the system. These variables are displayed on a dual beam oscilloscope in the form of a dot (target) and a line (integrated operator output). Visual representation of the sum of four nonharmonically related sinusoids insures a random appearing motion of the target dot. The operator responds by manipulating the steering wheel which moves the vertical line at a rate proportional to the steering wheel displacement.

Simulated inertia, stiffness, and damping (input impedance) of the steering system are controlled by the torque motor. Power is obtained from a servo-amplifier and amplidyne. The output from the potentiometer and tachometer are the inputs to the servo-amplifier. Simulated impedance can be varied by altering coefficients of the servo-amplifier.

A variety of disturbances can be superimposed upon the torque motor input to simulate steering wheel shimmy or sudden wheel displacement. The operator can be made to experience kinesthetic stimuli characteristic of adverse road conditions, blowouts, and/or misaligned or unbalanced wheels.

Elements of the vehicle mock-up are experimentally variable to facilitate driving behavior research of various control system configurations.

7. There was developed by RCA at Bethesda, Maryland, under contract with U.S.P.H.S., a modern version of a simulator first devised by T. W. Forbes (1931) and called by him, 'The Miniature Highway Test.' In the RCA device, a vehicle mock-up is operated in response to a 20 foot long scale (½″ = 1′) model of a roadway scene viewed through an aperture. Moving belts provide a representation of traffic lanes and roadside elements in much the same manner as the roadway scene in the Ohio State device. However, the illusion of traffic in this case is created by model vehicles that are fastened to the moving belts and all of the apparent speed relationships are controlled by adjusting the belt speeds. Just as in the Forbes device, opposing traffic, as well as traffic in the same direction, will be presented. Lateral movements of the viewing aperture relative to the belts will create the illusion of lateral placement changes when the steering wheel is moved. Improvements over the Forbes' device will be through the introduction of a lens system and by the use of computers to regulate the movements of the various belts. The lens system is designed to make the scale-model scene appear life size. An out-of-sight experimenter will place and remove model vehicles on appropriate belts to create various traffic situations for study.

8. There was developed by Goodyear Aerospace Corporation at Akron Ohio, under contract with U.S.P.H.S., a closed circuit T.V. visual display and related model landscape and vehicle mock-up to provide a projected image (approximately 45° azimuth field) of what the pick-up lens sees as it is maneuvered over the model landscape by the control actions of the driver. The landscape will contain not only roadways but moving model vehicles remotely controlled so that the driver may interact with traffic in an unprogrammed manner in much the same way as that planned for the Liberty Mutual device. A large portion of the visual field at the sides of the projected T.V. image may be filled with displays of still or moving pictures. Both daytime and night driving will be simulated.

9. Miles Electronics Ltd. has produced a simulator for the British Army to use in training tank drivers. This device employs a closed circuit projection T.V. system and a model landscape in much the same fashion as that described in item 8 above."

Two major additions have been made to the 1964 list of types of driving simulators. One is the creation of a moving-base device at General Motors Corporation Research Laboratory (Beinke and Williams, 1968). This simulator uses a color motion picture visual display and a pitch-and-roll mechanism to create the visual illusion and "feel" of driving. The other is a conversion of a television flight simulator at North American Corporation at Columbus, Ohio, where a black and white image is augmented by a three-color traffic signal light projector and the image of a lead vehicle is superimposed from a separate television camera and projector.

Other activities have to do with improving the data acquisition from simulators and the exploration of new methods of creating the visual display. Both Professor Norman Heimstra at the University of South Dakota and Allen L. Cudworth at the Liberty Mutual Research Center have developed methods for measuring lateral placement on the Sim-L-Car point-light source display. At South Dakota the system uses a proximity detection principle to measure displacement from an electrically generated magnetic field that stretches along the model roadway. Liberty Mutual uses a photocell principle to detect and measure the position of the shadow created by the edge of the model roadway. Both groups are also working to improve the realism and control of "other vehicles" that are made to appear in the driving scene. For example, a mirror arrangement is being used at Liberty Mutual to simulate the glare of oncoming headlights.

Work is continuing at the Providence, Rhode Island facility of United States Public Health Service to improve the Goodyear closed-circuit television simulator and the RCA moving-belt device that were described in the 1964 survey report (Hulbert and Wojcik, 1964). For the Goodyear television system, virtual image displays are being developed to create a more realistic driving scene. This group also has added a Sim-L-Car point-light source device and is working to improve lateral measurement capability.

THE UCLA SIMULATOR

The UCLA Driving Simulation Laboratory (Wojcik and Hulbert, 1965), as presented in block diagram form in Figure 1, has been developed to measure performance of highway-transportation systems (man-machine-environment), Figure 2. This simulator is a projection room in which an automobile is driven on steel rollers of a standard chassis dynamometer while the driver views the road scene that is projected onto a curved screen 8.5 feet in radius. The driver also views the road scene behind him by looking through the rear-view mirror at a motion picture projected on a screen placed beyond the rear window of the vehicle. The field of vision of the front view is 150 degrees. The projection technique used is a special type of motion picture presentation called Dimension 150, in use under contract with Dimension 150, Inc. of Hollywood, California. Dimension 150 is a single-lens process that nearly

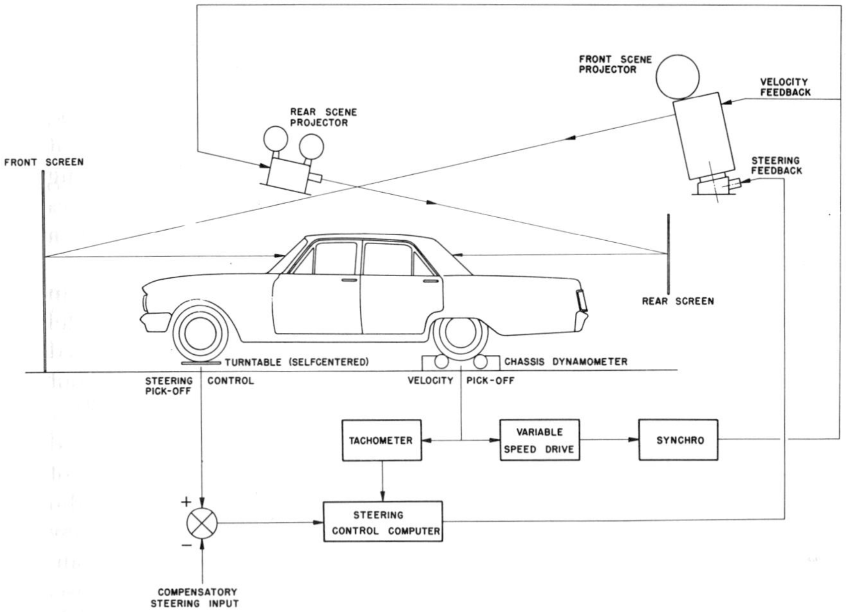

Figure 1. Block diagram of driving simulation laboratory (S. F. Hulbert and C. K. Wojcik).

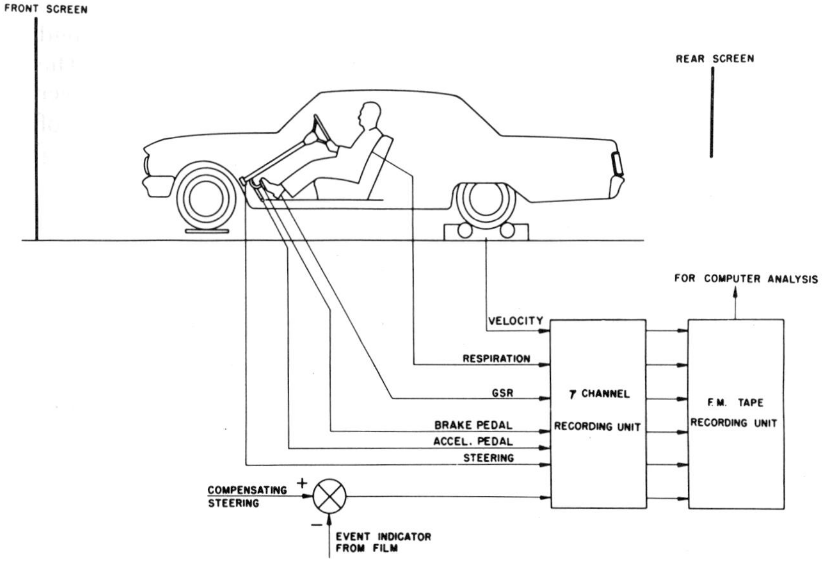

Figure 2. Measuring system in driving simulation laboratory (S. F. Hulbert and C. K. Wojcik).

duplicates the human binocular field of vision (Hulbert and Wojcik, 1959). It entails use of a unique anamorphic-type optical system that photographs and projects a distortion-free field of 150 degrees including the central and peripheral portions thereof. This technique utilizes standard cameras, lenses, film, projection booths, projectors, and a special screen material.

There are two variable-speed projectors mounted on a turntable in the projection booth. The projectors are manufactured by DeVry, Model NDX-35, modified for selsyn control, and their capacity was increased to 3000 feet of film. This length of film constitutes an average of about 30 minutes of projection time, depending on the speed the driver chooses to drive. Since there are two projectors, one can be reloaded while the other is in operation. Hence, the only limitation on time of projection comes from the total length of film (number of reels). Film used for the front-view projection is 35-mm colored film. The rear-view projectors are Dumont 16-mm, continuous-image projectors, custom-built and modified for selsyn control. They are mounted on a fixed base.

The speed of the projectors is governed by the speed of the vehicle placed on the chassis dynamometer; to be more specific, by the two synchro generators which are interlocked electrically with synchro motors of the projectors. One of the synchrogenerators is interlocked with two synchromotors of the projectors in the projection booth; the second synchrogenerator is interlocked with two rear-view projectors. The range of simulated velocity is limited by the projector speed. The lower boundary of 12 frames per second represents an average threshold of human perception of flicker. There are two revolutions of the shutter per frame giving 24 light interruptions per second at 12 frames per second. The upper boundary of 45 frames per second is the maximum speed the projector can operate without risk of breaking the film.

The front-view projectors in the projection booth are mounted on a turntable driven by a servomotor. The voltage input signal to this motor is a product of two voltages; one representing the velocity of the car and taken directly from the tachometer of the chassis dynamometer and the second representing the rotation of the front tires of the vehicle. The front tires are placed on two turnplates that are spring-loaded to simulate the resistance present when making a turn. One of the turnplates is geared to a potentiometer. The voltage signal is proportional to the displacement of this potentiometer.

Because a motion-picture technique is a programmed visual-presentation technique, a negative voltage signal, representing the steering-wheel displacement during the ride when the picture was taken (also

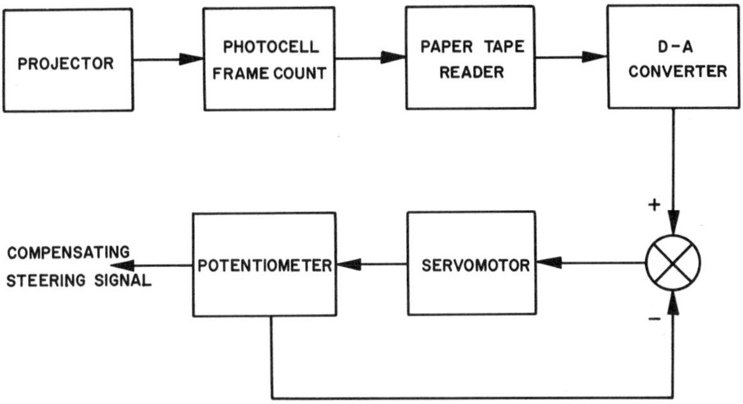

Figure 3. System for generating compensating steering signal (S. F. Hulbert and C. K. Wojcik).

called compensating steering) is introduced to the control system. This signal is generated by the system shown in Figure 3.

The steering wheel displacements, appropriate for a given film, are recorded on a paper tape in a discrete fashion for each frame of the film. The motion of the paper tape is interlocked with the motion of the film in such a way that for each frame advancement of the film, the paper tape moves one step forward. When the recorded steering signal and the signal from the potentiometer are equal in magnitude but of opposite polarity, they cancel out; then the input signal to the servomotor is zero and the turntable and the projectors remain at rest. When signals do not cancel out, the turntable and the projectors rotate, causing the picture to move from its center position on the screen and thus simulate a change in the direction of motion of the vehicle. This method of opposite sign signals is used to force the subject to control the steering wheel as he would in real driving. Furthermore, the driver's control of the steering wheel is compared with the recorded steering signal when analyzing the data obtained during experiments.

The heading feedback and the wide range of control of the projection speed eliminate, to a large degree, the drawbacks of programmed presentation.

Additional features incorporated in the system to improve its fidelity are simulation of road incline, and atmospheric conditions such as rain, wind, and fog. The simulation of the road incline is done by means of the chassis dynamometer power-absorption unit. The power-absorption unit is similar to a centrifugal pump having vanes or blades on the rotor to throw the water outward. Unlike the centrifugal pump, however, the outside housing or stator also has vanes that oppose the flow of the rapidly moving water. Thus, the power-absorption unit acts as a water brake. The dynamometer water is circulated by the pumping action of the rotor in a closed system. By maintaining a constant amount of water in this closed system, any desired load may be held indefinitely, or the load may be changed instantly by varying the amount of water circulating within the system.

Simulation of rain is achieved simply by sprinkling water over the windshields of the vehicle. Used water is then diverted to a special drain.

Simulation of wind is done in two ways. For winds along the path of the vehicle the power-absorption unit of the chassis dynamometer is used. To simulate transverse winds a torque is applied to the turnplates supporting the front tires. This torque is transmitted through the steering mechanism to the steering wheel, giving the driver a feeling of side thrust on the vehicle exerted by wind and a resulting drifting off the road. Simulation of the wind is heightened by strong circulation of air within the room provided by the ventilating system.

Simulation of fog is accomplished by placing special moving filters in front of the projector lens to create any desired level of vision impairment.

In addition to these developments, recent progress has created a method of casting a shadow on the motion picture screen (Hulbert and Wojcik, 1969) into which a second projector (16-mm) throws an image of the roadway and vehicles. At this time, the resulting image is useful only for nighttime driving scenes. Films depicting various experimental patterns of roadway reflectors have been created using an animated (frame by frame) filming technique of tabletop models. A similar, more complicated, technique has been used to create 16-mm films not only of the roadway, but of groups of vehicles with which the test driver (in the simulator) can interact. A 3:1 zoom projection lens provides this driver interaction capability with respect to car-following distance. Model vehicles in these films are shown with active headlights and rearlights.

CLOSED-CIRCUIT TELEVISION

The research usefulness of the UCLA Driving Simulation Laboratory has been increased lately through addition to the system of a closed-circuit television display and two animated model landscapes. A block diagram of the modified facility is shown in Figure 4.

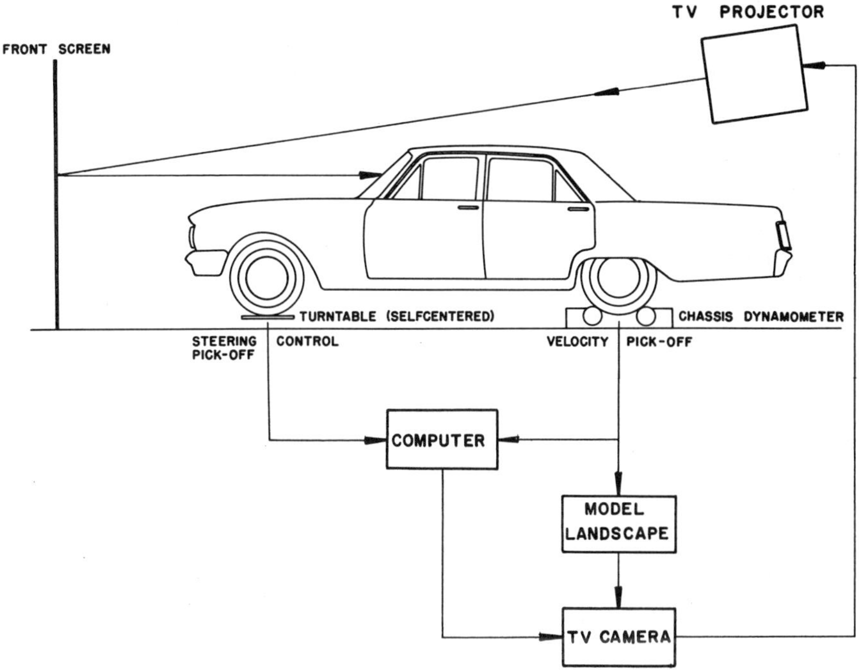

Figure 4. Block diagram of driving simulator with television display (S. F. Hulbert and C. K. Wojcik).

One model landscape is in the form of a disc, 8 feet in diameter, for near-circular roadways; another model landscape is in the form of a continuous belt for near-straight roadways. Each of the landscapes is driven by the rollers of the chassis dynamometer through the system of a selsyn generator and a selsyn motor. Because of this arrangement the velocity of the television camera, relative to the model landscape, is directly proportional to the speed of the vehicle in the driving simulator. Both model landscapes have moving vehicles; the circular landscape has one such vehicle, while the "straight roadway" landscape has two such vehicles that move in opposite directions. Each of the moving vehicles has its own drive.

Since the motion of the television camera with respect to the model landscapes is a plane motion, only 3 degrees of freedom in the system are required. One of the degrees of freedom, in the forward direction, is provided by the motion of the model landscape with respect to the stationary television camera stand. The remaining 2 degrees of freedom—translation in the transverse direction, and rotation (yaw) about a vertical axis—are designed into the camera mount. Both these motions are generated by servomotors that receive appropriate input signals from an analog computer.

The television camera is a GPL Precision 1000 model, two-unit, solid-state camera. Its main features are: resolution up to 1000 lines (horizontally), 15 mc band width, and a scan rate of 525 lines per frame. The lens used in this camera is a Schneider, Xenon lens, its focal length is 16 mm, and its "*f*" number is 2.0. The television projector is a Prizomatic 5XTP projector. The image from this unit is projected on a 6- by 8-foot lenticular screen placed in front of the vehicle.

The video signals from the camera pickup tube go through the camera control unit to the projector. The image of the road scene is then projected onto the screen. The driver viewing the screen responds, in turn, to changes in the highway scene. Thus the driver-vehicle-environment system is a closed loop just as it is during actual driving.

The instrumentation of the system is used to measure and record positions and velocities of the television camera and the animated vehicles with respect to the model landscape.

The television system just described is capable of producing the completely unprogrammed display that is so important in studies of driver performance of such driving tasks as tracking, car-following, passing, and overtaking in the presence of on-coming traffic.

INSTRUMENTATION SYSTEMS

Two basic classes of instrumentation are in use in driving simulator facilities:

1. Instrumentation necessary for the functional operation of the simulator.
2. Instrumentation required to measure and record the performance of the man-machine system.

In some cases the two classes overlap since some information necessary for operation is also of interest to research.

The first class includes the instrumentation measuring system of vehicle performance and conditions including velocity of the vehicle, power consumed, displacement of the steering wheel, room and water temperature, and so forth. The second class of instrumentation includes recording devices. Research needs have been met by various electronic recording systems. A typical example of data recorded includes:

Vehicle speed.
Brake and gas-pedal displacements (separately or in combination).
Steering wheel displacement.
Time reference (pips) of certain traffic events in the film or on the model roadway.
Galvanic skin response (GSR).
Respiration.
Heart rate.
Timing track for synchronized data conversion for all channels.

Figure 5 shows a typical recording of a driver's responses during a simulated drive in the UCLA Simulator. On this tracing, channel 3, for the steering wheel displacement shows two ranges of full-scale displacement:

1. Small motions of the steering wheel, up to a quarter of a turn.
2. Large motions of the steering wheel, in excess of a quarter turn.

Pips, in channel 4, represent electrical impulses received from a photocell actuated by opaque markings on the edge of the film.

The GSR continuously measures the electrical resistance of the skin. For that purpose two electrodes are placed on the left foot of the driver.

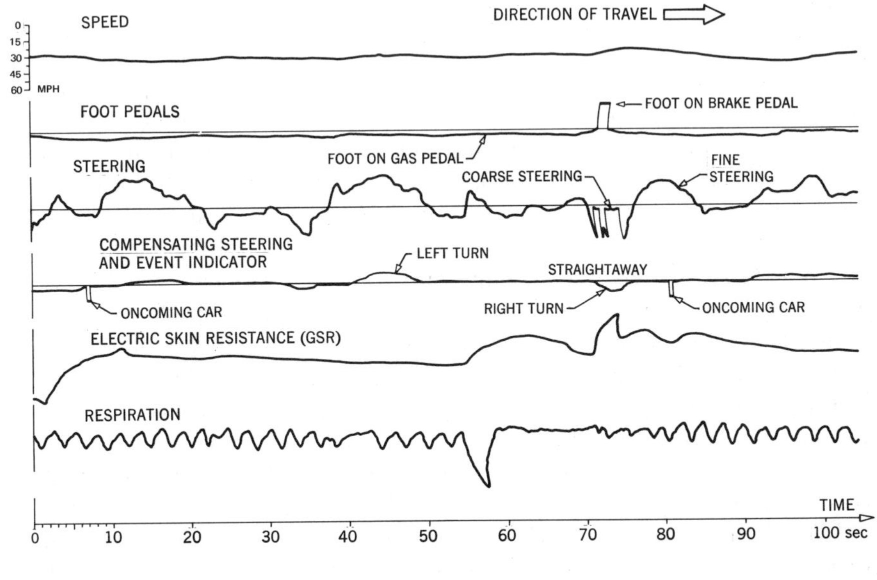

Figure 5. Record of driver's responses during a simulated ride (S. F. Hulbert and C. K. Wojcik).

To measure the driver's respiration a belt is placed around his chest. This belt has a built-in strain gage that measures chest expansion.

SIMULATION OF MOTION

The purpose of the motion-simulating system in a driving simulator is to provide the driver with the kinesthetic cues that are appropriate for the driving situation presented to him by the visual display. These kinesthetic cues are derived from the forces acting on the driver's body. Among these forces, the inertia forces are of primary importance since they signal changes in motion of the vehicle.

With the exception of the case of the vehicle moving at constant speed on a straight and level road, the driver is subjected to some changes in motion. These changes are usually expressed in terms of the tangential and normal components of acceleration or in terms of the inertia forces associated with these components. The magnitudes of these accelerations or inertia forces vary widely from below human thresholds to dangerously high values as in an automobile crash. Because of these great differences in magnitudes, it is convenient to distinguish here two classes of accelerations:

1. Low magnitudes of various durations as experienced in normal driving.
2. High magnitudes of extremely short durations as encountered in an automobile crash.

Investigations of inertia forces have different aims for each of these classes. The purpose of investigating inertia forces of low magnitudes is to study the effects of their actions on the driver and his performance. On the other hand, the purpose of investigating high magnitude forces is to study the traumatic effects of their actions on the driver's body and the vehicle. In discussing driving simulation requirements, only those magnitudes encountered in normal driving will be considered.

Inertia forces are of great importance to the driver. They inform him about the dynamic state of the vehicle and they affect his performance. Naturally, the driver expects their presence. Lack of inertia forces in various simulators has not only diminished the realism of the simulated ride or flight, but also, in the opinion of some researchers, has been the reason many simulators cause some subjects to become motion sick (Miller and Goodson, 1960; Hulbert and Wojcik, 1963; Testa, 1969). For these reasons, a high-fidelity driving simulator should include a system to simulate inertia forces.

The human body has the fundamental property of mass; it therefore develops inertia forces under the influence of external forces acting upon it. Normally, the force of gravity is the only considerable force acting upon the body; hence, weight is fundamental in human experience. However, if other forces are acting on the body, the effects of these forces can be appreciated only in terms of their common resultant. This is a very important fact that is utilized in creating an illusion of motion by tilting the subject (together with the vehicle and the visual display) to a position at which the tangential component of gravity force is equal to the inertia force being simulated at that instant. Since the vehicle moving in a plane has 2 translational degrees of freedom, along the two principal dimensions of the vehicle, the tilting mechanism must have 2 rotational degrees of freedom (pitch and roll). Rotation about a vertical axis (yaw motion) is not sensed by human operators; hence, no simulation of that motion is required.

In simulating inertia forces by means of tilting the subject, it is important to select an appropriate location for the axis of rotation. In perceiving changes in motion, both the vestibular system and the seat contact play very important roles (Hulbert and Wojcik, 1963; Wojcik, 1969). Placing the axis of rotation through one of them, say the vestibular system, would produce a large error in the simulated accelerations, both tangential and normal, for the lower part of the body. A compromise seems to be the best solution; that is, the axis of rotation should be placed halfway between the vestibular system and the seat so the errors for these two points can be minimized.

The above method of simulating the inertia forces employs only the rotations of the subject about the pitch and roll axes. In order to diminish the influence of the undesired components of the angular acceleration associated with such a simulation technique, one can use a combination of translational and rotational motions (Booz and Allen, 1968) to simulate the inertia forces. In such a case, a translational acceleration of given amplitude is applied to the system for a certain period of time; at the same time, the system rotates to a predetermined angular position, as shown in Figure 6. There are three phases in such a simulation:

1. Onset of the force; initiated by translational acceleration and gradually transferred to gravity acceleration by means of rotation. (The resultant acceleration produced by translation and rotation is equal to the simulated acceleration.)
2. Steady-state condition; the magnitude of the force is held constant by maintaining the appropriate angle of rotation for as long as it is required.

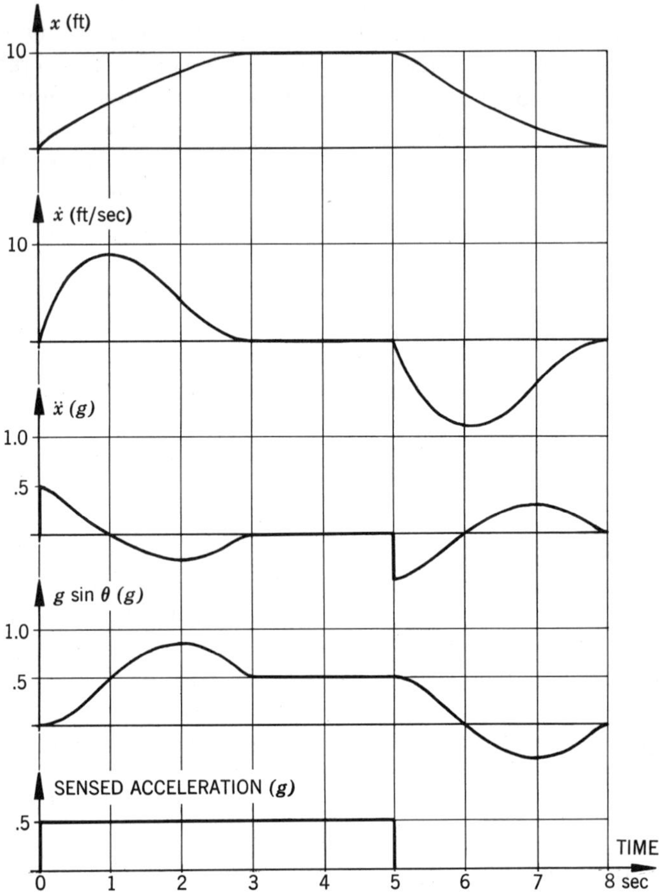

Figure 6. Combined translation and rotation to simulate braking (S. F. Hulbert and C. K. Wojcik).

3. Termination of the force; this phase requires a translation and rotation program that is an inverse of phase 1.

The advantage of this method of simulation is that the rotation here can be performed at much lower rates, and thus, the undesirable components of the angular acceleration can be held to small values. However, this method can be used only in a completely programmed situation because, in order to resolve the acceleration to be simulated into the translational and rotational components, one must know its value in advance and decide on the rate of rotation, compute the translational acceleration, and then program the system accordingly.

Besides the inertia forces acting in the horizontal plane, we have to consider the forces acting on the driver in the vertical direction. When driving along a perfectly flat and level road, there is no vertical motion in the system and the vertical force acting on the driver is simply equal in magnitude to the gravity force. However, when the road surface is coarse or wavy, the driver is subjected to some vertical motion that causes variation of the vertical force. This type of motion can be duplicated by devices specially built for this purpose. Such devices are placed between the vehicle (or vehicle mock-up) and the moving base that is used for simulation of horizontal motion. A simple model of a driving simulator with a tilting mechanism, moving base, and system for simulating the vertical motion is shown in Figure 7.

Human perception of motion is strongly influenced by visual and tactile cues. This fact has been utilized, with some degree of success, in

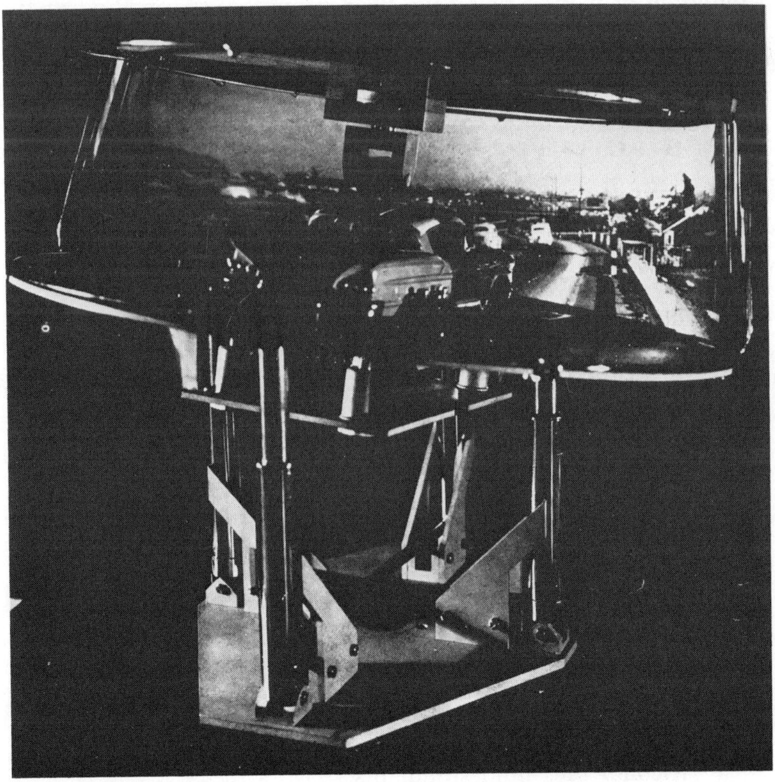

Figure 7. Scale model of a moving-base driving simulator (S. F. Hulbert and C. K. Wojcik).

several flight simulators to simulate the vertical motion. In one such simulator, a series of straps hold the pilot down against the seat. Variations in accelerations are simulated by changing the tension in the straps and, consequently, the pressure between the seat and the pilot. Another method employs an inflatable seat cushion in which both the inflation pressure and seat contour are varied as a function of the vertical acceleration to be simulated. In this way, contact pressure and contact area are programmed to simulate changes in magnitude and distribution of seat pressure. The last technique can be extended to include the longitudinal accelerations commonly encountered in driving.

In summing up, we can state that simulation of motion is necessary for a high-fidelity driving simulator. The task of simulating inertia forces is facilitated by the fact that human perceptions of motion and position in space are rather crude and strongly influenced by visual cues (Wojcik, 1969; McConnell, 1957; Clark and Stewart, 1962). Of all techniques for simulation of motion that have been proposed, the method of tilting the whole assembly (driver, vehicle, and visual display) seems to be most suitable for this application.

RESEARCH ACTIVITY

The relatively few existing research simulators have been and are being actively used in studies of the following important categories of driving behavior:

- I. Traffic Control Devices
  - a. Wrong way driving warnings
    - 1. Signs and pavement markings at off-ramps and on-ramps
    - 2. Red-colored raised pavement markers on the highway
  - b. Tangent off-ramp exit signs placed in the gore
  - c. Passing zone markings and signs
  - d. Automatic passing control system for rural highways
  - e. Route guidance system
- II. Drug Effect
  - a. Alcohol
  - b. Tranquilizers used for mental patients
  - c. Marihuana
  - d. Cold remedies (antihistamines)
  - e. Alcohol plus mild tranquilizers
  - f. Alcohol plus mild stimulants
  - g. Alcohol plus carbon monoxide

III. Driver as Control Element
   a. Car-following behavior
   b. Random path following
   c. Overtaking and passing
   d. Speed estimation
   e. Vigilance
   f. Fatigue effects
   g. Age effects
   h. "Bad" versus "good" driving record groups
IV. Vehicle Characteristics
   a. Steering system response
   b. Vibration and large-amplitude vertical displacement
   c. Visibility
   d. Rear lighting systems
V. Highway Design
   a. Left-hand off-ramps
   b. Tangent off-ramps
   c. Freeway interchange design
IV. Driving Conditions
   a. Reduced visibility in fog
   b. Against glare of oncoming headlights

An example of this research activity is a fatigue study in which 11 drowsy drivers and 9 alert drivers and a control group of drivers not selected on this basis were tested in the UCLA Driving Simulation Laboratory at the end of their workday and before eating their evening meal. On most testing days two drivers were run, one at 5:30 P.M. and the other at 7:00 P.M. Subjects drive approximately 25 miles, simulated distance, on a film made up of several driving scenes, blended into a single continuous drive of 45 to 65 minutes duration, depending upon the driving speed preferred by the individual driver.

Scoring

At nine places along the filmed drive, there is an impending collision with a moving object. None of these actually occur because these objects change their speed and/or their path. Drivers are scored as "failing" or "passing" in their response to these impending collisions, depending on whether they responded appropriately and in sufficient time to have avoided the collision that would have occurred if the other objects had proceeded as they threatened to do.

Each such pass or fail score must take into account the speed the test driver was traveling and then a calculation must be made to determine the "action point" which is the point along the roadway before which he must have begun his attempt to stop in order to accomplish that stop before reaching the "collision point." This, in turn, requires the determination of the collision point for each of the 9 traffic situations.

Since all of the traffic scene is on film, both the collision point and the action point are particular frames of film. The collision point is always the same frame but the action point varies with the speed of the driver. The response values are generated from the computer printout of accelerator pedal and brake pedal times taken from an arbitrary starting point in the film which point is near (a few seconds before) the collision point.

The following notes describe how the pass or fail score is determined for the various columns on the data work sheet:

1. "Speed" of the DSL driver is read from the computer output as average FPS (frames per second) and is the measurement currently being scored which is the closest to the film speed and consequently the truest estimate of feet-along-the-road for the driver. The mph speed is calculated from FPS.

2. Deceleration: the column marked "max time" is speed dependent, assumes constant velocity before deceleration, and constant deceleration. The number is the maximum allowable lapse time in seconds, at the end of which the driver *must* decelerate in order to come to a forceable stop and avoid the potential accident. That is, if he has not begun to decelerate by that time, he *cannot* come to a stop in time. No reaction time less than 0.5 second is considered a valid reaction to the indicated event.

3. Brake: the column marked "max" is calculated by adding 0.5 second to the "max decel" time; the additional being considered an average foot-to-brake reaction time (RT). Thus it would represent the RT from the beginning of the event to the first brake press. S (subject) RT is read from the computer output in seconds. No RT less than 1 second is valid.

4. Scoring failures: S is deemed to have "failed" to respond adequately to the event *indicated* if:

a. his speed is excessive to the extent he *could not* have stopped within the length of the event, or

b. *none* of the four possible RT is equal to or less than their corresponding "maximums."

Due to the arbitrariness of 0.5 and 1.5 as being "average" RT for acceleration to brake and GSR, respectively, some leeway is given before marking a "fail" on very close (but over) RT comparisons. The working hypothesis is that one would expect the driver to see and react to the events that were created on the film. Therefore, where there was a doubt the S was considered *passed.*

OUTLOOK FOR THE FUTURE

Computer-Generated Images

The University of California at Los Angeles had conducted a study of the feasibility of using a digitally computed image (CGI) for the visual display of a research driving simulator (Kamnitzer and Hulbert, 1969).

A CGI is obtained from information stored within the memory of a digital computer. In order to understand this system, we must realize that photographic images are projections of a three-dimensional environment upon a two-dimensional surface. As the viewpoint (or station point) is changed, the projection changes, even though the environment may remain the same. To obtain equivalent results in a CGI system, an "environment" is stored, in terms of numerical data, in the computer's memory. This environment is described in three dimensions: it consists of objects of various shapes at specific locations, oriented in a particular manner. Using mathematical rules of perspective, the computer is programmed to supply data upon which a planar projection of its stored environment is made. If the coordinates of the viewpoint are changed, the projection will change, as in the photographic situation.

Using CGI techniques, it is possible to represent an environment, whether it is urban, rural, real, or imaginary, and observe it from any desired location, left, right, above, below, far, near, with extreme ease and without building a physical model. If successive images are generated at motion-picture frame rates while the viewing coordinates are gradually changed, the illusion of moving through the environment is created. Thus, a new and highly flexible method has been developed for creating a driving simulator visual scene.

Because the environment exists only as data in a computer store, it may be easily modified to suit the needs of a particular experiment. A city may be rearranged; a building removed. A freeway may be narrowed, a curve elevated, or better markings added. In driving simulation, since there are no physical components, there is nothing to be damaged, even when collisions occur. Dense traffic may be added to a highway, or a child may dart across a street before the driver. A tire could blow out while passing on a curve. There is an endless range of opportunities for exploring driver behavior with a sophisticated simulator employing computer-generated images. Situations that could never be created in the real world and that would be difficult to implement with model terrain boards become relatively easy with CGI.

COMPARISON OF VISUAL SYSTEMS

In order to further assay the future state of visual displays for research in driving simulation, it is important to attempt to make evaluative comparisons among three major types of visual simulation techniques, namely Terrain Board Television (TBTV), Photographic (PT), and CGI. Several general categories are provided for the following discussion of comparative advantages among these types of visual simulation for various research requirements.

Quality of Image

This criterion is important for all visual display simulators. It becomes even more significant when the bulk of information being used by the operator comes to him through his sense of vision as is the case in automobile driving.

The overall effect caused by poor image quality is difficult to quantify. Some persons develop eyestrain headaches from trying to make blurred images clear. In the UCLA Driving Simulation Laboratory, when the fog-effect filter is placed in front of the projector lens, the driver's speed drops immediately and he directs the major share of his attention to the roadway in order to accomplish the guidance or tracking task. Such behavior is typical of driving in reduced visibility condition, but is *not* typical of driving under normal visibility conditions, and could not be tolerated in a driving simulator.

Realism

This is a highly subjective quality. It is the combination of factors that makes the subject feel as if he were actually in the environment that is being visually simulated. The effects of high image detail have not been fully evaluated, although it is evident that increased information content in a picture may tend to distract as much as it helps.

Research Opportunities

It is in this area that the versatility of the CGI system gives it a strong advantage over the other systems. The ability to simulate practically any set of conditions for a driving situation that may exist or might be hypothesized reduces the threat of obsolescence.

In driving and highway safety programs in general, the present state of research with visual simulation systems customarily obtains driving environments and circumstances from previous and existing roadway configurations. Completely novel environments and *new* experiences are just beginning to come within the grasp of researchers. Considering the rapid and increasing rate of technological development in the vehicle and highway field, it is essential that system conflicts be foreseen or pre-experienced in order to investigate the reasons for their occurrence and see to it that the means for compatible solutions are achieved before the system is built.

The freedom to organize an experiment and to control it so as to obtain the maximum significant data is of prime importance in obtaining a high benefit-to-cost ratio for research funds.

Growth Potential

The long-term utility depends upon the system's capability for growth, as well as its usefulness when initially acquired. Photographic systems provide practically no room for adding new features or increasing scope. TBTV systems can be added to, but at an expense proportional to the amount of terrain added; little upgrading or addition of new features is possible with this type of system; CGI, on the other hand, may be expanded in many directions by the addition of software only and it can grow in dimensions not possible with other systems.

Improvements of Moving Platform

As new vehicles and propulsion systems are developed, improved motion devices will need to be developed in order to simulate new handling characteristics. The CGI system can more readily adapt to changes in input requirements and there is no practical limit to the rate of change that can be simulated visually. This is not true of TBTV equipment or photographic systems.

Interface with Other Driving Simulation Subsystems

Accurate and precise timing is critical in relating subsystems such as sound effects, bumps, and so forth, to the driving experience. The quantified nature of the data inherent in the computer system allows predictable and repeatable measurement of status to be made. Terrain board techniques will not be capable of the precision or the comprehensiveness achievable in the computer system. Photographic simulators could provide only crude approximations due to the inflexibility of the filmed images.

Animating the Model

The number of moving elements can be increased by adding computer modules and computer-generated images allowing complete flexibility of motion with high resolution. Even with large-scale terrain boards, the vehicle and pedestrian models employed would be difficult to move in a realistic-appearing manner as observed in the simulator and the TBTV system would be quite limited in the number of moving objects that could be accommodated. Although photographic techniques are quite inflexible, limited use of superposition projection can provide some degree of realism under certain circumstances.

Ability to Add Stations with Interactive Capability

The computer system is far superior in that the only requirement is more computer capability and additional programming. Model systems would be severely limited since the probes would have to be disguised as vehicles. Photographic techniques cannot incorporate this feature.

Development Requirements

A modular design can be achieved with the CGI so that new elements merely add on with a minimum of down time and only more computer hardware/software is needed to improve the CGI system. Probe lenses, lighting, moving vehicles, and model size limit the terrain board system. There is little that can be done with purely photographic systems.

Ease of Adding Capabilities

Because only additional computer, and possibly display, capability is required, and they can be added on a modular basis, CGI systems would be easiest to expand. This would be true for a greater field of view, higher image quality, or additional stations for interactive studies or increased utilization factor. In TBTV simulators, a major reconstruction of the system would be required and the use of additional stations to increase the utilization factor is almost impossible.

Feasibility

Obviously a system is of little value if it cannot be built. It must be possible to meet adequate performance requirements without requiring technological advances in the future. Only existing photographic systems meet requirements within their fundamentally limited capability. Considerable extension of state-of-the-art is needed to make a wide-view probe suitable for TBTV. All components of CGI systems have been demonstrated; little extrapolation of technology is required to meet the essential goals.

Engineering Concept

Both the CGI and PT systems are based upon sound principles. The development of the terrain board probe is relatively unsound from an optical basis and clearly limited with respect to model size, illumination, and animation.

Relation to the State-of-the-Art

Probe limitations put the required TBTV system beyond current state-of-the-art. The other two systems are within the bounds of existing technology.

Potential for Hemisphere Projection

The TBTV concept encounters visual blockage in the vertical direction due to the gantry supporting the probe, thus preventing hemispherical views that are possible, if somewhat difficult, with CGI techniques. The photographic techniques are best suited for "total view."

System Control and Monitoring

CGI systems are best by far because monitoring stations can be provided with any desired vantage point without intruding upon the experiment. Monitoring is limited in the TBTV system, although the model can be viewed in its entirety. Only very limited monitoring can be done in PT systems. The all-digital CGI is more flexible and adaptable than the hybrid computer systems needed for TBTV.

Driver Training and Licensing

The dollar cost of research simulators make them out of reach for use in driver training or driver licensing test simulators. However, if a truly adequate research simulator is built, it can be used to evaluate simple devices that would be cost effective in driver training and driver licensing programs.

One example of this type of development strategy is the current use of a small simulator patterned after the UCLA motion picture type simulator. It uses the same wide-screen system as the parent simulator. However, in keeping with the scaling down process, 16-mm film is projected rather than the 35-mm version used at UCLA. The 16-mm film that is being used in driver licensing research depicts 13 minutes of driving scenes selected from the UCLA library.

SUMMARY AND CONCLUSIONS

Several types of driving simulators are described relative to their development and use in the United States and abroad.

In the past 12 years or so a great deal of discussion has taken place about the need and feasibility of building a truly high-fidelity driving simulator. These discussions are best exemplified by the National Conference on Driving Simulation (1961), Seminar on Research Applications of Driving Simulation (1963), and the Conference on Mathematical Models and Simulation of Automobile Driving (1967).

While these conferences stressed the *need* for a high-fidelity driving simulator, feasibility studies, such as those conducted by Cornell Aeronautical Laboratory, Inc. (1958) and Booz, Allen Applied Research, Inc. (1968), were concerned with technical aspects that must be considered before construction of such a system. These feasibility studies indicate that the visual display required for the driving simulator will constitute an advancement of the state-of-the-art of that field. This advance results from the fundamental requirements for high resolution, wide field of view, color, and so on.

The simulation of motion, on the other hand, is realistically achievable within the present state-of-the-art. As for the computer requirements, one must recognize that the digital computer mode does not operate well in the real-time domain, which is necessary for any system with man in the loop; for this reason an analog computer is essential in the system. However, an all-analog approach is not sufficient for reasons such as the wide range of variables, nonlinearities in equations of motion, and drift in voltage level in analog computer components. To make use of the best of both, the accuracy and repeatability of the digital computer and the frequency bandwidth of the analog computer, a hybrid approach is suggested.

In spite of many arguments presented in support of developing a truly high-fidelity simulator, no definite plans for building such a system have been proposed. The simulators that have been built are of modest scale and of limited applications. Even so, their usefulness to current and future research in highway safety has been widely recognized. A survey of driving research simulators, published in 1970 (Kuratorium für Verkehrssicherheit, 1970) lists 17 devices in use in 11 locations in the United States and 11 in 9 locations overseas.

REFERENCES

Anonymous, Two-Page Press Release #00649, Goodyear News Bureau, Akron, Ohio, 1963a.

Anonymous, Driving Simulator Could Help Solve Traffic Woes, *The Wingfoot Clan,* **22**, 18 (September 5, 1963b), 1, 2.

Beinke, R. E. and Williams, J. K., Driving Simulator, paper presented at General Motors Corporation Automobile Safety Seminar, July 1968.

Booz, Allen, Applied Research, Inc., Motion Simulation Techniques Analysis for the

Driving Simulation Laboratory Facility, Report prepared for U.S. Department of Transportation, National Highway Safety Bureau, October 1968.

Clark, B. and Stewart, F. D., Perception of Angular Acceleration about the Yaw Axis of a Flight Simulator, *Aerospace Medicine,* December 1962, 1426.

Conference on Mathematical Models and Simulation of Automobile Driving, Massachusetts Institute of Technology, September 1967.

Cornell Aeronautical Laboratory, Inc., Automobile Driving Simulator Feasibility Study, Report No. YM-1244-V-6 (November 1958).

Forbes, T. W. Visual Estimation of Velocity in Connection with Highway Safety, *Abstract of Dissertation,* Ohio State University Press, 1931.

Forbes, T. W., Age Performance Relationships Among Accident-Repeater Automobile Drivers, *Journal of Consulting Psychology,* **38**, 2 (1938), 143–148.

Highway Research Board, Highway Research in the United States, Needs, Expenditures and Applications, Special Report 55, Washington, D.C. (1959).

Hulbert, S. and Wojcik, C., Human Thresholds Related to Simulation of Inertia Forces, *Highway Research Record 25,* Highway Research Board, 1963.

Hulbert, S. and Wojcik, C., Driving Simulator Devices and Applications, *SAE Paper 803A,* presented at Automotive Engineering Congress, January 13–17, 1964.

Hulbert, S. F. and Wojcik, C. K., Visual Display for U.C.L.A. Driving Simulator, *S.P.I.E. Seminar Proceedings,* **17** (1969).

Kamnitzer, P. and Hulbert, S., Highway Transportation System Simulation: The Visual Subsystem by means of Computer Generated Images, *UCLA Report for Contract FH-11-6879* (August 1969).

Kuratorium Für Verkehrssicherheit, Verkehrspsychologie IV, Vienna, Austria, May 1970, 149–184.

Mathewson, J. H., Driving Simulator for Research in Street and Highway Safety, Technical Memo L-11, Institute of Transportation and Traffic Engineering, University of California, 1957, 7.

McConnell, W. A., Motion Sensitivity as a Guide to Road Design, *SAE Transactions,* **65** (1957), 493.

Miller, L. W. and Goodson, L. E., Motion Sickness in a Helicopter Simulator, *Aerospace Medicine,* March 1960, 204.

National Conference on Driving Simulation, New Horizons for Highway Safety through Driving Simulation, A Report on National Conference on Driving Simulation, Santa Monica, California, February 27–March 1, 1961.

Neuberger, T. P., Visual Simulation for Rendezvous Training, *Space Rendezvous, Rescue, and Recovery,* **16**, Part I, Advances in Astronautical Sciences, 1963, 507–524.

Seminar on Research Applications on Driving Simulation, Proceedings of the Seminar on Research Applications of Driving Simulation, The Ohio State University, Columbus, Ohio, September 1963.

Testa, C. J., The Prediction and Evaluation of Simulator Illness Symptomatology, Ph.D. Dissertation, Department of Engineering, University of California, Los Angeles, Cal., 1969.

Williamsburg Conference, Special Report on the Williamsburg Conference, February 23–28, 1958, *Traffic Safety,* **2**, 2 (June 1958).

Wojcik, C. K., Motion Simulation Techniques for Driving Simulators, *ASME Paper 69-WA/BHF-10* (1969).

Wojcik, C. K. and Hulbert, S. F., The Driving Simulator—A Research Tool, *ASME Paper 65-WA/HUF-13* (November 1965).

IV

CHARACTERISTICS OF DRIVERS

Albert Burg

Albert Burg is associate research psychologist with the Institute of Transportation and Traffic Engineering at the University of California, Los Angeles. He has been on its staff since 1953, and serves as a consultant to member departments of the California Business and Transportation Agency as well as to other governmental and private organizations. He received his Ph.D. degree in psychology from U.C.L.A.

Dr. Burg's present fields of major scientific interest include human factors in transportation, visual requirements of the driving task, and accident prevention. Since 1961, he has directed research on a long-range project relating visual capability to driving performance.

Dr. Burg is affiliated with the American Psychological Association, Western Psychological Association, Human Factors Society, and Society of Engineering Psychologists. He is a member of several Highway Research Board Committees and is chairman of its Visibility Committee. He is a subpanel member of the U.S. National Committee of the International Commission on Illumination. He serves on the Editorial Advisory Board of the journal *Accident Analysis and Prevention,* and has authored or coauthored many research reports in his areas of interest.

In applying the "human engineering" approach to driving, an attempt is made to coordinate the demands of the job (driving) with the capabilities of the operator (driver) in such a fashion as to produce safe and efficient operation. This, of course, is an end highly to be desired.

The success of the human engineering approach, however, depends upon the availability of sufficient detailed knowledge of *both* major components: the job and the operator. Unfortunately, to date no one has been able to provide a clear description of just what the driving task is comprised of and, until valid and reliable performance measures become available, any attempt to "match the job and the man" will, of necessity, fall short.

In the absence of such data, operational agencies concerned with the regulation and control of driving behavior have tended to orient their activities in accord with the traditional trichotomy of *driver, vehicle,* and *environment* (highway), and to a certain extent they have made an attempt to define the interaction among these three components in order to arrive at operational decisions.

These decisions are based, in part, upon known or assumed facts about the three system components and, in part, upon known or assumed *interactions* among them. The purpose of this chapter is to review the known facts about one of these components, namely, the driver. More specifically, the chapter will deal with (1) characteristics of the driving population, (2) what is known about the relationships between these characteristics and driving performance, and (3) where justified, some implications of this knowledge for operational decisions.

The emphasis will, insofar as possible, be placed on normative data, that is, data describing the *average* performance, as well as the *range* of performance, of a large number of drivers on a number of different descriptive variables. The usefulness of normative data lies in the fact that such data permit definition of a range of behavior to be considered "normal" or "acceptable" from the standpoint of its regulation or control. The validity of prediction of group behavior depends on the adequacy of normative data, and an attempt will be made to point out those instances in which it is felt that the quality of available information does not justify its use as a basis for action. As will be seen, the quality of data is extremely variable.

BIOGRAPHICAL DESCRIPTORS OF THE DRIVING POPULATION

Available Data. According to data compiled by the National Safety Council, there were some 107,500,000 licensed drivers in the United States in 1969. Of these, 58 percent were male and 42 percent female. Table 1 presents an age-sex breakdown of licensed U.S. drivers for several years. The 1969 figures describe, in a gross way, the total population of drivers with which we are to be concerned. The sex and age breakdowns are normative data describing distributions of "behavior" on two of many possible parameters. Age and sex are variables of great impor-

Table 1 Age and Sex Distribution of Licensed Drivers in the United States by Year (Percent)[a]

Age Group	1969[b]	1965	1960
Under 20	10.2	9.8	7.2
20–24	11.0	10.4	11.2
25–29	10.0	9.6	12.7
30–34	9.5	10.1	12.5
35–39	9.9	11.1	11.6
40–44	10.5	10.8	10.3
45–49	9.8	9.7	9.1
50–54	8.6	8.5	7.8
55–59	6.8	6.8	6.2
60–64	5.2	5.2	4.7
65–69	3.9	3.7	3.1
70–74	2.7	2.6	2.1
75 and up	1.9	1.7	1.5
Total licensed drivers	107,500,000	98,000,000	87,000,000
Percent male	58	61	70
Percent female	42	39	30

[a] From National Safety Council figures.
[b] Latest figures available.

tance, influencing many actions concerned with driver regulation and control, and are two of the possible predictors of future driving performance.

Not only is the information presented in Table 1 useful in describing the current driving population, the data for prior years can be used to demonstrate trends in the composition of the driving population. For example, the figures clearly indicate the following:

1. Females are comprising an ever-increasing proportion of the driving population, with the male/female ratio approaching that which exists in the general population.
2. Both old and young drivers comprise an increasing proportion of the total driving population.

This type of information is useful in deriving estimates of the future composition of the driving population, which is essential to effective planning for future needs. For example, should an increasing proportion of drivers fall into the older age brackets, then the capabilities (sensory, response, judgmental and so on) of this age group must be given increasing consideration in the design of vehicles, highways, signs and all other aspects of the system where age-related performance differences may influence efficiency or effectiveness. This type of advance planning has, up to now, not been too common in the field of transportation.

Other biographical variables of interest in describing the driving population include marital status, education, and occupation, among others. No comprehensive survey has yet been made that can provide reliable population distributions on these dimensions on a nationwide basis.

A recent UCLA study provides some interesting regional information on these variables, however, based on a reasonably random sample of over 17,000 California drivers (Burg, 1967a, 1968c). Table 2 shows the marital status breakdown of the sample, while Table 3 provides data on occupation. The UCLA study did not gather information on educational background; however, it did accumulate data on how the study drivers had learned to drive. These data are presented in Table 4. Tables 2, 3 and 4 all contain previously unpublished data from the UCLA study.

Unlike the age and sex data presented earlier, distributions for several years are not available for marital status, occupation, and educational

Table 2 Marital Status of California Driver Sample by Age and Sex (Percent)

Age Group	*N*		Married		Single		Divorced or Separated		Widowed	
	M	F	M	F	M	F	M	F	M	F
Under 20	1185	736	5.1	21.3	94.9	78.3	0.0	0.4	0.0	0.0
20–24	1387	779	38.9	63.7	60.1	33.4	1.1	3.0	0.0	0.0
25–29	1163	667	67.0	79.8	30.9	15.3	2.1	4.6	0.1	0.3
30–34	1123	631	79.9	83.2	17.8	11.7	2.0	4.4	0.4	0.6
35–39	1120	700	83.2	83.0	12.9	10.9	3.7	5.3	0.3	0.9
40–44	1124	723	85.7	85.6	10.7	6.1	3.2	6.5	0.4	1.8
45–49	941	646	87.7	82.0	9.1	7.1	2.9	6.0	0.3	4.8
50–54	861	582	87.1	75.8	9.3	11.0	3.1	6.4	0.5	6.9
55–59	640	381	84.8	72.4	10.0	9.7	3.8	7.1	1.4	10.8
60–64	499	275	84.6	62.2	9.6	10.9	3.0	5.5	2.8	21.5
65 and up	914	389	83.8	44.7	8.1	15.4	1.0	2.3	7.1	37.5
All ages	10957	6509	68.2	69.2	28.6	21.0	2.2	4.5	1.0	5.3
All ages, both sexes	17466		68.6		25.8		3.1		2.6	

Table 3 Occupational Breakdown of California Driver Sample by Age and Sex (Percent)

Age Group	*N*		Occupation[a] 1		2		3		4		5		6		7		8		9		10	
	M	F	M	F	M	F	M	F	M	F	M	F	M	F	M	F	M	F	M	F	M	F
Under 20	1186	736	1.0	0.7	0.7	0.0	2.4	9.4	2.2	0.1	8.0	0.5	2.0	2.4	0.3	0.1	0.0	14.0	78.5	69.2	4.9	3.5
20–24	1388	780	5.8	7.8	1.6	0.1	10.0	27.8	14.3	1.3	19.2	2.1	4.8	5.8	0.0	0.0	0.0	34.7	21.5	15.4	22.8	5.0
25–29	1164	668	20.3	15.4	1.6	0.3	15.8	17.8	17.0	1.2	20.5	1.3	5.8	4.2	0.0	0.0	0.0	55.2	6.2	2.1	12.7	2.4
30–34	1124	633	28.1	11.7	0.4	0.2	15.7	15.0	21.2	1.7	20.1	2.5	5.3	6.8	0.0	0.0	0.0	59.7	1.5	0.9	7.6	1.4
35–39	1120	700	28.8	9.9	2.0	0.3	17.1	16.1	21.3	1.1	18.8	3.6	4.9	7.0	0.3	0.0	0.0	60.3	0.4	0.4	6.3	1.3
40–44	1125	723	31.3	11.1	1.6	0.3	16.4	18.1	22.6	2.1	17.0	3.7	5.5	7.7	0.7	0.0	0.0	54.9	0.1	0.6	4.8	1.5
45–49	941	646	26.0	13.9	2.3	0.2	14.8	21.1	25.8	1.5	19.1	3.7	5.6	8.4	1.4	0.0	0.0	49.7	0.2	0.5	4.7	1.1
50–54	861	582	27.3	17.0	1.6	0.2	14.4	22.2	26.0	1.7	19.5	5.2	5.7	7.7	2.1	0.9	0.0	43.0	0.1	0.2	3.3	2.1
55–59	641	381	25.3	14.4	2.3	0.3	14.2	18.1	25.0	1.6	19.5	3.1	4.2	10.5	5.5	2.9	0.0	46.5	0.0	0.3	4.1	2.4
60–64	499	275	22.0	12.7	2.0	0.4	16.8	12.7	19.2	0.7	14.6	1.8	5.6	4.4	17.6	14.5	0.0	52.4	0.0	0.0	2.0	0.4
65 and over	915	389	12.0	7.2	1.2	0.3	6.2	3.9	6.6	0.0	3.7	1.0	1.9	2.3	66.9	43.4	0.0	39.8	0.3	0.3	1.2	1.8
All ages	10964	6513	19.9	10.7	1.5	0.2	12.8	17.3	17.7	1.2	16.5	2.6	4.7	6.1	7.1	3.5	0.0	45.9	12.1	10.2	7.8	2.2

[a]

1. Professional and semi-professional, proprietors, managers, and officials.
2. Farmers, farm managers, and farm workers.
3. Clerks, salesmen, and agents.
4. Craftsmen, foremen, skilled laborers.
5. Operatives, semiskilled workers, laborers and unskilled workers.
6. Protective services and personal service workers.
7. Retired.
8. Housewives.
9. Students (primary occupation).
10. Others, not elsewhere classified (including military personnel and unemployed).

Table 4 How Sample of California Drivers Learned to Drive (Percent)[a]

Age Group	*N*	1	2	3	4	5	6	7
Under 20	1921	47.1	0.9	11.9	0.7	9.9	29.1	0.4
20–24	2168	60.3	2.0	9.5	1.1	6.0	20.2	0.9
25–29	1831	74.7	3.2	6.9	1.7	4.2	8.7	0.6
30–34	1755	85.5	4.3	3.4	1.4	1.3	3.8	0.3
35–39	1820	90.5	4.1	1.8	1.3	0.5	1.6	0.2
40–44	1848	89.8	4.0	1.8	2.1	0.3	1.5	0.6
45–49	1587	93.1	2.7	1.1	1.3	0.1	1.4	0.3
50–54	1443	92.6	3.7	0.6	1.1	0.2	1.5	0.3
55–59	1022	93.8	2.7	0.8	1.3	0.1	1.1	0.2
60–64	774	92.0	4.3	1.2	1.2	0.5	0.8	0.1
65 and up	1304	91.4	4.2	1.9	1.7	0.1	0.5	0.2
All ages	17473	80.5	3.2	4.3	1.4	2.5	7.7	0.4

a

1. Taught by family, friends and/or "picked up."
2. Paid instruction.
3. Driver education (classroom plus on-the-road).
4. 1 above plus paid instruction.
5. 1 above plus classroom course only.
6. 1 above plus driver education.
7. Miscellaneous and not stated.

level, making trend analysis for those variables purely speculative in nature.

The California Department of Motor Vehicles (DMV) has collected an immense amount of data over the past six years describing the California driving population on various dimensions, including age, sex, marital status, height, weight, license restrictions, and a host of driving record variables. The major findings of this study are described in a set of nine reports, entitled "The 1964 California Driver Record Study."

In addition to its Driver Record Study, which involved a sample of nearly 150,000 California drivers, the California DMV has also been conducting a follow-up study of some 10,000 young male drivers, between the ages of 19 and 22, in which educational level is one of the variables under analysis.

One additional study is worthy of mention. Heath (1957) studied driving records and a number of biographical variables for 763 traffic offenders (three or more traffic accidents and/or moving traffic violations over a specified period of time), and also for a control group of 195 drivers who had unblemished driving records for the same period of time. Heath's findings are discussed below.

Relationship to Driving. With regard to biographical predictors of driving record, the data collected in the California DMV studies, as well as those from the UCLA study mentioned earlier, represent the largest body of information currently available. The results of these studies are in general agreement with each other as well as with previous studies, summarized in several reports (Goldstein, 1962; Antia, 1969; and the 1966 A.D. Little report, "The State of the Art of Traffic Safety").

The research results to date may be summarized as follows:

1. *Age.* Accidents and convictions for traffic offenses generally decrease with increasing age; however, when miles driven are taken into account, then both young and old drivers have poorer driving records than do middle-aged groups. A recent publication reporting additional findings from The 1964 California Driver Record Study (Harrington and McBride, 1970) indicates there are differences in violation patterns as a function of age. Specifically, the authors feel that those violations most prevalent among young drivers (e.g., speeding) reflect a greater propensity for risk-taking behavior, while the violations most common among older drivers (sign, turning, passing, and right-of-way) may be associated with increasing decrements in physical and judgmental skills that are known to occur with increasing age. There is some evidence that *accident* type also varies with age, but this has not as yet been studied in detail (Burg, 1970).

2. *Miles Driven* (Quantitative Exposure to Risk). Generally speaking, mileage appears to be the variable most closely correlated with driving record variables. Accidents and convictions increase with increasing mileage, but not linearly.

3. *Sex.* Males have more accidents and convictions than females; however, when miles driven are taken into account, the differences essentially disappear.

4. *Marital Status.* Generally speaking, married drivers have better driving records than single drivers. This relationship tends to hold true for both males and females, at all age levels, and whether or not exposure (miles driven) is taken into account. To be more explicit, it should be said that these driving record differenecs between married and single drivers are not completely uniform; that is, they are more evident for convictions than for accidents, show up more often for raw conviction or accident frequencies than when these figures are corrected for exposure, and tend to shrink with increasing age, becoming insignificant in the older age groups (Burg, 1970).

5. *Occupation.* There are no data presently available to describe adequately the relationship between occupation and driving. Heath found

that few of his experimental group (those with accidents and/or citations) were engaged in the professions or in managerial or official capacities; moreover, they reported smaller earnings and higher job turnover. This is a difficult area to research, due to the high degree of interaction between occupation and a number of other variables, notably socioeconomic level, age, sex, race, education, and so on.

6. *Educational Background.* No definitive research findings are available in this area. However, preliminary results from the aforementioned "Young Driver Follow-Up Study," presently near completion by the California Department of Motor Vehicles, indicate that a significant relationship does indeed exist between educational level and driving record. Specifically, driving record is found to worsen with decreasing number of years of schooling, and as a group, school dropouts have poorer records than do school graduates. Heath also found that a greater proportion of his experimental group had failed to complete high school or college.

Practical Applications of These Findings. From the standpoint of the *practitioner,* that is, the individual whose responsibility it is to regulate or control the driver's behavior, research results are meaningless unless they can be translated into working rules and standards. In the larger picture, the "practitioner" can be one who is concerned with driver licensing, law enforcement, highway design, vehicle design, automobile insurance, lawmaking, and a host of other activities. For the most part, however, this chapter will consider practical applications of research findings primarily from the viewpoint of driver licensing, with but occasional reference to some of the other activities named above.

It is difficult to specify practical ways in which the above information on biographical variables can be utilized in the driver licensing procedure. While licensing officials can and do restrict driving privileges on the basis of past driving performance (as reflected in driving record information), it is inconceivable that a driver license applicant, whether new or renewal, be denied a license on the basis of age, sex, mileage driven annually, marital status, occupation, educational level, or any of a host of other biographical factors.

At present, there are, however, two possible applications of this information in the licensing area. The first one, already in effect in some states, calls for the issuance of restricted-term licenses for both young, novice drivers and elderly drivers. In the first case, the poor driving record usually demonstrated for this age group justifies maintaining closer control over driving privileges which, in actuality, is the intent and effect of issuing shorter-term licenses. In the case of elderly drivers, their increasingly poor driving record (when exposure is taken into consideration), plus the increasingly rapid rate at which their physical (and, perhaps, judgmental) capacities deteriorate, again justify the restricted-term license. It is not possible to specify the length of term most effective for such licenses; however, either one- or two-year licenses appear to be indicated, with the one-year license probably more desirable. The exact ages at which this restriction should be imposed on the elderly driver, or lifted from the young driver, cannot yet be specified.

The other possible application of a biographical variable to driver licensing bears a relationship to education, and is already in effect in several states. This is the use of high school driver education as a factor in determining the earliest age at which a driver can be licensed. In California, for example, successful completion of a high school driver education course enables licensure at age 16; otherwise, licensure cannot occur for first-time applicants until the age of 18. In view of the lack of conclusive evidence regarding the role of driver education in providing lasting benefits for safety, the value of this particular application of biographical information cannot properly be assessed.

MEDICAL DESCRIPTORS OF THE DRIVING POPULATION

It has been only recently that large quantities of data have come to be generated concerning some of the physical and physiological characteristics of drivers. Of interest to the researchers are permanent physical disabilities, such as loss of limb and defective vision, and physical diseases such as epilepsy and cardiovascular problems. Related to these areas, and also the subject of increased interest on the part of researchers, are *temporary* physiological conditions caused by such factors as fatigue, and drugs, alcohol, and chemical agents, which are discussed in detail in Chapters 12 and 13, and psychological or psychiatric problems, covered in Chapter 14.

Loss of Limb

Available Data. A recent report (McFarland et al., 1968) provides a critical evaluation of previous research efforts, as well as a description of a carefully planned and executed study conducted by the authors. In their review, the authors found that all of the previous research studies, without exception, contained methodological limitations that made it impossible to make valid inferences concerning the relative accident experiences of disabled and nondisabled drivers. Typical shortcomings cited by the authors are failure to take relative exposure to risk into account, incomplete data, lack of a comparison population, contradictory findings, and small sample size.

In order to avoid some of these shortcomings, the authors undertook a controlled study of the comparative driving records of disabled and nondisabled drivers in Massachusetts. A random sample of 625 disabled licensed drivers was selected, as was an equal number of nondisabled licensed drivers matched on age, sex, and years licensed in Massachusetts.

Relationship to Driving. The study results showed a significantly lower ratio of involvement in violations and accidents for the disabled drivers than for the nondisabled drivers. Specifically, the nondisabled drivers were involved in approximately *twice* as many accidents and nonaccident traffic violations as the disabled drivers.

Practical Applications of These Findings. These results are suggestive, rather than definitive. As the authors point out, there are several constraints on interpretation of the data: The two groups of drivers were not equated for exposure; the reliability of the accident data was not established; accident records are not complete, since minor accidents (under $200.00 property damage) are not reported; and while the disabled drivers were restricted to passenger car operation under terms of their licensure, no such restriction was imposed on the nondisabled control group.

Obviously, the results of this study call for no action; however, a more controlled replication would seem to be desirable.

Disease

Available Data. One of the most comprehensive studies of the relationship between chronic medical conditions and traffic safety was conducted by Waller (1965; Waller and Goo, 1969). Waller studied a sample of 2672 California drivers with known chronic medical conditions, including epilepsy, cardiovascular diseases, diabetes, alcoholism, drug usage, mental illness, and miscellaneous conditions. A comparison group of 922 randomly selected drivers with no known (to DMV) chronic medical conditions also was studied. The following information was obtained for all drivers in both samples: age, sex, marital status, occupation, annual mileage, and three-year driving record (accidents and convictions for traffic violations on file with the California Department of Motor Vehicles). One caution emphasized by the author is that the experimental sample represents only those drivers whose medical conditions are *known* to the licensing authorities, and it is not possible (in the absence of additional data) to assume that the findings apply equally to *unreported* drivers with the same medical conditions.

This same issue is discussed in a series of studies conducted by the Washington State Department of Motor Vehicles (Crancer and McMurray, 1967; Crancer and Quiring, 1968; Crancer and O'Neall, 1969). Obviously, it is not possible to study all drivers with impairments or diseases, because there is no effective means for uncovering all such drivers. Ordinarily, such drivers come to the attention of the licensing authorities in several ways, for example, when they volunteer information regarding their condition, when their condition is observed or accidentally discovered by the examiner at the time of license application, or when they are reported to the licensing authority by the courts, enforcement officers, medical people, or concerned citizens. There is no way of knowing how many drivers with medical conditions fail to be uncovered by these means, but it is likely to be a substantial number. A British study (Rees, 1967), utilizing medical records for 76.6 percent of the *entire licensed population* of a rural area, found that 9.2 percent had at least one significant mental (2.7 percent) or physical (6.5 percent) illness severe enough to deny licensure to drive public service vehicles. Rees found that some severely disabled people continued to renew their licenses but no longer drove. He also feels that less than 1 percent of all motorists *declare* a disability when applying for a license.

In the Washington State studies, 39,240 Washington motorists whose licenses bore medical driving and licensing restrictions were studied. Their restrictions fell into seven categories: vision deterioration, heart disease, diabetes, epilepsy, fainting, other conditions, and medical driving restrictions. The last-named category involves regulations for drivers with physical impairments such as stabilized vision defects (e.g., one-eyedness), arthritis, paralysis, and loss of limb.

The number of recorded accidents and violations accumulated over a 6½-year period was obtained for these medically restricted drivers, and compared with equivalent driving record data for *all* Washington motorists, analyzed by restriction category, age, and sex. Two follow-up studies expanded the findings by studying in detail the driving records of diabetics and drivers with specific types of cardiovascular illness.

Relationship to Driving. The Waller study found that drivers with diabetes, epilepsy, cardiovascular disease, alcoholism, and mental illness averaged twice as many accidents per 1,000,000 miles of driving and 1.3 to 1.8 times as many violations per 100,000 miles as did the comparison group on an age-adjusted basis. (It should be pointed out, however, that the two groups differed in their distributions on age, sex, marital status, and socioeconomic status, a fact which lessens the impact of the findings.) Drivers convicted for illegal use of drugs averaged 1.8 times as many violations but no more accidents than those in the comparison group.

The Waller and Goo study elaborated on the above results by finding that drivers with medical conditions tend to have different *types* of accidents.

The Washington State studies generally support the Waller findings, when taken as a group. They found drivers with diabetes, epilepsy, fainting, and other conditions to have more accidents per unit time than the comparison group, but no more violations. The findings for drivers with permanent physical impairments (medical driving restrictions) were equivocal. Initially, it was found that drivers with heart disease and vision deterioration did not have driving records differing significantly from the comparison population; however, in the second study, a more severely ill group of cardiovascular drivers was found to have a higher number of violations, and different types of violations, than the comparison population; and in the third study, drivers with specific types of heart disease (i.e., arteriosclerotic and hypertensive) were found to have more accidents than matched drivers with no heart disease, while two other heart disease groups (rheumatic and other heart disease) showed no difference.

It seems clear that the results of the Waller and Washington State studies are suggestive, but not conclusive. Each set of studies has at least one serious weakness: the Waller study fails to use a carefully matched comparison group, and the Washington State study does not take exposure (annual mileage) into account, in evaluating driving records. Both of these shortcomings can drastically affect the research findings, in an unpredictable fashion.

As pointed out in the A. D. Little report (1966), epileptic drivers have been studied more than drivers with any other chronic medical condition; yet, concrete evidence to back up a firm conclusion is still lacking. Similarly, the data on the role played by other diseases in accident causation is not sufficiently unequivocal to justify an action program on the part of an operational agency.

West et al. (1968) point out one of the major obstacles to obtaining definitive information in this area. They conducted a special study in which examinations were made of 1026 California drivers who died within 15 minutes of their involvement in single-vehicle accidents. The study found that 15% died of natural causes, 94% of whom died of heart disease. The authors point out, however, that this was a special study, and that normally there is no record made of recognized natural deaths of drivers in accidents and, hence, the extent of this problem is not known. This points up one basic (and universal) shortcoming in all studies of accident causation—the lack of adequate data describing the nature of and circumstances surrounding the accident.

Practical Applications of These Findings. It is not possible to effect any immediate operational decisions relative to the licensing of drivers with chronic diseases based on the information presently available. However, the following steps *can* be taken:

1. Improve the quality and quantity of accident-describing data.
2. Conduct a carefully controlled study, utilizing a large sample of licensed drivers with chronic medical conditions who are actually *driving*, and a comparison sample of drivers without disease. Be sure to match the two groups on every important dimension, including exposure.
3. Develop an effective program for uncovering as many as possible of the licensed drivers with chronic medical conditions (through passage of appropriate legislation, if necessary).

Until the "definitive" study is done, there is little justification for action with regard to differential licensing of chronically ill drivers. The results that have been produced to date are not without value, however. They are suggestive, and will tend to make those concerned with traffic safety aware that deviant driving behavior may be beyond the control of the driver. As Waller (1970, p. 75) explains it: "The most highly motivated driver with epilepsy or cardiovascular disease will still have trouble on the highway if his physiologic mechanisms are not functioning properly." In addition, the research results suggest that the commonly encountered emphasis on epilepsy as the major medical handicap to safe driving is too narrow an approach in driver licensing. These concepts, in themselves, represent meaningful contributions to our still meager body of knowledge regarding accident causation.

Defective Hearing

Available Data. It is generally believed that in driving, as in most of man's activities, vision is the most important sense. It is the one whose impairment is most feared and, consequently, it is the one most often studied. As a result, the traffic safety literature contains many references to vision and driving, but few concerning the importance of any of the other sense modalities in proper performance of the driving task.

Audition is usually mentioned as being the next most important sense in driving, yet very little is known about its role, or of the consequences to the driver's performance of impaired hearing. The only study of consequence in this area was conducted by the California Department of Motor Vehicles (Coppin and Peck, 1964). The study involved 310 totally deaf licensed California drivers, 170 males and 140 females, who were compared with a sample of nondeaf licensed drivers carefully matched with regard to several critical variables: age, sex, annual mileage, occupation, and area of residence. The matched samples were then compared with one another on the basis of their three-year driving records (accidents and convictions for traffic violations).

Relationship to Driving. The Coppin and Peck study found: (1) no evidence that deafness results in either an increase or a decrease in traffic violation frequency; and (2) that deaf males have a disproportionately high number of accidents (1.8 times as many as the nondeaf males), whereas deaf females are no different from nondeaf females in this respect. These findings are significant, since in an earlier phase of the same study, in which no attempt was made to match the samples on the basis of mileage, occupation, or area of residence, significant differences in both violation and accident frequency had been found for both sexes, favoring the nondeaf driver.

These dissimilar results clearly indicate the importance of taking into account ("controlling for") those variables that are relevant to the relationship under investigation.

Practical Applications of These Findings. The results of the study have several implications. First of all, the findings obviously offer no support to the widely held theory that deaf drivers are better drivers than nondeaf drivers, due to compensatory development of their remaining sense modalities. The question is, are they *worse* drivers? Coppin and Peck feel that some type of driving disadvantage for deaf drivers is, at least, suggested by the results. One possible explanation is that there are certain types of driving situations in which lack of hearing is a definite handicap, and further, that male drivers, by virtue of their work or other habit patterns, are more likely to be placed in these situations than female drivers. It is quite clear that no action by licensing officials is called for on the basis of these results. What *is* called for is additional research to clarify some of the questions, such as the following, raised by the Coppin and Peck study.

1. Are the results of this study in any way artifactual? What is necessary is a replication of the study, exercising the same or even more stringent controls over the effects of extraneous variables.
2. If the results are confirmed by subsequent research, then would formal specialized training of deaf drivers be an effective means of re-

ducing their accident likelihood? Only additional research would provide the answer to this question.

3. Are deaf drivers involved in different types of accidents than non-deaf drivers? Under different circumstances?

4. Does driving performance of deaf drivers vary as a function of the etiology of their deafness (e.g., age at onset, precipitating factors, other defects related to the hearing impairment, and so on)?

In view of the provocative findings of the Coppin and Peck study, it is surprising that no significant follow-up research has been conducted to date. Perhaps it is felt that the magnitude of the problem, if indeed there *is* a problem, is too small to warrant the large-scale research effort that would be required to study the problem adequately. It would appear logical, however, to at least *attempt* to ascertain whether a problem exists, before writing it off as unworthy of attention. To date, no such attempt has been made. One can only hope that this situation will not be permanent.

Vision

Available Data. Goldstein (1962) reviewed research on vision and driving up to 1961, and concluded that at best, accident records were only slightly predictable from measures such as visual acuity. Burg (1964) extended this review to 1964, at which time he stated that ". . . at the present time there is no widely recognized evidence that vision is related to driving" (p. 20). The A. D. Little report (1966) added two more years to the survey, and made the following statement: "At the present time, valid information is not available on relationships between various visual impairments and accidents" (p. 76).

Since the A. D. Little report was issued, however, a major study of vision and driving has been conducted in California, directed by UCLA in conjunction with the California Department of Motor Vehicles. This study for the first time has provided conclusive evidence that a small but significant relationship exists between vision and driving. The major findings from the study are given in two reports (Burg, 1967a, 1968c).

In this study, visual performance measures were obtained for a representative sample of nearly 18,000 California driver license applicants, along with personal and driving habit information. In addition, three-year driving records were obtained for all subjects, and six-year records were obtained for nearly 8000 of these drivers. Detailed driving record information (accidents and convictions for traffic violations) was obtained from three sources: DMV records, accident report files of the California Highway Patrol and, for approximately 5400 of the subjects, insurance company records. (This study represents the first time that insurance records were made available for detailed analysis on a large scale for a traffic safety research program.)

The visual performance data accumulated in the California study included binocular and monocular static visual acuity (three measures), dynamic visual acuity (ability to resolve an acuity target moving horizontally at various speeds), horizontal visual field, form perception under low illumination levels, glare recovery, lateral phoria (the "aim" of the eyes in the horizontal plane), and eyedness, or sighting dominance.

Relationship to Driving. The principal finding from the California study was that dynamic visual acuity, among the vision variables studied, demonstrated the strongest and most consistent relationships with driving records (both 3-year and 6-year). In addition, there was substantial, but not conclusive, evidence that static acuity, form perception under low illumination levels, and visual field are also related to driving record. All relationships are in the "expected" direction, that is, poor visual performance is positively associated with poor driving record.

To be more specific, the vision-driving relationships obtained were not large, but were statistically significant.* (Age and mileage, for example, are better predictors of driving records than any vision variables.) Also, the vision-driving relationships are not consistent under all circumstances —they vary as a function of age, sex, and the driving record variable under consideration. For example, conviction experience is a much more stable and, hence, more *predictable* characteristic than is accident experience. Thus, relationships between conviction record and vision performance (and other variables, as well) are stronger than is the case with accident record. In addition, significant age and sex differences are evident in all the analyses. The relationships vary both qualitatively and quantitatively between males and females; in general, driving record variables are not as "predictable" for females as for males (that is, the relationships between predictor variables, including vision, and driving variables are smaller for females than for males). Age differences are also striking: vision-driving relationships are much stronger for middle-aged and older drivers than for younger drivers. As a matter of fact, for the youngest drivers the vision-driving relationships are in the "unex-

* The principal statistical techniques used were correlational analysis and multiple regression analysis. The latter is a technique for determining that combination of factors (the "independent" or "predictor" variables) that will optimally predict another factor (the "dependent" or "criterion" variable) and permits the assessment of each independent variable's *unique* contribution in the prediction of the criterion variable.

pected" direction, that is, poor vision is associated with *good* driving record. This indicates that for the young drivers, variables other than vision overwhelmingly predominate in influencing driving behavior. Young drivers, as a group, have the best vision and the worst record. Quite obviously, factors such as immaturity, inexperience, propensity for risk-taking behavior, and so on, are extremely critical determinants of driving behavior for this group, while vision is not.

Practical Applications of These Findings. The results of the California study suggest several specific courses of action.

First of all, it is clear that the study left a number of unanswered questions, such as the following:

1. What relationship exists between specific visual performance measures and specific types of accidents and violations?
2. How might the obtained vision-driving relationships change if *qualitative* exposure to risk (type of driving) is taken into account, instead of only quantitative exposure, as was the case?
3. Is it possible to specify "cutoff scores" for the various tests that might be useful to driver licensing administrators?

Work is currently underway at UCLA in an attempt to find answers to these questions, which is the first course of action implied by the results.

Second, the results are encouraging enough to warrant effort toward developing an acceptable vision-testing device for driver licensing purposes. Such a device should be compact, reliable, not too expensive, easy to administer and score, and should permit measurement of several aspects of vision. These measures should include, at a minimum, some dynamic test of visual performance, a static test of visual resolution, and horizontal visual field, and the instrument should permit these measurements to be made under a range of illumination levels. This course of action is currently in progress, in the form of a research and development program supported by the U.S. Department of Transportation.

In addition, the study results indicate that static acuity vision testing, in universal use in the driver licensing procedure at the present time, is of some value, and its use should be continued until such time as the vision-testing device currently under development is completed and validated. The same statement may be made with regard to visual field testing, currently used for screening driver license applicants in approximately one-third of the states.

Finally, it should be pointed out that during the course of the study, an enormous amount of data was collected that can be used to describe driver characteristics, both personal and driving. Included are visual performance scores, the distributions of which are analyzed and described in detail in a series of separate reports (Burg, 1966, 1967b, 1968a, 1968b). These data can be useful in themselves in formulating operational decisions. For example, the distribution of static acuity measurements indicates what percentages of the driving population fall below certain acuity levels. This information can be used by highway sign designers, for example, in establishing specifications for the "design driver" to be used in drawing up signing standards (letter size, sign placement, etc.). As another example, all of the study data clearly show the decline in visual performance capabilities with advancing age. This finding, of course, is in agreement with all other similar studies, and suggests the institution of more frequent licensing examinations (i.e., vision testing) and consequently, shorter-term licenses, for older drivers. This practice is already in effect in several states. Further research is necessary, of course, before it can be recommended that such more frequent testing should begin at a specified age level, or at the point where the driver's vision has deteriorated to a specified level.

SUMMARY AND CONCLUSIONS

The foregoing represents a brief overview of some of the major areas of concern in the study of driver characteristics. The writer's purpose was not to present a complete picture, but rather to help provide the reader with an understanding of the present state of knowledge in these areas, and to foster in the reader an appreciation of the complexities involved in studying the relationships between various characteristics of drivers and various measures of driving performance.

An additional purpose of the discussion presented here is to impress upon the reader the difficulties faced by officials of operational agencies such as motor vehicle departments. The driver licensing official, for example, is charged with the responsibility for screening out those applicants who should be denied driver licenses; yet, he has not been provided with the type and quantity of information needed to make these decisions most effectively. The information needed consists of highly meaningful, unequivocal results that can be translated into operational decisions. One cannot expect the administrator to implement findings he cannot understand; nor can he justify initiating programs based on research findings that are statistically significant but of little practical value.

With this fact in mind, the information presently available concerning those driver characteristics discussed earlier may be summarized as follows:

1. *Biographical Descriptors.* A justification exists for differential li-

censing for both young and old drivers, and implementation of such a program is feasible. Not feasible, however, is differential licensing on the basis of such factors as marital status, education, or annual mileage, although research results would suggest such a move.

2. *Chronic Medical Conditions.* There is sufficient evidence relating certain severe medical conditions to accidents to suggest that short-term licensing of such individuals might prove beneficial. However, final action of this sort should not be taken without confirmation of present findings through a carefully controlled study.

3. *Hearing.* Present evidence suggests that the deaf driver may be at a disadvantage, and that special training programs and/or special aids might be of benefit; however, additional research again is needed before action is warranted.

4. *Loss of Limb.* There is no evidence to justify taking any action in this area.

5. *Vision.* Research results indicate that vision is indeed related to driving. However, the magnitude of the relationship appears to be small, and the question of practical significance arises. How much improvement in the traffic accident picture can be effected by more effective vision screening? By the same token, of what value are present licensing techniques such as written examinations and drive tests? These are questions that have no clearcut answers, for definitive research has yet to be done, and other factors, such as "face validity" and "tradition" serve to confound the issue.

All of these issues need resolution, and it is clear that such resolution is not close at hand. Rather, a carefully designed series of studies to provide more reliable information, plus judicious application of those facts already known to us, will eventually provide the administrator with meaningful information upon which to base his decisions.

REFERENCES

Antia, Kersey H., Biographical and Medical Data About the Automobile Driver—A Review of Literature, *Highway Research News,* **37** (1969), 51–61.

Burg, Albert, *An Investigation of Some Relationships Between Dynamic Visual Acuity, Static Visual Acuity and Driving Record,* University of California, Department of Engineering Report No. 64-18, Los Angeles, Cal., April 1964.

Burg, Albert, Visual Acuity as Measured by Dynamic and Static Tests: A Comparative Evaluation, *Journal of Applied Psychology,* **50**, 6 (1966), 460–466.

Burg, Albert, *The Relationship Between Vision Test Scores and Driving Record: General Findings,* University of California, Department of Engineering Report No. 67-24, Los Angeles, Cal., June 1967a.

Burg, Albert, Light Sensitivity as Related to Age and Sex, *Perceptual and Motor Skills,* **24** (1967b), 1279–1288.

Burg, Albert, Lateral Visual Field as Related to Age and Sex, *Journal of Applied Psychology,* **52**, 1 (1968a), 10–15.

Burg, Albert, Horizontal Phoria as Related to Age and Sex, *American Journal of Optometry,* **45**, 6 (1968b), 345–350.

Burg, Albert, *Vision Test Scores and Driving Record: Additional Findings,* University of California, Department of Engineering Report No. 68-27, Los Angeles, Cal., December 1968c.

Burg, Albert, Previously unreported findings from the UCLA Driver Vision Research Project, 1970.

Coppin, Ronald S. and Peck, Raymond C., *The Totally Deaf Driver in California—Part II,* California Department of Motor Vehicles, Division of Administration, Report No. 16, Sacramento, Cal., December 1964.

Crancer, Alfred, Jr. and McMurray, Lucille, *Accident and Violation Rates of Washington Drivers with Medical Licensing and Driving Restrictions,* Washington State Department of Motor Vehicles, Administrative Services, Report No. 007, Olympia, Wash., December 1967.

Crancer, Alfred, Jr. and O'Neall, Peggy A., *A Record Analysis of Washington Drivers with License Restrictions for Heart Disease,* Washington State Department of Motor Vehicles, Research and Technology, Report No. 025, Olympia, Wash., December 1969.

Crancer, Alfred, Jr. and Quiring, Dennis L., *Driving Records of Persons with Selected Chronic Diseases,* Washington State Department of Motor Vehicles, Administrative Services, Report No. 015, Olympia, Wash., July 1968.

Goldstein, Leon G., Human Variables in Traffic Accidents: A Digest of Research and Selected Bibliography, *Highway Research Board Bibliography,* 31 (1962).

Harrington, David M., personal communication, 1970.

Harrington, David M. and McBride, Robin S., Traffic Violations by Type, Age, Sex and Marital Status, *Accident Analysis and Prevention,* **2**, 1 (1970), 67–79.

Heath, Earl D., The Relationships Between Driving Records, Selected Personality Characteristics and Biographical Data of Traffic Offenders and Non-Offenders, *University Microfilms,* Doctoral Dissertation Series, Publication No. 21, 705 (1957).

McFarland, Ross A., Domey, Richard G., Duggar, Benjamin C., Crowley, Thomas J., and Stoudt, Howard W., *An Evaluation of the Ability of Amputees to Operate Highway Transport Equipment,* Harvard School of Public Health, Boston, Mass., December 1968.

Rees, W. D., Physical and Mental Disabilities of 1,190 Ordinary Motorists, *British Medical Journal,* 5540, (March 11, 1967), 593–597.

The 1964 California Driver Record Study, California Department of Motor Vehicles, Division of Administration, Sacramento, Cal., Parts 1–9, December 1964–March 1967.

The State of the Art of Traffic Safety, Arthur D. Little, Cambridge, Mass., 1966.

Waller, Julian A., Chronic Medical Conditions and Traffic Safety-Review of the California Experience, *The New England Journal of Medicine,* **273**, 26 (1965), 1413–1420.

Waller, Julian A., Administrative and Research Problems in Identifying Individuals with High Crash Risk, *Behavioral Research in Highway Safety,* **1**, 2 (1970), 67–77.

Waller, Julian A. and Goo, James T., Highway Crash and Citation Patterns and Chronic Medical Conditions, *Journal of Safety Research,* **1**, 1 (1969), 13–27.

West, Irma, Nielsen, George L., Gilmore, Allan E., and Ryan, John R., Natural Death at the Wheel, *Journal of the American Medical Association,* **205**, 5 (1968), 266–271.

V

VISIBILITY AND LEGIBILITY OF HIGHWAY SIGNS*

T. W. Forbes

The problem of transmitting information to drivers on the highway has been with us since the early days of the automobile. Visual transmission by means of signs was a natural development and early signs were varied and often difficult to read. It soon became clear, therefore, that factors of visibility and legibility were important as highway and safety problems developed with increasing traffic.

DEFINITIONS

In an early study by Forbes (1939), the term "legibility" was adopted to indicate the ability to read the letters on a sign, and the term "attention value" for the characteristics resulting in a sign being seen in competition with other visual stimuli. "Visibility" as used here refers to attention-getting characteristics and does not mean detection threshold or greatest detection distance. The practical problem for the traffic engineer is whether the sign attracts enough attention to be read when it is within legible distance.

The 1939 study analyzed legibility into "pure legibility" with unlim-

* Modified from a paper entitled "Factors in Visibility and Legibility of Highway Signs and Markings," published in *Visual Factors in Transportation Systems.* Proceedings of Spring Meeting, 1969. NAS-NRC Committee on Vision, National Academy of Sciences, National Research Council, Washington, D.C., 1969, 131 pp.

ited time for reading the sign and "glance legibility" which refers to legibility when reading time is limited.

Visibility or attention value was analyzed into "target value" or characteristics making the signs stand out against its background and "priority value" which referred to other factors, such as location along the highway and mounting position affecting the order in which signs might be read. It was shown that contrast factors affected target value and that location, number of signs, reading habits, search procedure, and the "mental set" of looking for a road marker affected priority value.

LEGIBILITY FACTORS

There have been many studies of factors affecting sign legibility. Factors of importance are letter contrast, letter height, height-width ratio, stroke width, spacing between letters, and spacing between lines vertically.

Mills (1933) used a shutter-exposure technique to test color combinations and recommended first, black on yellow and, second, black on white or white on black, thus indicating the importance of letter contrast. Lauer in 1932, summarizing work of his laboratory at Iowa State University, recommended a light yellow as best for all seasons, and a letter width-to-height ratio greater than 33 percent, a stroke 20 percent of average letter width, and a spacing of 50 percent of average letter width. However, average letter width is difficult to use because of the varying widths of different letters of the alphabet.

Two later studies (Uhlaner, 1941; Kuntz and Sleight, 1950) indicated an optimum stroke width for block letters in the range of 15 to 25 percent of letter height. Also legibility increases with letter width up to a square letter as shown by several studies (Forbes and Holmes, 1939; Allen and Straub, 1955). A series of license plate legibility studies (Berger, 1944 to 1952; Herrington, 1960) confirmed this range except in the case of bright, internally illuminated letters where a narrower stroke gave better legibility. This is easily explainable in terms of an irradiation effect on the retina which produces an effectively wider stroke width.

This question of an irradiation effect plays a part in the relative effectiveness of dark letters on a light background versus light letters on a dark background. A number of studies have investigated the question of black-on-white versus white-on-black signs. Although differing in detail, these studies are consistent in indicating the light letter to be more effective when the letter design, stroke width, spacing, and brightness are such that a widening of the stroke produces a better balance of the letters and their internal and external spacing. For example, in a full-scale outdoor legibility distance experiment, Case et al. (1952) found black letters better at close spacing and white letters better with wide spacing [equal to letter height of (wide) Series E letters]. In a laboratory experiment, Allen and Straub (1955) using alphabets of three different width letters [Bureau of Public Roads Series (narrow) A, C, and (wide) F] found bright letters better at intermediate brightness using internally illuminated letters. Allen et al. (1967) found bright letters on a low-transmission background more legible than the reverse against low and medium ambient illumination but not against a high ambient background.

LEGIBILITY DISTANCES FOR HIGHWAY SIGN DESIGN —HUMAN FACTORS ENGINEERING

Based on the information from the earlier of the above studies, a standard block-letter alphabet, later a rounded-letter alphabet and still later, a lower-case alphabet design were developed by the National Committee on Signs, Signals and Markings and the U.S. Bureau of Public Roads. It has been known for many years that 1 minute of arc represents so-called normal vision for young subjects, but this was not of much assistance to the highway sign designer. The traffic engineer and those designing highway signs needed to know how far most drivers can read a sign of certain letter size and design.

Accordingly, a method for determining legibility distances for a standard block-letter alphabet was developed by Forbes (1939) and applied by Forbes and Holmes (1939). Letter size required to give sufficient warning time was calculated from speed, viewing time for glance reading, and needed maneuvering time (Mitchell and Forbes, 1942). This was one of the first applications of the engineering psychology or the human factors engineering approach in the highway field. Perhaps the highway field can claim a nationwide first, since most aviation psychology and military human factors engineering applications were developed in response to World War II problems shortly after this.

The Forbes and Holmes full-scale outdoor observations indicated a linear relationship between letter height and visibility distance of about 50 feet to the inch in daylight for black-on-white Series D (medium wide) letters. The narrower Series B letters gave about 33 feet per inch.

"Normal" versus Average Driver Vision

These 80 percentile values from observations by 412 different people represented "normal" or 20/20 vision. Six- to 24-inch letters and 6-letter place names with *one misspelling* were used for test signs. Floodlighted signs at night gave a legibility distance from 10 to 20 percent shorter. Results with button reflectorized signs under headlights were similar up to about 300 feet beyond which there was little increase with letter height. This study required subjects to record all letters accurately including the misspelling. Legibility distance of 60 feet per inch, stroke width 20 percent of height and smallest internal spacings equal to stroke width correspond rather well with the usually accepted 1 minute of arc for "normal" visual discrimination. However, most states require only 20/40 vision for a driver's license.

Lower-Case Letters and Familiarity Effects

A comparison of legibility distances of lower-case and capital letters using both familiar words and scrambled letters (Forbes, Moskowitz, and Morgan, 1950) showed distances similar to the Forbes-Holmes (1939) study for the scrambled letters, but familiar words gave longer distances. Legibility distances for lower-case alphabets in terms of "loop height" were comparable to those with capital letters. Longer legibility distances resulted with familiar names. The familiar place names shown a second time but in different orders gave slightly longer legibility distances than when first seen, even though originally the subjects had seen a list of all names that might be used (see Figures 1 and 2).

White-on-black signs of the wide Series E rounded-letter alphabet were used. Letter heights were 6, 9, and 13 inches for capitals and 5, 8, and 12 "loop height" for lower case. Lower-case letter height must be measured by "loop height" since this is the only constant dimension of all letters. Loop height in this alphabet was about three-quarters of the height of rising stems of the lower-case letters. Each word began with a capital letter. Fifty-five observers viewed all sizes and types of test sign on foot, starting from about 2000 feet, under day and night floodlighted conditions.

The normal or 20/20 legibility distance for the scrambled capital letters was about 55 feet per inch of letter height, while familiar words gave about 65 feet per inch of letter height. The median distances were somewhat greater. These distances showed the effect of familiarity but should not be used as design standards for the general public since most states require only 20/40 vision.

The shorter legibility distances of scrambled letters were quite comparable to those of the Forbes-Holmes study (where a one-letter misspelling was used).

Legibility distances on the order of 70 to 80 feet and in some cases 100 feet per inch of letter height reported by Allen and Straub (1955) and by Allen et al. (1967) corresponded well with the comparable distances of this study since they used three-letter familiar syllables.

For most effective sign design, a larger vertical spacing between lines will be required for capital-letter signs compared to that for lower-case signs.

Brightness Effect on Legibility Distance

The two studies by Forbes and others used floodlighted signs and therefore brightness remained constant. However, an increase of legibility distance occurs when sign brightness increases but distance values vary greatly depending on conditions.

An increase from 50 to about 90 feet per inch of letter height occurred (Allen and Straub, 1955) for wide Series F letters using three-letter familiar syllables, when brightness varied from 0.1 to 100 foot-lambert (ft-L) in laboratory tests. However, tests of 7-inch (narrow) Series C letters under headlights showed increasing high-beam legibility distances of only 30 to 40 feet per inch from 1 to 300 ft-L.

An even greater range of legibility distances was reported by Allen et al. (1967) with internally luminated bright on dark and dark on bright background signs using three-letter familiar syllables. They used outdoor full-scale observations using sign luminance values from 0.2 to 2000 ft-L with and without headlight glare and in three different levels of ambient illumination. As would be expected, legibility distances were greatly affected by headlight glare and by ambient illumination. Here again, resulting legibility distances were generally from 40 to about 60 feet per inch of letter height in the luminance range between 2 and 20 ft-L but ranged from 12 to 65 feet per inch in glare and in high surrounding illumination. From 10 to 100 ft-L sign luminance for rural and lighted areas, respectively, were recommended. Allen et al. commented that the driver does not ordinarily observe a highly luminous sign continuously on his approach as did their subjects. This might account for the high luminance values at which they obtained maximum legibility distance. Of importance is their comment that a large, very bright sign face will impair the driver's dark adaptation and his vision for low luminance objects on the road beyond the sign.

Need for Contrast

The need for over 40 to 50 percent contrast for day luminance and 50 to 60 percent contrast under night driving luminance levels is indicated in average values obtained by Richards (1966). He measured visual ability to discriminate letters rather than sign legibility distances. On

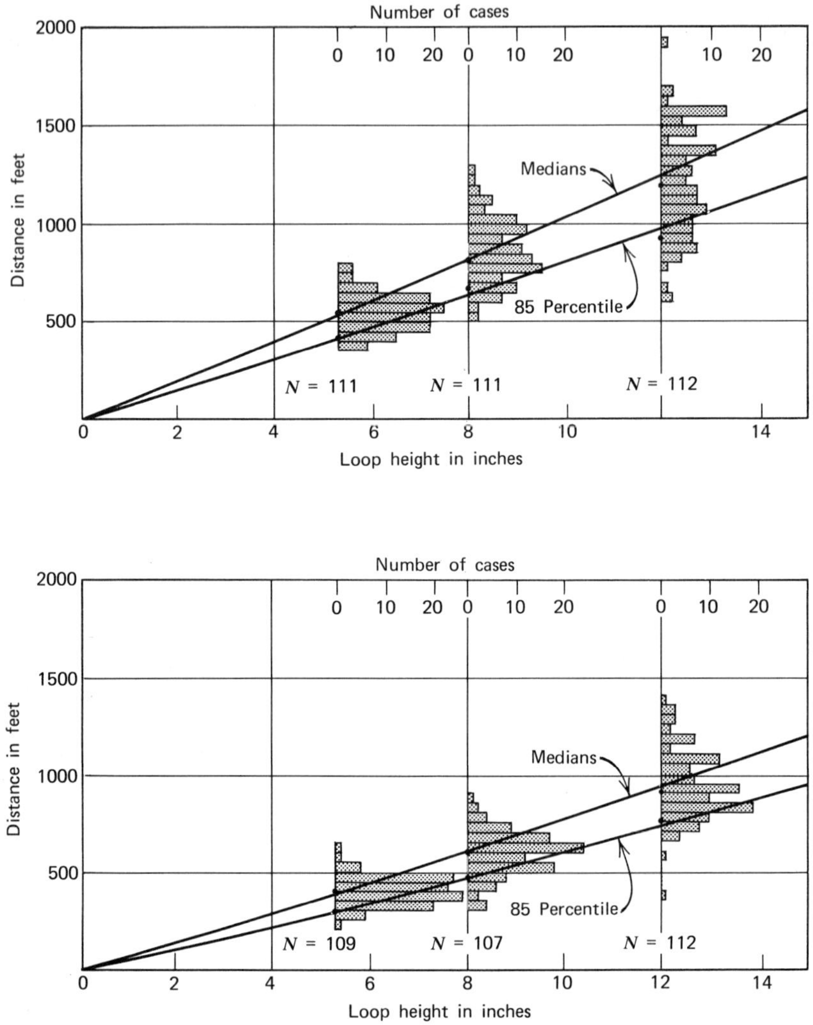

Figure 1. Daytime legibility distance distributions for lower-case (loop height) and capital letters (letter height). Scrambled letters below, familiar names, first observation above. (From Forbes et al., 1950.)

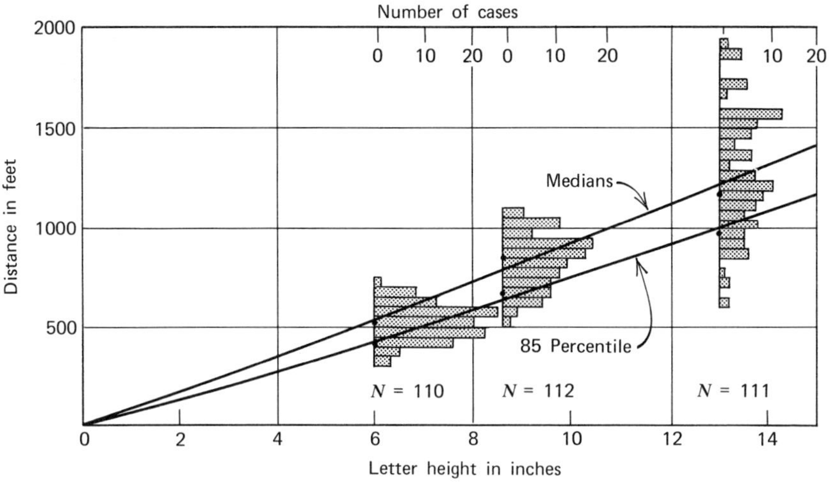
Number of cases
0 10 20 0 10 20 10 20
2000
1500
1000
500
Distance in feet
Medians
85 Percentile
N = 110
N = 112
N = 111
0 2 4 6 8 10 12 14
Letter height in inches

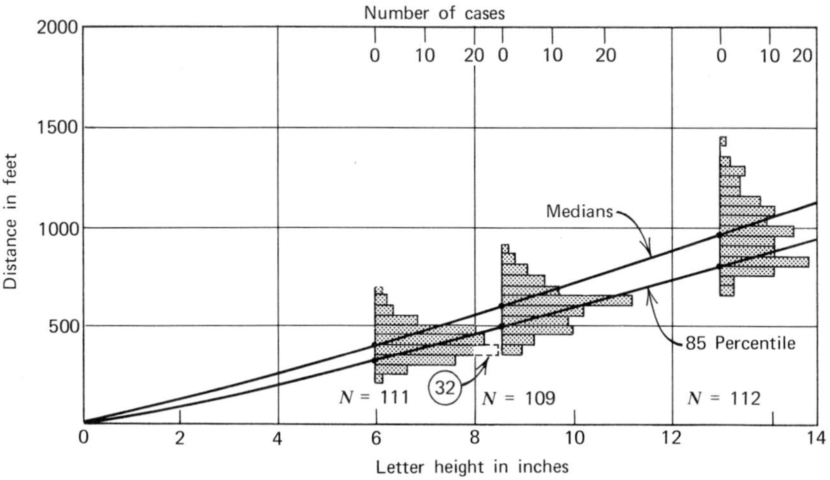
Number of cases
0 10 20 0 10 20 0 10 20
2000
1500
1000
500
Distance in feet
Medians
85 Percentile
32
N = 111
N = 109
N = 112
0 2 4 6 8 10 12 14
Letter height in inches

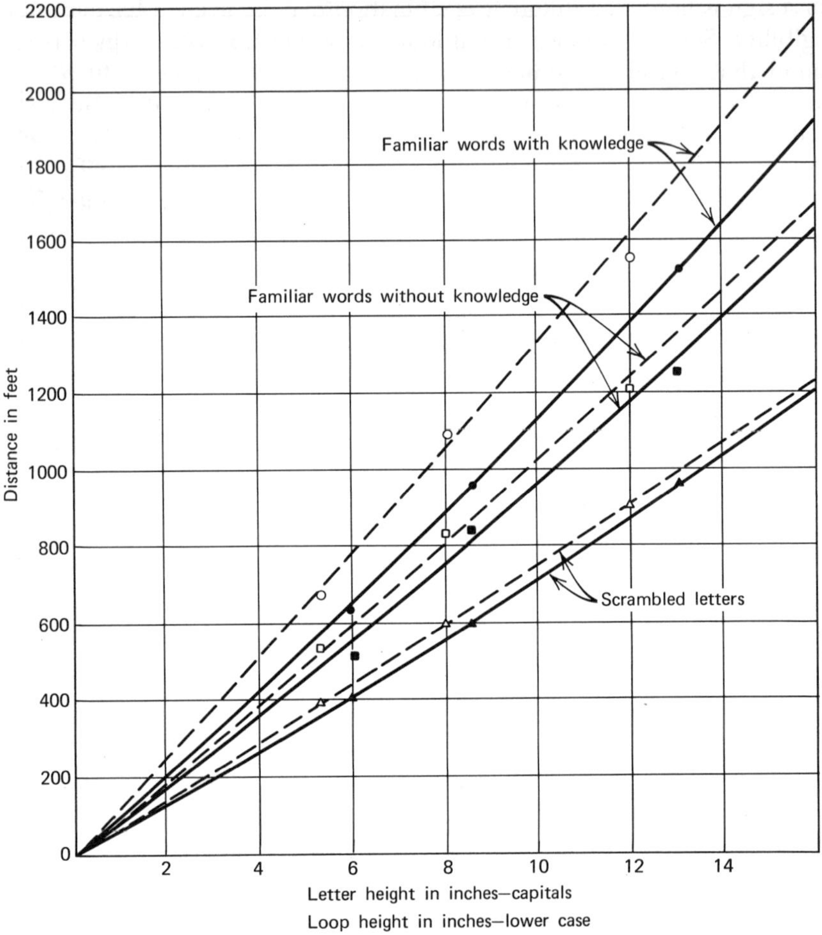

Figure 2. Effect of familiar names on lower-case and capital letter legibility distance, daytime. (From Forbes et al., 1950.)

the average his subjects showed greater need for high contrast targets with increasing age. In addition to some increasing average loss in low contrast vision in older groups, wide differences among individuals in all age groups in low contrast acuity at night driving levels was found by Forbes et al. (1969).

Tradeoffs Between Letter Height, Width, and Letter Spacing

As seen above, increased letter height, width, and letter spacing all give increased legibility distance. When either width or height available for a sign is limited, a different combination may be needed for maximum legibility. Solomon (1956) in outdoor measurements with 10-inch letters found that legibility distance increased up to letter spacing 40 percent above "normal" for both narrow- and wide-letter alphabets. He noted that for an overhead sign with vertical distance limited but horizontal space available, a square letter with wide spacing may be advantageous. The reverse might be needed for a sign located on the road side where horizontal space is limited. Whether lower-case or capital letters are more efficient for a given sign area depends on combinations of letter size, width and spacing used (Forbes et al., 1950; Christie and Rutley, 1961).

Glance Legibility

When time to view signs is limited to a short glance of about 1 second, as in much seeing by drivers on the highway, the legibility distances are reduced from 10 to 15 percent and about three to four short familiar words can be recognized. This was shown by Forbes (1939), and the limit for familiar words with about 1-second exposure was confirmed in a study by Hurd (1946). Thus, not more than three to four familiar words should be used on each sign at locations along a highway to require minimum reading time by the motorist (Forbes, 1941).

Calculation of Necessary Letter Sizes

A method for calculating required letter size for a given highway design speed and warning distance was suggested by Mitchell and Forbes (1942) in the United States and in England by Odescalchi et al. (1962) and by Moore and Christie (1963). To accomplish this, time to read signs and warning time needed for stopping or other maneuvers must be known or assumed.

Mitchell and Forbes used a 1-second glance for each three-word sign and a 1-second safety factor. Average perception response time of 1.5 seconds was assumed on the basis of previous experiments. Odescalchi measured "distraction time" for three-, six-, and nine-name signs when a subject in a car interrupted an auxiliary task to find a given place name on a map sign. The subject "canceled" four small lamps with one switch and pushed a button when he found the required place name.

The results of the United States and English studies differed somewhat but not to an unexpected degree considering the variability to be expected in this type of measurement. The equations of the English studies were more meticulous in including distance of sign from driver's path. However, either calculation can be applied to a given signing problem.

VISIBILITY FACTORS IN SIGN EFFECTIVENESS

In addition to being legible, a sign must be seen by the motorist to be effective. Thus, suprathreshold visibility factors that contribute attention value of the type previously called "target value"* are important (Forbes, 1939). These become even more important as greater volume and speed of traffic is encountered.

Attention Value or Conspicuity Factors

An early study (Forbes, 1939) analyzed "attention value" into "target value" and "priority value" as noted above. Subject drivers called out signs on rural highways. Signs that contrasted with background terrain were seen at much greater distances then others, but no equipment was available at that time to measure brightness and contrast of these high target value signs.

At intersections, signs were called in the order they were seen. This order in most cases involved: (1) route signs being followed; (2) placement along the highway; and (3) order from top to bottom and left to right in multiple-name signs. The effect of such factors was called priority value.

Odescalchi (1960) had observers rate various sized signs seen against open field and shaded background for "conspicuity" at 150 to 500 yards in a paired comparison presentation with different sized white panels to determine detectability while fixating a gray panel between them. Five colors also presented were effective in order of their luminance factors with one reversal.

A study of arrow signs with and without a reflective sign background (Powers, 1965) was inconclusive. It analyzed turn errors by a group of drivers following a route indicated by the experimental signs, but the number of drivers and erroneous turns was too small for reliable statistical evaluation.

This suprathreshold visibility or attention value of signs differs from the threshold of detection and is much more difficult to measure. Data on visibility factors in suprathreshold conditions, therefore, are needed but relatively few studies have been conducted (Forbes et al., 1964). A four-year study of such factors was recently reported (Forbes et al., 1968).

Several methods of measurement were tried. The most satisfactory and consistent proved to be an immediate subjective response to simu-

* The author is indebted to Guy Kelcey for suggesting this term in discussion of sign characteristics. "Conspicuity" has been used by other investigators more recently.

lated signs by subjects in the laboratory. A 1-second view of four simulated signs was presented without warning while the subjects simultaneously carried on an auxiliary task of relighting combinations of small red lights in a foreground matrix. Simulation by means of projected highway scenes with colored slides in a completely dark laboratory allowed control of the important variables. Results from the laboratory experiment were checked by outdoor observations later.

A number of different highway backgrounds were used typical of day, night, summer, and winter backgrounds in different parts of the country. Most of the experiments used simulated signs approximating the interstate green but one used seven colors in pairs.

Mathematical models based on certain assumptions were tested against the laboratory results. Showing the best fit was a model based on brightness *ratios* and almost as good was one based on percent brightness contrast of sign-to-background and letter-to-sign. For a single sign in which the legend usually covers about one-half of the area, the model applied to predict outdoor results was

$$D = \frac{C_{SB} + C_{LS}}{2} \times ER$$

where D = visibility distance, $C_{SB} + C_{LS}$ = percent brightness contrast of sign to background terrain and letters to sign, respectively, and ER = expected recognition distance (small dimension of sign in feet × 1200) or clear sight distance, whichever is smaller.

When the simplified model was used to predict outdoor sign observations, the calculated values were close enough to observed values to indicate fair validity for the laboratory results. The percent contrast calculation was suggested for estimating sign visibility against various backgrounds for traffic engineering purposes. Details will be found in Forbes et al. (1968) and Forbes (1969).

Other Factors: Mounting Position

The most effective mounting of signs with respect to the roadway depends to some extent on type of lighting. Straub and Allen (1956) found mounting position 5 feet to the right and 8 feet above the pavement most effective and the overhead position least effective. Their conclusions were from measurements with headlights and based on luminance levels. Forbes et al. (1968) found that sign position over the highway was seen first more often than beside the highway in the simulated sign presentations. With floodlighted signs, both sidemounted and overhead signs would be of approximately equal brightness characteristics, whereas headlights may favor side-mounted signs especially if on "dimmed" aiming.

Sign Color

Paired comparison presentation of seven different colored signs gave visibility ratings again clearly related to brightness of the sign colors. There was also, however, an effect of hue contrast with the background as shown by the individual curves (Forbes et al., 1968).

Brightness Ratio and Brightness Level

Pain (1969), using Munsell gray chips of different lightness, analyzed brightness ratio and brightness level using both an eye movement camera and subjective responses. He found the latter a more consistent measure and confirmed brightness ratio as a primary factor. Brightness level showed an interacting effect.

Importance of Backgrounds

Hanson and Woltman (1967) reported the wide range of backgrounds against which highway signs are seen in different parts of the country. Dark green trees, bright sky, and highway bridges furnished 23, 19, and 16 percent of the backgrounds. In winter, of course, snow backgrounds are common.

SUMMARY

Efficiency of highway signs has been analyzed into legibility and attention value. The former is composed of pure legibility and glance legibility, the latter of target value and priority value.

Numerous studies have shown that legibility depends on letter height, height-to-width ratio, stroke width, spacing between letters, spacing between lines, contrast, and illumination. These studies are quoted and optimum values for these factors are quoted.

For ordinary black-on-white or white-on-green highway signs with wide letters, legibility distances were 50 feet to 65 feet to the inch letter height. Some longer distances have been reported for signs with high luminance and high letter contrast. The distances given are for people with 20/20 or "normal" vision and must be reduced for 20/40 vision, the minimum allowed for driver's license in most states.

Lower-case letters and capital letters with similar stroke and width-to-height ratios gave about the same legibility distances per inch of loop height and letter height. Signs can be designed to be adequate for a given design speed and warning distance. Reports are quoted which described two methods of calculating letter size needed. Ordinarily at least 40 to 50 percent letter to sign contrast is needed. Three to four familiar words could be read at a glance.

Attention value for signs that are easily within legibility distance depends on a number of factors. Early studies showed that contrast with the background and location on the road, sign position, reading habits, and a "set" to find a certain route affect target value and priority value. A later study showed that, in general, visibility (which signs will be seen first) depends on brightness contrast of letter to sign and of sign to background. Color contrast (hue) might add to this effect but, in general, colors were effective in proportion to their brightness and brightness contrast.

Very bright signs will be seen to best advantage against a bright background but may interfere with dark adaptation in a dark rural setting.

A simplified mathematical model for estimating visibility distances was reported. Relative effectiveness of mounting signs over the highway as against on the side of the road, and relative percentages of backgrounds against which highway signs are seen were considered.

The proper design for signs, for both legibility and visibility is of primary importance for efficient and safe traffic on city streets and on high-speed highways and freeways.

REFERENCES

Allen, T. M., Night Legibility Distance of Highway Signs, *Highway Research Board Bulletin,* **191** (1958), 33–40.

Allen, T. M., Dyer, F. N., Smith, G. M., and Janson, M. H., Luminance Requirements for Illuminated Signs, *Highway Research Record,* **179** (1967), 16–37.

Allen, Terrence M. and Straub, Arthur L., Sign Brightness and Legibility, *Highway Research Board Bulletin,* **127** (1955), 1–22.

Berger, C., Four Reports on Legibility of Numerals and Symbols, *see* Abstracts in Forbes et al., 1964, 50–52.

Case, H. W., Michael, J. L., Mount, G. E., and Brenner, R., Analysis of Certain Variables Related to Sign Legibility, *Highway Research Board Bulletin,* **60** (1952), 44–54.

Christie, A. W. and Rutley, K. S., The Relative Effectiveness of Some Letter Types Designed for Use on Road Traffic Signs, Road Research Laboratory, Laboratory note, January 1961.

Forbes, T. W., A Method for Analysis of the Effectiveness of Highway Signs, *Journal of Applied Psychology,* **XXIII** (1939), 669–684.

Forbes, T. W., Factors of Adequate Sign Design, *Traffic Engineer's Handbook,* Institute of Traffic Engineers, New York, 1941, 106–107.

Forbes, T. W., Factors in Highway Sign Visibility, *Traffic Engineering,* **39** (September 1–8, 1969).

Forbes, T. W. and Holmes, Robert S., Legibility Distances of Highway Destination Signs in Relation to Letter Height, Letter Width and Reflectorization, *Proceedings of the Highway Research Board,* **19** (1939), 321–335.

Forbes, T. W., Moskowitz, K., and Morgan, G., A Comparison of Lower Case and Capital Letters for Highway Signs, *Proceedings of the Highway Research Board,* **30** (1950), 355–373.

Forbes, T. W., Pain, R. F., Bloomquist, D. W., and Vanosdall, F. E., Low Contrast and Standard Visual Acuity under Mesopic and Photopic Illumination, *Journal of Safety Research,* **1** (1969), 5–12.

Forbes, T. W., Pain, R. F., Fry, J. P. Jr., and Joyce, R. P., Effect of Sign Position and Brightness on Seeing Simulated Highway Signs, *Highway Research Record,* **164** (1967), 29–37.

Forbes, T. W., Pain, R. F., Joyce, R. P., and Fry, J. P. Jr., Color and Brightness Factors in Simulated and Full-Scale Traffic Sign Visibility, *Highway Research Record,* **216** (1968), 55–65.

Forbes, T. W., Snyder, R. F., and Pain, R. F., A Study of Traffic Sign Requirements II. An Annotated Bibliography, College of Engineering, Michigan State Univ., Lansing, Mich., 1964, 85 pp.

Forbes, T. W., Snyder, Thomas F., and Pain, Richard F., Traffic Sign Requirements I. Review of Factors Involved, Previous Studies and Needed Research, *Highway Research Record,* **70** (1965), 48–56.

Hanson, Douglas R. and Woltman, Henry L., Sign Backgrounds and Angular Position, *Highway Research Record,* **170** (1967), 82–96.

Herrington, C. G., Design of Reflectorized Motor Vehicle License Plates, *Proceedings of the Highway Research Board,* **39** (1960), 441–466.

Hurd, F., Glance Legibility, *Traffic Engineering,* **17** (1946), 161–162.

Kuntz, J. E. and Sleight, R. B., Legibility of Numerals: The Optimal Ratio of Height to Stroke Width, *American Journal of Psychology,* **63** (1950), 567–575.

Lauer, A. R., Improvements in Highway Safety. *Proceedings of the Highway Research Board,* **12** (1932), 389–401. Abstract in Forbes et al., 1964.

Mills, F. W., The Comparative Visibility of Standard Luminous and Nonluminous Signs, *Public Roads,* **14** (1933), 109–128. Abstract in Forbes et al., 1964.

Mitchell, Adolphus and Forbes, T. W., Design of Sign Letter Sizes, *Proceedings of the American Society of Civil Engineers,* **68** (1942), 95–104.

Moore, R. W. and Christie, A. W., Research on Traffic Signs, British Road Research Laboratory, Engineering for Traffic Conference, 1963, 113–122.

Odescalchi, P., Conspicuity of Signs in Rural Surroundings, *Traffic Engineering and Control,* **2**, 7 (1960), 390–393. Abstract in Forbes et al., 1964.

Odescalchi, P., Rutley, K. S., and Christie, A. W., The Time Taken to Read a Traffic Sign and its Effect on the Size of Lettering Necessary. Road Research Laboratory, Laboratory note, September 1962.

Pain, Richard, Brightness Ratio as Factors in the Attention Value of Highway Signs, *Highway Research Record,* **275** (1969), 32–40.

Powers, Lawrence D., Effectiveness of Sign Background Reflectorization, *Highway Research Record,* **70** (1965), 74–86.

Richards, Oscar W., Vision at Levels of Night Road Illumination XII. Changes of Acuity and Contrast Sensitivity with Age, *American Journal of Optometry,* **43** (1966), 313–319.

Solomon, D., The Effect of Letter Width and Spacing on Night Legibility of

Highway Signs, *Proceedings of the Highway Research Board,* **35** (1956), 600–617.

Straub, Arthur L. and Allen, Terrence M., Sign Brightness in Relation to Position, Distance and Reflectorization. Highway Research Board Bulletin, **146** (1956), 13–34.

Uhlaner, J. E., The Effect of Thickness of Stroke on the Legibility of Letters, *Proceedings of the Iowa Academy of Sciences,* **48** (1941), 319–324. Abstract in Forbes et al., 1964.

VI

DRIVER INFORMATION SYSTEMS

Slade Hulbert

DRIVER INFORMATION NEEDS

Drivers, as a whole, perform their tasks very well considering the difficult nature of the task. The driver must constantly process a stream of information coming to him from the environment, primarily through his visual faculties. Since any vehicle (or object) in motion is committed to occupy a certain amount of space directly in its path within the next instant, the driver must make a continuous series of such spatial commitments. Hulbert and Burg (1970) describe the shape of this spatial commitment for automobile drivers as fan-shaped, extending in front of the vehicle, as shown in Figure 1. The exact configuration of this spatial commitment, of course, varies from vehicle to vehicle and is effected by road surface and highway design features. Generally, however, this fan-shaped area grows in size with increased speed and/or reduction in the pavement friction. As the driver proceeds along, he makes an unalterable commitment to be somewhere in this fan-shaped zone immediately ahead of his vehicle. The portion of this zone that he actually uses is his path. At the same time the immediate path is being chosen, the driver is making provisional commitments extending out beyond the immediate zone (to which he is totally committed).

The various bases upon which these provisional commitments are made is the subject of this chapter and we shall attempt to describe the information processing that underlies these successive spatial commitments that are continually being made and re-made as the driver proceeds along the highway.

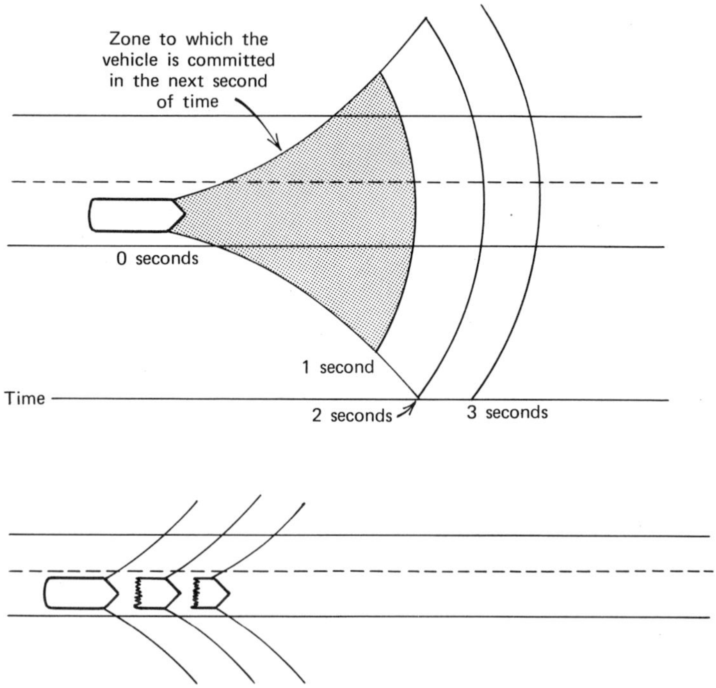

Figure 1. The exact configuration of this fan-shaped zone will depend upon the vehicle speed, turning radius, and stopping distance as they interact with the driver's reaction time. As each driver proceeds, the fan-shaped zone extends in front of his path and changes shape as velocity and pavement conditions vary (Hulbert and Burg, 1970).

INFORMATION PROCESSING BY DRIVERS

In a recent textbook Hulbert and Burg (1970) set forth a generalized framework for considering the role that humans play in transportation systems. This framework is shown in Figure 2 where, for the sake of simplicity, human decision-making is classified into pre-trip decisions about route selection and scheduling (the timing of a trip); decisions about vehicle path, speed, and failure. These types of decision-making create an information need, some of which is met by pre-trip planning and the balance of which is met during the actual act of driving. We will concentrate our attention on the driving and deal with traffic control devices, vehicle control feedback, and traffic situation judgment.

Unfortunately, man, although he may appear otherwise, is essentially a single-channel information processing system. His ability to rapidly

Human Functions Common to All Transportation Systems			Sources of Information	Range of Performance	Selection and Placement	Training of Personnel	Performance Evaluation
MAKING DECISIONS	TRIP PLANNING	Schedule					
		Route					
	VEHICLE OPERATION	Path					
		System Failure					
		Speed					
EXECUTING	DECISIONS	(+, 0, −) Acceleration					
		Direction					
MAINT.	VEHICLE	En Route					
		At Home					

Figure 2. Generalized framework for considering human factors in transportation systems.

shift his attention from one task to another enables him to carry on more than one simultaneous task. The driving task has two major simultaneous elements—namely, tracking and object avoidance. If man's single central processing channel is occupied with one type of information, it cannot be utilized to process additional information. Therefore, time spent reading a highway sign or looking at a pedestrian is time taken away from the tracking task and vice versa. For this reason designers of roadways and vehicles have striven to make the tracking task easier, and traffic control devices have been designed over many years of trial and error to be relatively unambiguous information generators, demanding a minimum of the driver's attention to comprehend.

DRIVER INFORMATION FROM TRAFFIC CONTROL DEVICES

The role of standardization and uniformity of traffic control devices is obvious in respect to simplifying the driving task. Uniformity is reflected in the *National Manual on Uniform Traffic Control Devices* (U.S. Department of Transportation, 1971) where both shape and color coding are employed, along with standardization of the placement and the size of traffic control devices, in order to avoid confusion among drivers.

Warning signs are yellow in color, diamond in shape, and are placed where the driver needs some advance notice about the nature of the roadway or traffic situations he will soon encounter. Such warnings are necessary because the driver cannot see very far ahead of his vehicle, especially at night or when roadside objects block his view; and yet, as we have shown earlier, he has committed himself to be somewhere in a fan-shaped space extending in front of his vehicle. Wherever a warning sign is placed, it is there because experience has shown that many drivers, at that location, will unknowingly commit themselves (spatially) beyond their limits to respond to the situation.

Pavement markings also play a major role in warning drivers about such situations as "no passing" and "ped Xings" which is a cryptic way of saying "pedestrian crossing." Color is used in pavement markings with yellow standing for "no passing," which is a regulatory traffic control device.

Regulatory signs are rectangular and black and white which distinguishes them as having the force of law. Red and white is used for extremely hazardous situation regulatory signs such as STOP and YIELD and WRONG WAY. For both warning signs and regulatory signs it is important to know more about how signs attract the attention of passing drivers. Recent studies at Michigan State University by Forbes, Snyder, and Pain (1963) have produced formulas that relate such things as the size, the brightness, and the contrast ratio of the sign against the background scenery. In general, the problem facing highway and traffic engineers is to create signs that attract enough attention for the driver to be able to read them before they pass from his view. The legibility or reading distance of each sign, therefore, must enter into the formulas used.

Research beginning as early as 1932 (Lauer, 1932) has resulted in the current format of letter height and width ratios, stroke width, spacing between words and letters and lines of message. Several subtle factors have emerged such as the "irradiation effect" that white letters have against black backgrounds which causes them to have the appearance of larger stroke width letters. Also, interactions have been found between letter contrast and letter and word spacing.

It was in this part of the driver information problem that the first "human factors" contribution was forthcoming when Forbes and Holmes (1939) studied the alphabet for highway signs that had been approved by the U.S. Bureau of Public Roads. This alphabet produced a reading distance of about 50 feet for every inch of letter height in daytime and 33 feet at night. Forbes, in Chapter 5, states:

"Legibility distance of 60 feet per inch, stroke width 20 percent of height, correspond rather well with the usually accepted figure of one minute of arc for normal (20/20) visual discrimination. However, most states only require 20/40 vision for a driver's license."

Green and white signs display guidance information although current practice does permit the use of black and white guide signs on city streets and county roads. This should not prove confusing because directional information obviously does not carry the force of law and guide signs have their own characteristic appearance and location along the roadway.

Freeway Information Requirements

Freeway or expressway driving is creating special demands on drivers to quickly interpret directional signs and there is a continuing effort to improve these signs. In 1968 the House of Representatives Blatnik Committee conducted hearings about safety and freeway signing (U.S. Congress, 1968). Witnesses called attention to a 1960 study by Schoppert et al. where 12,000 motorists were interviewed concerning their experiences with finding their way on the California freeways. These interviews led the researchers to conclude that out of every ten trips in new territory, one trip would involve getting lost due to poor signing. The primary recommendations of these researchers were set forth as the following six basic principles:

"*1. Interpretation.* All possible interpretations and misinterpretations must be considered in phrasing sign messages (words and symbols).

"Messages must be complete and clearly stated. Cryptic messages, which are easily misinterpreted, must be avoided. The difference between two alternatives must be emphasized and, where possible, choices offered must be between things of the same kind, for example, two route numbers. Care must be exercised to avoid giving more information than can be read and comprehended in the time available.

"There are two important general points to be remembered. The first is that a motorist's interpretation of a sign message is based not only on what the message says but also on what it does not say. The second point to be kept in mind is that literal interpretation results in the motorist doing exactly what the sign indicates exactly at the sign location. For example, drivers reported turning into alleys and driveways by mistake because the on-ramp sign appeared to direct them to do so.

"*2. Continuity.* Each sign must be designed in context with those which precede it so that continuity is achieved through relatively long sections of highway.

"The driver should be expected to evaluate not more than one new alternative at any advance sign. At the decision point he should never be given new information about either the through route or the turnoff. For example, sometimes several communities (or streets) are served by one turnoff. The advance sign will say 'Orangevale Exit 2 Miles,' the next sign, 'Orangevale Exit 1 Mile,' and finally, at the exit the sign says 'Orangevale, Jamestown.' The "Jamestown" on the third sign violates the principle of continuity and throws the motorist for a loss. He says to himself, 'I wonder if this is the exit they have been referring to as the one for Orangevale, or is this just an alternate route to Orangevale?' For another example, the advance signs say 'Castro Blvd 1 Mile,' then 'Castro Blvd ½ Mile,' and finally, at the exit, 'Castro Blvd.' Then a few seconds later the driver comes upon a sign like the one shown in Figure 3. He is

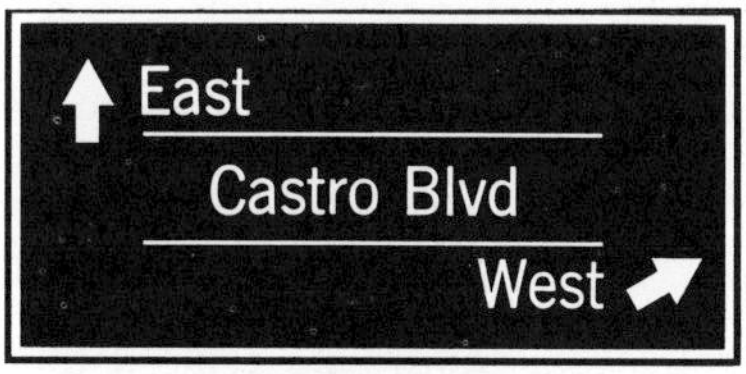

Figure 3

totally unprepared for this new information. He has 8 sec to digest it, visualize a map, mentally turn the map upside down if he is southbound, and finally take action.

"3. ***Advance Notice.*** Signing must prepare the driver ahead of time for each decision he has to make.

The term "advance notice" is frequently used by traffic engineers and motorists, but is practically never analyzed. Essentially, when the motorist is surprised to find that he has to make a decision, he assumes that he was not told about it ahead of time. Very large signs, and signs well in advance of decision points, have been in place on California freeways for many years and still there are many surprised motorists. In almost all of the cases investigated during this study where the motorist said he did not have advance notice such signing did, in fact, exist. This signing, however, did not adequately prepare the driver for his decision.

"The real point is that the motorist does not want to learn suddenly about the decision, regardless of how far ahead he is told or how vividly (that is, how big the letters are). He wants to know where he is located in relation to the point of decision throughout the trip. This is the only advantage that repeat motorists have over unfamiliar motorists.

"A single advance sign can easily be missed, as can one sign of any kind, especially in dense traffic (*cf.* principle 5, below). Two advance signs can also be missed, although the probability is not as great. Of course, the size of the sign and the distance in advance have a bearing on this problem, but more 'advance notice' cannot be achieved merely by increasing the size or distance or both.

"4. ***Relatability.*** Sign messages should be in the same terms as information available to the driver from other sources, such as touring maps and addresses given in tourist information and advertising.

"To insure this result, maps used by engineers as the basis for sign design should also include some which correspond in scale to touring maps. Outside of large metropolitan areas, signs should relate to a state road map. In a city represented on the map by a small circle or dot, signs preparing the driver for an important junction within the city should take into consideration that there will be many turnoffs from the main route to other streets, while the map may show only the one junction. In metropolitan areas, he must be expected to receive more detailed information than a state map can show.

"5. ***Prominence.*** The size and position, as well as the number of times a sign or message is repeated, should be related to the competition from other demands on the driver's attention.

"These demands can come from other visual aids, other signs or parts of the message, as well as the task of driving. One huge sign in a group or one huge word in a message tends to attract so much attention that the other signs or the rest of the message may not be comprehended. Thus, it often happens that the sign designer defeats his very purpose.

"When the road is very wide, the traffic very dense, and there are numerous competing 'spectacular' commercial signs or buildings (as is typical of a downtown urban freeway), the directional signs must be very large, well-illuminated and well-placed, even if this means costly overhead installations. There is no certainty that a motorist will, in the face of such competition (particularly dense traffic on curves) see a given sign no matter how large it is. Repetition suggests itself, not only for 'advance notice,' but for initial notice. On the other hand, the use of a gigantic sign in a sparsely settled rural area where there is no visual competition will serve to lessen the impact of using extra large signs where they are really necessary.

"On city streets, where proper signing is just as important to the motorist as is signing on a freeway, the signs do not have to be as large, but the competition is much greater. Trees, poles, parked cars, signs on buildings, and traffic regulation signs all make it difficult to find the essential sign saying how to get to the freeway. Although standardization of color, shape, and style (uniformity) is one way to make the essential sign distinctive, it should not be relied on too heavily. Location, size, and contrast with surroundings are more important factors.

"6. Unusual Maneuvers. Signing must be specially designed at points where the driver has to make a movement which is unexpected or unnatural.

"The driver's natural inclination to turn a certain way frequently will lead him to do the wrong thing. Clarity in signing wins the driver's confidence and helps him avoid mistakes resulting from instinctive movements. Although cloverleaf interchanges are becoming more prevalent, the unfamiliar driver never knows whether or not the next interchange is a cloverleaf, and if it is, whether or not it has a collector-distributor road. Standard directional arrows used for near-side turnoffs cannot be used successfully to prepare a first-time user for the series of decisions he must make within a short time interval if his proper course of action is to take the far-side turnoff."

Unfortunately, over ten years later, these principles still are not being followed in many areas of the United States with resultant driver confusion and highway accidents (U.S. Congress, 1968), as was documented in a 1966 report (Schoppert, 1966), of observations of hundreds of confused motorists on the Beltway that encircles Washington, D.C. These data clearly show that the more of the six basic principles that are violated, the more drivers are confused. This study reached the conclusions that 0.2 of 1% of the traffic volume is a "normal" proportion of confused drivers to be found at choice points in the highway.

Currently, studies are underway (Eberhard and Berger, 1970) to develop some form of graphic symbols that will more clearly inform the motorist about the geometry of the off-ramps he is approaching. Several types of ramps have been selected for study, among which are the following:

1. Those where you must take a right-side off-ramp in order to go left, or vice versa (Figure 4).
2. Where a major fork occurs and therefore both choices appear equally important (Figure 5).
3. A cloverleaf (Figure 6).
4. Those interchanges where a through lane is discontinued at the turnoff (Figure 7).
5. Where two right turns (or left) are required in quick succession (Figure 8).
6. Where there are sequential choice points after a main exit (Figure 9).

The superhighways also have made the availability of motorist services less obvious than when the roadway actually led through the city. A study by Foody and Taylor (1969) indicates that special signing to indicate the availability of services does increase the motorist's awareness of these services and in some cases changes the use patterns.

Another, more serious, problem created by superhighways is wrong-way driving. Several years of research effort in California and other states

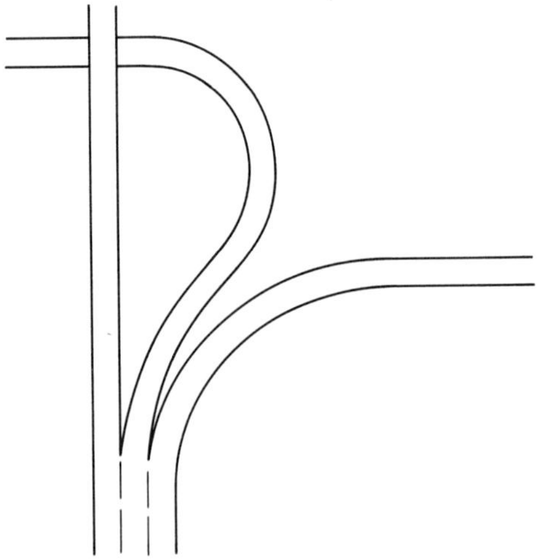

Figure 4

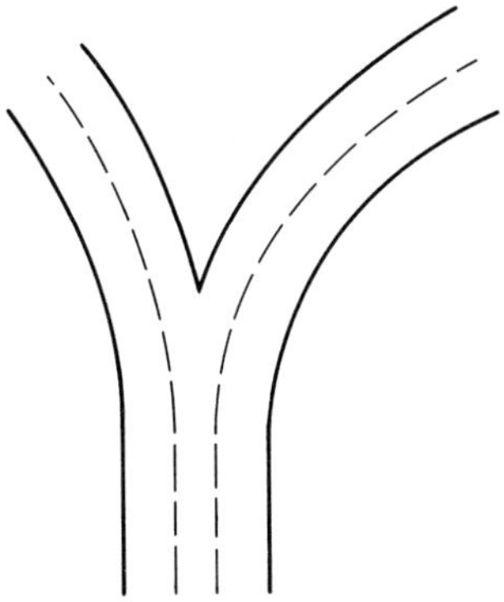

Figure 5

Figure 6

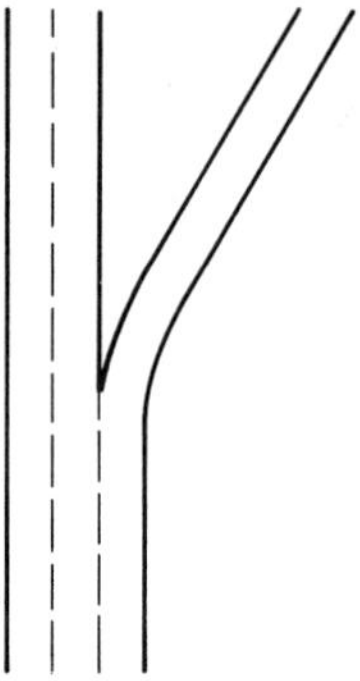

Figure 7

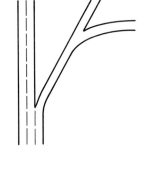

Figure 8

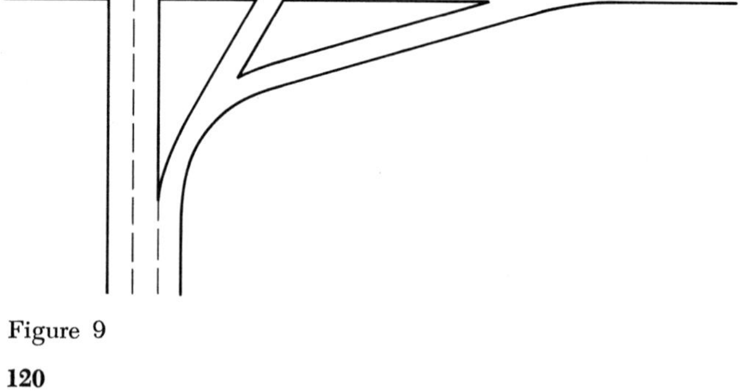

Figure 9

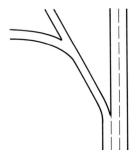

have resulted in special traffic control devices to warn motorists of this hazard. There is a definite interaction between the geometry of off-ramps and the alignment of adjacent roadways that causes more confusion at certain types of ramps. Research in the field and in the UCLA Driving Simulation Laboratory (Hulbert and Beers, 1966, see Chapter 3) resulted in design of special green-colored "Freeway Entrance" signs and red "WRONG WAY" signs and large white pavement arrows. Accident records (Tamburri, 1969) clearly show that these devices are effective in reducing wrong-way accidents by as much as two-thirds. The effect of red-colored raised pavement markers is still being evaluated.

Advance Information at Railroad-Highway Crossings

Traffic control devices at railroad-highway grade crossings were among the earliest of roadway hazards marked by signs, but they have not been improved greatly for at least 30 years. This unfortunate condition was documented in a 1968 study by Schoppert and Hoyt (1968) in which a human factors analysis is made of the special problems these crossings pose for motorists. The report recommends that a clear difference be established between those crossings that are "protected" by signal devices and those where the driver must actually detect the approaching train without any assistance from traffic control devices. As it is now, there is *no difference* in the advance warning signs.

This study also considered rumble strips as an alerting device to help notify the driver he is approaching a crossing. These devices have been used in Texas rather widely since 1956, and New Jersey as early as 1947 reported experimental use at approaches to tollgate plazas.

Bellis (1969) describes two basic types: one composed of actual strips of material placed at intervals across the highway to cause intermittent jolts and bumping vibration, and the other made of a rough surfacing material to create a "rumble area" of perhaps 25 feet in length or longer. Results indicate the rumble *strips* to be more effective than the rumble *area* tested. Several important considerations are raised in this report, namely,

"1. Serious consideration should be given to the question 'Does the motorist require advance notice of the oncoming rumble strip.' And if so, how should it be given?' This seems nonsensical in a way because the rumble strip in itself is to warn, alert, wake up, the motorist. However, quite a few alert drivers, given no advance notice of the experience, and apparently not acquainted with such experience, pull off to the side and examine their car for mechanical trouble. This type of reaction slows down traffic and is hazardous to the motorist.

"2. Consideration should be given as to whether or not a series of strip patterns, rather than only one, would better suit the purpose.

"3. That when the decision is reached to use rumble strips, consideration be given to whether they should be installed on more than one of the roads which form the dangerous intersection.

"4. Consideration should be given to the possible necessity of developing ways and means for preventing the local motorist, familiar with the installation, from deliberately driving around it. This 'driving around' practice is not only very hazardous in itself, but it becomes much more so when non-local motorists unwittingly follow the local driver in this dangerous manner.

"5. Every consideration be given to establishing the proper distance between the warning device and the critical area. If the distance is too great, acceleration rather than deceleration can be effected by the determined aggressive motorist; if too short, the alert motorist, who however, is exceeding the speed limit, is in trouble."

The railway crossing report (Schoppert and Hoyt, 1968) suggested the possible use of "quiet strips" which more rightly should be called "quiet areas" to create an unusually smooth surface immediately preceding a rumble strip.

A rumble strip installation was reported by Bellis (1969) to be successful in creating a 20 percent reduction in accidents during a two year before-and-after tabulation of collisions at a traffic circle. Injuries were reduced 40 percent during the same period.

Symbols or Pictographs

In the United States, traffic signs contain fewer symbols than the Canadian or Mexican system and far fewer symbols than are generally used in Europe. As more and more drivers have the opportunity to drive in foreign countries, the need for universal traffic signs is increasing (Elliott, 1960). In general, there are two types of symbol signs. The abstract symbols bear no obvious relation to the traffic situation and their meaning must be learned by the motorist. Graphic symbols, on the other hand, are pictographs that attempt to depict the highway situation and thereby create an immediate awareness without any prior learning. If a pictograph is completely successful, it will require *no* uniformity because it requires no language or prior learning. Therefore, the problem lies with those many traffic situations for which no clearly understandable graphic has been devised. Examples are "slow," "no parking," "do not enter," "resume speed," and many others.

One solution for these situations is to adopt a universal symbol and have all drivers learn its meaning; the other solution is to adopt a single language for a certain sign. The United Nations has attempted these solutions and before them the League of Nations. Several European countries have announced they are going to adopt the American stop sign and the U.S. Committee on Uniform Traffic Control Devices is recommending many symbol signs for the *National Manual.*

Information from Traffic Signals

The red, yellow, green signal light at intersections has become so well known that it is hard to imagine how traffic could move without it. Various styles of mounting and types of lenses are continually being developed but several factors generally are found in all signals. They all take into account the fact that upwards of 8 percent of drivers (mostly males) are color weak in the red-green area. Therefore, there is considerable blue in the green lens and yellow in the red lens (Hoxie, 1961).

In addition, for the placement of lens, there is a position code of red over green that generally is followed and is relied upon by color-weak drivers. In order to be more effective in attracting drivers' attention, there is increasing use of 12-inch diameter lens (particularly for red) to replace or augment the standard 8-inch lens. For the same reason, redundancy of signal is created by multiple signal heads that reduce the unfortunate consequences of lightbulb failures. Complex control of traffic has brought about the use of arrow symbols in traffic lights and uniformity of usage is slowly coming about, but drivers can still expect to see yellow, red, and green arrows at various locations and unfortunately carrying different meanings.

The time it takes for pedestrian movement across intersections is the most limiting time factor that traffic engineers have to cope with in attempting to set the signals for "green wave" movement. In order to increase pedestrian safety and better control the time cycle problem, special pedestrian signals are being added to many urban traffic signals. Soon these "walk—don't walk" type of signals will be standardized as to color and message, but at present, as with all new traffic control devices, there are several variations of these signals. One unexpected and not generally recognized consequence of pedestrian signals is their use by drivers as a pre-amber indication which can be a safety improvement.* To the extent that pedestrian signals are uniform in their use, drivers will learn to pace their approach speed so as to avoid emergency braking

* Some before-and-after evidence has been found that installation of pedestrian signals reduced not only pedestrian accidents, but also vehicle accidents, in comparison with a parallel and similar boulevard where the pedestrian signals were not installed (Los Angeles City Traffic Department, 1969).

or even running the signal when they are caught in the so-called "dilemma zone."

The major difference between signals and other traffic control devices is that the message changes. This, of course, produces a group of problems having to do with the timing of these changes and the way that drivers can or cannot be expected to react. Traffic engineers try to time signals so as to create a "green wave" of signals at the speed they wish traffic to flow. When they can do this, motorists (particularly commuters) learn to pace their speed so as to move along without encountering a red signal. The yellow (or amber) signal timing creates a so-called "dilemma zone" for vehicles traveling at certain speeds approaching a signal that goes to yellow for too short a time period for the car to clear the red and not soon enough for them to be able to stop. This problem is far from simple and the latest study by Jenkins (1969) lists the following driver tasks that are involved:

1. Detect presence of signal.
2. Detect color of signal.
*3. Estimate time of change to yellow.
*4. Estimate time remaining on yellow.
*5. Estimate braking distance at driven speed.
*6. Estimate time to clear intersection far enough so starting or moving vehicle on other legs will not contact.
7. Estimate discomfort if stop is made.
8. Estimate effects of action on others.
*9. Decide on action.
10. Take action.
11. Reappraise all factors.

Factors influencing errors in connection with "items most likely to be in error by driver" listed above are:

Item 3. Estimate time of change to yellow.
- a. Short- or long-term conditioning of driver to nonexpressway driving and signal operation.
- b. Driver familiarity with the specific location.
- c. Visibility distance of signal.

Item 4. Estimate time remaining on yellow.
- a. Conditioning—same as (3a).
- b. Familiarity—same as (3b).
- c. When yellow was detected or how long since previous scrutiny of the signal.

Item 5. Estimate braking distance at driven speed.

* Items most likely to be in error by driver.

a. Conditioning—same as (3a).
b. Familiarity—same as (3b).
c. Type and condition of surface.
d. Knowledge of vehicle characteristics.
e. Human capability for distance estimating.
f. Availability of estimating aids and cues.

Item 6. Estimate time to clear intersection.
a. Conditioning—same as (3a).
b. Familiarity—same as (3b).
c. Initial velocity.
d. Knowledge of vehicle accelerating ability.
e. Actions of or presence of inhibiting traffic.

Jenkins concludes that further research is needed before an optimum yellow interval can be determined or a national standard recommended.

This same type of problem plagues the engineers who are planning for the use of changeable message highway signs. A few such signs, remotely controlled, are already in use for limited situations such as when mountain roads are blocked with snow requiring use of tire chains or when desert roads are flooded. But more extensive use on heavily traveled streets and freeways will require far more complex signs and messages. The changeover time and methods are causing engineers to have to consider such things as the creation of a dilemma zone and the effect of partial messages. This type of freeway sign is being considered for a 17-mile section of a Los Angeles freeway where a vastly improved new system is being tested for continuously monitoring traffic movement and adjusting sign messages and radio messages to cope with accidents and other types of congestion. These messages would give drivers advance warning of slowdowns ahead and also divert them to alternate routes if that becomes necessary.

Another special message traffic signal is the red X symbol for controlling the direction of traffic in certain lanes where at times, it is necessary to reverse the flow of traffic. These situations occur on bridges, in tunnels, and major arterials, and on expressways where, due to heavy in-bound or out-bound traffic demand in peak hours, it is efficient to use several more lanes in the direction of heavy demand than in the direction of lesser demand. The research work that led to the development of the red X symbol for this special purpose is described in Forbes et al. (1960).

Detours and Construction Zone Warning Principles

A general principle of handling construction zone traffic is stated in a 1967 publication of the California Division of Highways (Obermuller, 1967) as follows:

"The safest and most convenient construction trafficway is one that has been designed to provide a facility which is geometrically equal to or better than the approach roadway in order to present the motorist with a condition of sufficient continuity of function and appearance that he will react properly, naturally and without confusion.

"If the above objectives can be attained, the construction trafficway can be treated as a continuation of the approach roadway using standard signing, delineation, etc., and it need not be designated as a 'Detour.'"

To the extent that this principle is followed, the trafficway through construction would not be noticeably different from the approach roadway and the motorist would not be aware that he is moving along a temporary path. However, for many reasons, this ideal trafficway, in most instances, cannot be created and it is necessary to warn the motorist that he is in a construction area. For this reason the *National Manual* calls for the use of orange instead of yellow warning signs in construction zones so that even if standard warning signs are used, and this certainly is desirable, they will offer a color cue that will notify the driver when he enters and when he leaves a construction zone.

Special problems of roadway delineation arise in construction and a variety of portable and temporary products are marketed to help guide the motorist. One such device, the battery-operated flashing light, has been found excellent for attracting the nighttime motorist's attention to obstacles, but very confusing as to showing their location. Thus the California report strongly recommends that only reflectors or steadily burning lights be used to mark the roadway. Oddly enough, the old flame pot that was used in the past has two desirable human factors characteristics. The flame is a constant light, and yet, it does move and thus attracts attention. The flame pots have other features that are undesirable and the modern devices are superior when they are properly used. A special circuit can be purchased to sequentially operate flashing lights in order to produce a strobe effect similar to those used in some airport runway approach lighting systems. The strobe effect is attention-getting but of questionable value for delineating the roadway.

Color and texture of roadway surfaces are often likely to present misdirection cues to the motorist in construction areas where the temporary pathway joins or departs from the approach roadway. Special attention must be given to these false cues so that they either are concealed (by covering) or are overwhelmed by lane markers, painted arrows, traffic cones, or other devices available to the traffic engineer. Devices that reveal a continuous connection with the road surface (e.g., cones) are more easily comprehended than reflectors on stands or paddles that at night appear to float or be suspended somewhere over the roadway. For this reason, raised pavement markers (containing reflectors) that are fastened to the road surface are excellent delineators not only for construction, but for all roadways where they can be kept free of snow or mud.

Information Functions of Highway Markings

Yellow stripes designate the center line separating opposing traffic. Other lane markings are white. No-passing zones are designated by double, solid yellow stripes that are a clearly visible cue but that unfortunately have two different meanings depending on the state law. In some states the no-passing stripes mean that the motorist may never legally drive to the left of the double yellow marking. In other states, however, the law states that motorists may not *begin* a passing maneuver that would cause them to cross the double yellow lines, but they are permitted to complete a pass as soon as possible if they began the pass before reaching the double yellow stripes. This unfortunate ambiguity has not been resolved and the law enforcement policy (as well as the distance preceding the curve), of course, agrees with the law in each state. Therefore, it constitutes a safety hazard for those out-of-state drivers who expect to be able to safely complete a pass before encountering head-on traffic, because the beginning of the double stripe is placed closer to the curve in those states where driving to the left of the stripes is not permitted.

Raised, reflectorized markers are available in colors that can be used to carry through the color coding for pavement markings. They are particularly effective in fog and when there is water on the road surface because the markers stick up through the glare surface and are thus clearly visible day or night. Steel snowplow blades tend to scrape off the raised markers, which makes them more difficult to use in snow country. A side benefit of tire rumble noise when crossing these markers may be helping to "wake up" tired or drunken drivers as they drift out of the lane. Some observers believe that motorists tend to make more abrupt lane changes in order to receive a minimum duration of rumble noise and vibration. If true, this is not necessarily unsafe.

Another aspect of raised markers is that the other side can be made as a red reflector to warn wrong-way drivers. A recent study using specially created animated films in the UCLA Driving Simulator has concluded that some irregular pattern of red-sided markers will be more attention-getting than having every marker red (Case, Hulbert, and Beers, 1970).

Ten years of trial installation evaluation preceded the adoption by the State of California (1968) of raised markers. Texas Highway Department (1969) thoroughly documents their positive evaluation of these extremely effective devices for clearly showing motorists lane lines and freeway ramps in foggy and inclement weather as well as in normal day- and nighttime driving conditions. Yu (1970) included raised markers in his study of delineation in which he reports cost and maintenance factors for various types of devices. He finds, for example, the effectiveness and maintenance costs of providing edge striping to delineate the outer, right-hand edge of the pavement, are significantly greater than the costs of providing median delineation.

In urban areas where there are many midblock opportunities for left turns, pavement markings are now authorized to create a two-way left-turn area in the center of the roadway. Into this lane, created by two pairs of dashed double yellow stripes, drivers may enter from either direction in order to make their left turn. This clears the through traffic lanes from being obstructed by left turners waiting for a gap in opposing traffic. This two-way left-turn area also creates a wide "buffer zone" separating opposing traffic.

Left-turn pockets at intersections require special pavement markings and many intersections are now marked for two pocket lanes that must turn and one optional turn or straight-through lane. Drivers are able to cope successfully with these complex situations probably because they are placed at locations where multilane turns are demanded by the predominant flow of traffic and these moves are "protected" by green arrow traffic signals and are depicted both by large symbol signs overhead as well as pavement arrows and legends.

Changeable Message Signs

As highway systems become more complex and carry greater volumes, the need for better communication with motorists has led to the development and trial use of several traffic surveillance systems. These systems use airborne observers patrolling overhead, vehicle detecting devices, or remote-control television installations to monitor traffic flow. This flow information is then either directly relayed to motorists via their car radios or, in the case of Chicago and Detroit, relayed indirectly through remote activation of lane control and ramp control signal systems.

These signal and radio message systems are proving only partially satisfactory (Highway Research Board, 1968), therefore, a system now under design for a portion of the Los Angeles freeway network is planned to include changeable message signs in addition to car radio messages.

Several types of changeable message signs are available ranging from those that can display any message (such as news signs or scoreboard signs) by illuminating appropriate bulbs in a matrix, to simpler mechanical type signs that can show only a limited number of predetermined messages in a predetermined sequence. At this time it is not known how many messages are needed for any given roadway nor what driving safety hazards may be created by various rates of change and partially visible messages. Neither the importance of random access to messages nor the relative desirability of using a novel color are known. Research will soon be started on these important questions.

Radio Messages to Drivers

Two basic types of radio systems are available. The general commercial broadcast bands are in use in at least 20 major United States cities (Highway Research Board, 1968) and many have several stations that devote some time during rush-hour morning and evening traffic to provide a wide range of traffic flow information. These systems originated in Los Angeles and have spread widely due to the large radio audience that they attract. This is evidenced by the fact that commercial time is far more expensive during traffic broadcasts than at other times of the broadcast day.

Unfortunately, no standardization of terminology has been developed or required of these many different broadcasts. Therefore, there are many different styles of messages as well as different input sources. The results are systems whose usefulness to the motorist are of unknown value. Even a casual acquaintance with these systems reveals many inadequacies and much room for improvement and standardization.

Roadside, limited range, radio systems have been developed for highway use (Covault and Bower, 1964). They make use of induction type radio transmission that can be initiated either from fixed location or portable transmitters that are activated either remotely or on-site for live broadcast or taped messages. Some systems automatically turn on the specially adopted radio receiver in the passing vehicle, other systems are less fully automatic and require a signal system to alert the driver to turn on his receiver. Messages from these transmitters can be very specific to the area, perhaps 80 to 100 feet along the roadway, or longer as may be required.

A two-way communication system has been thoroughly planned (Bauer, Malo, and Quinn, 1969) using citizen band radios for use in emergencies. This system has been in experimental use since 1966 by the City of Detroit, Department of Streets and Traffic not only for emergency reporting but also for traffic flow and other related information. Informal use of these two-way radios is reported in the Washington,

D.C. area and most likely is occurring in other locations. These calls for assistance are placed on the emergency channel 9 that often is monitored in relays around the clock by volunteer members of the local citizens' band radio group. Well over 100 traffic related calls per month are reported and in Washington, D.C. over 50 calls per month are reported from lost or confused motorists asking for directions.

ROADWAY ESTHETICS

An intangible communication from the roadway is associated with the general aspect it presents the motorist. Of late there is increasing attention to the humane considerations involved in highway placement and in landscaping. Also there is pressure to consider not only "cleaning up the roadside," but to include artistic concepts in the original engineering. Bridges have long been evaluated not only functionally but also artistically; but consideration of highways as things of beauty is a more recent concept. Snowden (1966) has dealt with this difficult topic of describing the relation between engineering design of highways and the artistic aspects of their dynamic appearance. He touches upon, but does not unravel, the complex interactions that may subtly, yet profoundly, influence motorists as they move along any given section of roadway. It will remain for future research, perhaps utilizing ultra-sophisticated brain wave analyses to eventually describe these important effects.

HOLOGRAPHIC IMAGES

In ever so many instances, traffic engineers would like to be able to place a sign message exactly in front of the driver and thereby eliminate ambiguity and related confusion due to parallax. The phenomenon of holography has been extended so that is now possible to project visual images in space so that they appear as solid tangible material. These techniques have been demonstrated and soon may actually be used in highway situations. Harry Forster describes these possibilities in an article (Forster, 1968) in which he states, "holography is a technique for storing information about the phase and amplitude of light waves so that the original light waves coming from the object holographed can be reconstructed."

Wrong-way driving situations seem to be an ideal application for these images because they characteristically are visible only from a limited cone of viewing angle and therefore can be so placed that they would be invisible to right-way drivers and yet squarely in the path of the wrong-way driver. Imaginative traffic engineers, in contemplation of this possibility, already have suggested a wide variety of images other than signs that might be effective in reaching the befuddled or rum-soaked mind of the wrong-way drivers (Tamburri, 1969).

GENERAL SUMMARY

An all-embracing description of driving has been set forth and related to current and near future systems for communicating to the driver the information he needs using methods and traffic control devices that are based on awareness of man's limited ability to process information. Improvements have been frustratingly slow, but there has been progress and there is great hope for accelerated progress in the future if public funds are directed to meet the challenge that booming traffic volumes, highway speeds, and age range of drivers is certain to provide.

REFERENCES

Bauer, H. J., Malo, A. F., and Quinn, C. E., Response to a CB Radio Driver Aid Network, *Highway Research Record,* **279** (1969), 24–39.

Bellis, W. R., Development of an Effective Rumble Strip, *Traffic Engineering,* April 1969, 22–25.

California, State of, Raised Reflective Markers for Safer Night Driving, *Public Works Magazine,* State of California, August 1968, 4 pp.

Case, H., Hulbert, S., and Beers, J., Wrong-Way Driving Studies: Part IV, Highway Reflectors, Institute of Transportation and Traffic Engineering, UCLA 1970, 17 pp.

Covault, D. O. and Bower, R. W., A Study of the Feasibility of Using Roadside Radio Communications for Traffic Control and Driver Information, *Highway Research Record,* **49** (1964), 89–106.

Eberhard, J. W. and Berger, W. G., Empirically Derived Criteria for Graphic Highway Guide Signs, Serendipity, Inc., Washington, D.C., 1970, 14 pp.

Elliott, W. G. III, Symbology on the Highways of the World, *Traffic Engineering,* **31** (1960), 18–26.

Foody, T. and Taylor, W., Service Signing and Motorists' Choice, *Highway Research Record,* **279** (1969), 13–19.

Forbes, T. W. and Holmes, T., Legibility Distances of Highway Destination Signs in Relation to Letter Height, *Proceedings of the Highway Research Board,* **19** (1939), 321–325.

Forbes, T. W., Snyder, T. E., and Pain, R. F., Traffic Sign Requirements, Michigan State University, 1963, 15 pp.

Forbes, T. W., Gervais, E., and Allen, T. M., Effectiveness of Symbols for Lane Control Signals, *Highway Research Board Bulletin,* **244** (1960), 16–29.

Forster, H., Holosigns, *Traffic Engineering,* April 1968, 20–24.

Highway Research Board, Conference Session of the Highway Research Board Annual Meeting, 1968 (not published).

Hoxie, J. P., Color and Intensity Relationships in Traffic Signals, *Proceedings of the 31st Annual Meeting of the Institute of Traffic Engineers,* 1961.

Hulbert, S. and Beers, J., Wrong Way Driving Off-Ramp Studies, *Highway Research Record,* **122** (1966), 35–49.

Hulbert, S. F. and Burg, A., Human Factors in Transportation Systems, chapter in New York McGraw, Hill, *Systems Psychology,* ed. by K. DeGreene (1970), 471–509.

Jenkins, R. S., A Study of Selection of Yellow Clearance Intervals for Traffic Signals, *Michigan Department of Highways Report* T50-TR-104-89, February 1969, 66 pp.

Lauer, A. R., Improvements in Highway Safety Design, *Proceedings of the Highway Research Board,* **12** (1932), 389–401.

Los Angeles City Traffic Department, Florence Avenue Study, Informal Staff Report of Los Angeles City Traffic Department, March 1969, 5 pp.

Obermuller, J. C., A Final Report on a Cooperative Appraisal of Devices to Guide Traffic Through Construction, California Division of Highways and U. S. Department of Transportation, April 1967, 36 pp.

Schoppert, D. W., Freeway Signing Concepts and Criteria, Alan M. Voorhees & Associates, Washington, D.C., June 1966, 59 pp.

Schoppert, D. W. and Hoyt, D. W., Factors Influencing Safety at Highway-Rail Grade Crossings, *National Cooperative Highway Research Program,* Report 50. Highway Research Board, 1968, 113 pp.

Schoppert, D. W., Moskowitz, K., Burg, A., and Hulbert S., Some Principles of Freeway Directional Signing Based on Motorists' Experiences, *Highway Research Board Bulletin* **244** (1960), 30–87.

Snowden, W. H., Formulas for Beauty, Institute of Transportation and Traffic Engineering Staff Paper, University of California, Berkeley, February 1966, 16 pp.

Tamburri, T. N., Wrong-Way Driving Accidents are Reduced, *Highway Research Record,* **292** (1969), 24–50.

Texas Highway Department, Driver Communication through Roadway Delineation, Department Research Report No. SS 12.1, Texas Highway Department, August 1969, 20 pp.

U.S. Congress, Highway Safety, Design and Operations: Freeway Signing and Related Geometrics, *Hearings Before the Special Subcommittee on Federal Aid Program of the Committee on Public Works,* House of Representatives, Ninetieth Congress, Second Session, U.S. Government Printing Office, May and July 1968, 661 pp.

U.S. Department of Transportation, *Manual on Uniform Traffic Control Devices for Streets and Highways,* U.S. Department of Transportation, Federal Highway Administration, 1971.

Yu, J. C., Driver Performance Related to Median Visibility, *Highway Safety, Special Report,* **107**, Highway Research Board, p. 180 (abridgment), 1970.

VII

SKILLS, JUDGMENT AND INFORMATION ACQUISITION IN DRIVING

Thomas Rockwell

Dr. Thomas H. Rockwell*, Professor in Ohio State University's Department of Industrial Engineering, has been a faculty member since 1955. He also serves as director of the Driving Research Laboratory and as Principal Investigator of the Systems Research Group of the Engineering Experiment Station.

Born in Loma Linda, California, he received the Bachelor of Science degree in Chemical Engineering from Stanford University in 1951. From Ohio State he was awarded the Master of Science degree in 1953 and Ph.D. degree in 1957, both in Industrial Engineering.

Dr. Rockwell is currently carrying on research projects in such areas as risk acceptance in man-machine systems, driver education curriculum evaluation, driver eye movements, effects of alcohol and carbon monoxide on driving, measurement of driver performance, evaluation of highway signing, the use of electronic guidance devices for traffic safety and flow, systems performance in light aircraft control, and simulation of insurance operations. His research program currently receives support from the U.S. Public Health Service, Ohio Department of Highways, National Highway Traffic Safety Administration, Federal Highway Administration, Society of Automotive Engineers, Ohio Department of Education, and from local industry.

Active in professional affairs, he holds memberships in many professional societies and is a fellow of the American Association for the Advancement of Science and the Human Factors Society. In 1969 he received the A. R. Lauer award from the Human Factors Society. Dr. Rockwell also serves on two committees of the Highway Research Board.

* This resumé appears also in *Who's Who in Engineering*, 8th ed., 1959, and *American Men of Science*, 1965 Edition, published 1967.

In 1966 he received a five-year grant from the U.S. Public Health Service for the training of graduate students in transportation accident research.

Skill and judgment in driving form the heart of the driving task. Lack of skill and poor judgment undoubtedly are factors in a majority of accidents and materially affect the flow conditions on our high-density highways. The two concepts, skill and judgment, cannot be separated since judgment can often be offset by driving skill and vice versa. In the context of this discussion, skill is not the mere manipulation of controls but rather the safe, smooth processing of information in the driving environment. Despite the efforts of many researchers, an accepted task analysis of driving has defied description, suggesting that driving consists of more than simple control manipulation and obstacle avoidance. Although the automobile is a forgiving system permitting operators of a wide skill range to use our highways successfully, the driving task also demands a great deal of attention since a lapse of a few seconds in information sampling can lead to catastrophic results.

In order to assess the dimensions of driving skills, it is first necessary to structure a few of the basic driving control subprocesses, such as information acquisition, decision-making, and control in the context of three major control tasks:

1. longitudinal control with and without traffic (this might also be described as open-road driving, car following, and the transition states between these states);
2. lateral control of the car in the roadway including curve negotiation, lane changing, cornering, and so forth; and
3. situational demands for specialized skills that are demonstrated in passing, parking, backing, and merging maneuvers.

A PROPOSED CONCEPTUALIZATION OF THE DRIVING TASK

A basic conceptualization (see Figure 1) helps to put these tasks into a framework for analysis.* Driving may be viewed as a negative feedback control system wherein the driver samples the lateral and longitudinal status of the vehicle and compares this to a target or reference input and acts on any observed deviation between the two. This con-

* "Proceedings, Conference on Mathematical Models and Simulation of Automobile Driving," Massachusetts Institute of Technology, September 28, 29, 1967, Appendix II, p. 179.

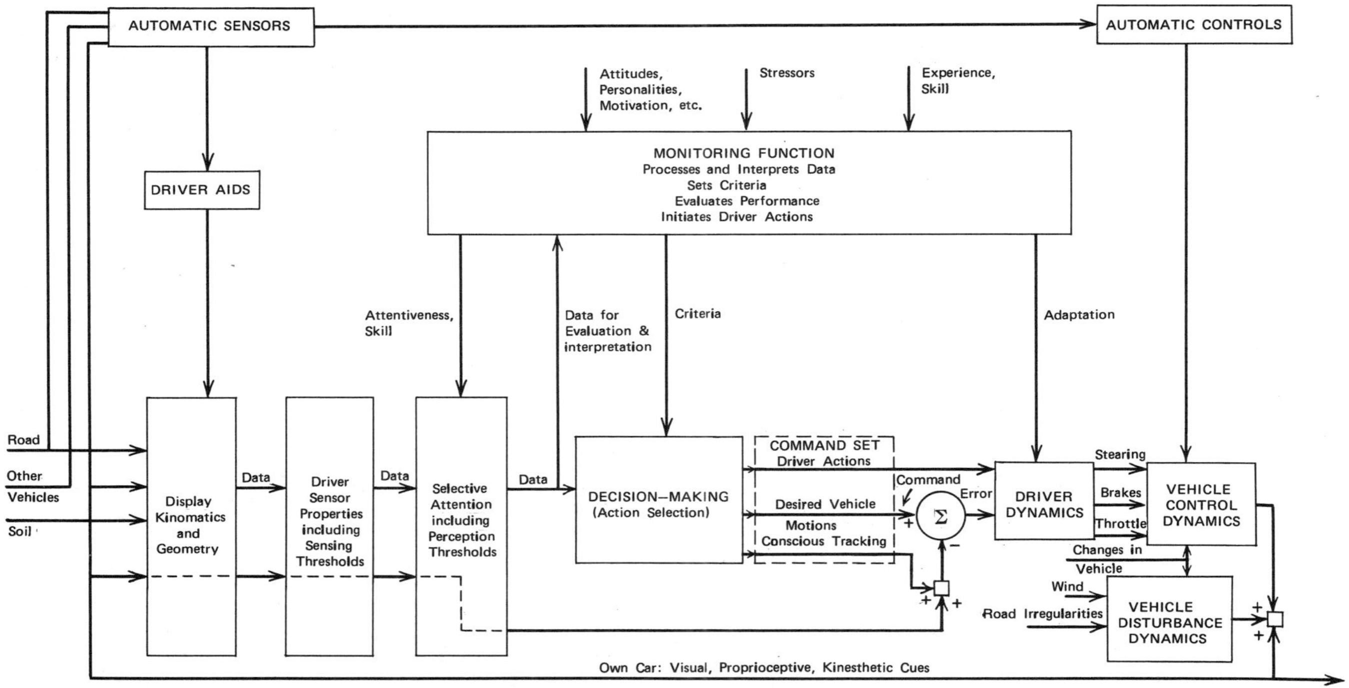

Figure 1. Generalized block diagram of the car-driver-roadway system.

ceptualization relates the sensory aspects of driving to decision-making and control. The entire process is embedded in various environments forced by the demands of the traffic and roadway conditions involved and is sensitive to vehicle dynamics. Using this qualitative model, we can readily note how failure in various components can lead to accidents or flow disturbances. Failure on the input side is immediately apparent. The driver may sample the wrong information, the right information too late for processing, or fail to sample at all. Clearly the information acquisition aspect of the driving task is subject to degradation from the following factors:

1. within the individual, such as emotion, alcohol, or fatigue;
2. from vehicle design and corresponding eye height (that is, can the driver see the necessary cues for driving); and
3. from the environment, for example, traffic, glare, rain, fog, or lack of illumination.

The system can also fail in the information processing or decision-making stage. In this case, information may be used incorrectly, such as, risk-taking in passing operations. Finally, errors in control selection and usage can also cause system failure.

There are also situations in which traffic conditions develop so fast that the driver cannot effectively convert information into control behavior in sufficient time. The classic example of this is found in multiple rear-end collisions in high-density traffic where drivers are forced into very small time spacing between cars. An initial flow perturbation results in accumulated response time, that is, a standing shock wave results in which virtually no hope for accident avoidance exists for the drivers who by chance or by choice operate with such short time headways.

A further advantage of this conceptualization is that we can readily see the role of aiding in driving control, for example, sensory supplementation using electronic sensors that enable the driver to get information sooner and more accurately than he can visually, and decision aids that assist in passing. Providing time headway* information in car-following is another aiding possibility. Obviously, aiding in control manipulation exists today with power steering and power brakes. These have been extended to anti-skid devices to compensate for driver overbraking.

Thus, this conceptualization is useful in examining the driving task, particularly those elements of skill and judgment that make up this complex man-machine system.

* Headway—the interval, time or distance, between a lead car and the following car.

The above discussion has viewed the several modes of driving in a qualitative context. In the literature (Weir and McRuer, 1967; Crossman, 1967; Sheridan, 1962) there are mathematical models of various restricted uses of the servo model, for example, transfer functions that predict drivers' lateral control in curve negotiation.

Rockwell, Ernst, and Hanken (1968) have studied regression type models that predict driver acceleration or deceleration as a function of the changing intervehicular dynamics in car-following. To date, models of "driver transfer functions" have been limited to very specific driving situations. Our ability to predict driving performance is largely limited by the difficulty in understanding driver reference input signals, that is, what the driver desires to do in any given situation. In addition, the nonlinear, intermittent, adaptive nature of drivers makes application of classic feedback models difficult. Nonetheless, these mathematical models are powerful tools in analyzing the driving task and perhaps represent the best approach to predicting driving control that exists today.

In studying driving skill, it is necessary to first define (a) the input measures to the driver, (b) his output relative to vehicular control action, and (c) the output of his vehicle. In the case of open-road driving, this implies that the driver must be able to sense velocity and change of velocity. In car-following, he must sense acceleration, headway, and relative velocity related to his car and the vehicle ahead. Driver outputs are gas pedal, brake, and steering wheel inputs to his vehicle while vehicular outputs consist of speed changes, lane position, relative velocity status, headway status, and lateral and longitudinal acceleration. In the main most human factors researchers have elected to view the driver vehicle system as one unit, concentrating on predicting vehicle acceleration as a function of changes in intervehicular spacing, relative velocity, and velocity. Mean and variances of speed and lateral placement are reasonably good measures for open-road performance. In car-following, headway mean and variance, time headway, relative velocity variance, and the variance transmission ratio (defined as the ratio of the lead car velocity variance divided by the following car velocity variance) have all been used to measure car-following performance of the driver. In the discussion to follow, these measures of performance will be developed more extensively.

THE DRIVER AS SENSOR

Before describing actual open-road and car-following performance of drivers, it is first important to establish the sensory capabilities of man for these tasks. The conceptualization above indicated that the driver must sense changes in spacing and/or relative velocity and/or relative acceleration as a basic input(s) to his control response. The question of how well the driver can make such judgments is an important concept in understanding the longitudinal control task. Research has indicated that man is a fairly accurate sensor of his own car's dynamics (Rockwell and Snider, 1969). In general, drivers can sense $\pm$ .01 g in the form of vehicle acceleration. They are capable of producing or estimating velocities very well—overestimating speeds at higher velocities and underestimating at lower velocities—acting much in the same way as the speedometer. Their capability for estimating changes of velocity range in the neighborhood of 4 to 5 mph.

This capability to estimate velocity is degraded, however, when we begin to study the two-car case where the driver must act upon intervehicular spacing and rates of change in order to make proper decisions in car-following. Research by Mortimer (1969) and Ernst and Rockwell (1966) have indicated the change necessary for detection in headways obeys Weber's law with ΔH (headway change) $\approx KH_i$ (initial headway) where $0.1 < K < 0.2$, that is, at 100 feet it would take the driver 10 to 20 feet to detect a change in spacing. Headway estimation or production is woefully poor in most driving situations with errors ranging anywhere from 20 to 100 percent for various drivers. Novice drivers overestimate headways by as much as 300 percent early in their training. To date, it is not known why drivers are such poor sensors of spacing. Relative velocity change detection is somewhat more accurate. Whether relative acceleration is indeed capable of being sensed by man is a moot point at this stage of our knowledge of intervehicular sensing. Tables 1 and 2 summarize data on perceptual sensing capabilities of acceleration, velocity change (no speedometer), speed estimation, production, headway change detections and headway estimation.

Sparse data exist for intervehicular sensing between cars traveling in opposite directions. Silver and Farber (1969) suggest that the driver has little skill in determining velocity of oncoming cars and in quantifying relative speed in such situations. However, their data have indicated that subjects could reasonably predict the time of arrival of oncoming cars, especially in the 10- to 12-second range. In terms of protensity (time sensing) measurement, drivers tend to overestimate elapsed time particularly as speed increases.

The data in Table 1 illustrate typical perceptual skills of normal alert test drivers. Under stress or with low motivation, perceptual errors would likely increase. These studies do not tell us how the driver arrives at these skills. Research by Gordon (1966) and Gordon and Michals

(1965) and others has begun to suggest the cues (e.g., rate of change of visual angle) the driver uses to make psychophysical judgments. Mourant and Rockwell (1970b) have studied driver search and scan patterns to identify perceptual cues for various driving situations. These will be discussed later. Until the sensory decision-making process is developed, it is sufficient to say that the present question is how good is the driver in ascertaining information necessary for proper control.

In general, alert test drivers can maintain constant speeds of plus or minus 3 mph without the use of a speedometer (Rockwell and Ernst, 1965). Decelerations from 50 mph to a specified stopping point revealed consistent deceleration patterns for individual drivers but widely varying patterns between drivers. Deceleration rates in nonpanic stops rarely exceed 5 feet per second^2 in residential driving. Novice drivers tend to begin with rates of 3 feet per second^2 but, with training, rapidly approach levels of the experienced driver. As precision in required deceleration is increased, lateral placement accuracy decreases. In a series of nighttime illumination deprivation studies, it was found that lateral and longitudinal accuracy could not both be maximized (Matanzo and Rockwell, 1967). If the subject emphasized precision in either velocity maintenance or lane position, the other performance measure was degraded suggesting a single-channel processing characteristic of man.

Test drivers can generally equal or exceed the precision of automatic velocity control systems in modern cars at least for roads with little or no vertical curvature.

CAR-FOLLOWING SKILLS

Considerable research has been directed to car-following skills. Some of this research began with traffic flow researchers (Herman, et al., 1959) who were interested in the macro-system of platoon* flow and the stability characteristics of vehicles at various traffic speed and density conditions. In this case the acceleration of the following car ($\ddot{x}_2$) was predicted by headway, H, relative velocity, RV, stream speed† conditions, vehicle mass, M, and a constant (λ), depicting driver and vehicle response time as in the general equation below (when τ = time lag).

$$\ddot{x}_2(t) = f\left[\lambda \frac{RV\ (t - \tau_1}{H\ (t - \tau_2}\right]$$

* Platoon—a group of n cars with $n - 1$ engaged in car following.

† Stream speed—the average vehicle speed for a given section of highway at a defined time. For a platoon, may be $(v_1 + v_2)/2$.

Table 1 Driver Sensing Capabilities[a,b]

Single-Car Case without Knowledge of Results

Task	Number of Subjects	Number of Observations per Subject	Dependent Variables	Initial Velocity − = deceleration + = acceleration	Results				
Acceleration sensing	27	20	g's	v_i ± in mph	−35	+35	−50		+50
				Average acceleration threshold	0.0117 g	0.012 g	0.035 g		0.0115 g
				95% C.I. Upper	0.0123 g	0.0129 g	0.0145 g		0.0125 g
				C.I. Lower	0.0105 g	0.0111 g	0.0124 g		0.0108 g
Velocity change detection	10	18	mph	v_i in mph	−35	+35	−65		+65
				Average velocity threshold	3.5 mph	5.9	5.0		4.2
				95% C.I. Upper	4.1 mph	7.0	6.4		5.3
				C.I. Lower	2.9 mph	5.0	4.0		3.3
Velocity estimation	12	48	mph	Actual v in mph	20 mph	30	50	70	80
				Average estimated velocity	15 mph	27	50	75	88
				95% C.I. Upper	29 mph	38	62	82	92
				C.I. Lower	3 mph	15	38	60	75
Velocity production	12	48	mph	Requested v in mph	20 mph	30	50	70	80
				Average produced v in mph	22 mph	31	45	62	68
				95% C.I. Upper	32 mph	40	56	73	80
				C.I. Lower	12 mph	18	45	50	59

C.I. = Confidence Level

Table 1 (Continued)

Two-Car Case without Knowledge of Results

Task	Number of Subjects	Number of Observations per Subject	Dependent Variables	Results						
				Velocity	50 mph			70 mph		
Headway estimation (*H*) in feet	12	140	feet	Actual headway (ft)	100	300	500	100	300	500
				Estimated headway (ft)	70	180	280	50	130	210
				95% Upper (ft)	180	300	400	130	220	300
				C.I. Lower (ft)	—	40	160	—	50	120
Headway production (*H*) in feet	12	140	feet	Specified headway (ft)	100	300	500	100	300	500
				Produced headway (ft)	90	180	240	60	130	180
				95% Upper (ft)	250	350	450	140	210	250
				C.I. Lower (ft)	—	50	120	—	50	90
				Results						
				Polarity	Positive Acceleration					
Headway change detection (positive polarity)	6	80	feet	Original headway (ft)	50	100	200			
				Threshold (subject) (ft)	3	8	10			
				95% Upper (ft)	10	13	20			
				C.I. Lower (ft)	—	—	5			
				Polarity	Negative Acceleration					
Headway change detection (negative polarity)	6	80	feet	Original headway (ft)	50	100	200			
				Threshold (subject) (ft)	4	10	15			
				95% Upper (ft)	12	18	23			
				C.I. Lower (ft)	—	—	8			

[a] From Ernst and Rockwell (1966).
[b] From Rockwell and Snider (1967).

Aerial photogrammetry provides insights into actual car-following performance. Recent studies by Lee (1971) indicate drivers operate in moderately high-density traffic (60 to 90 vehicles per mile) at time headways as low as one-half second although 0.8 second represents typical lower values. Response time of drivers depends upon flow density conditions. Forbes and Matson (1939) found the driver reaction time was shorter in high-density, short time-headway situations. Lee found that during queue build-up "driver-vehicle" response lag is approximately 0.6 second. As the queue dissipates the response lag approaches 1.3 seconds. In general, drivers attempt to maintain a minimum of 2-second headways. These data are supported by experimental studies on forward reference distance and velocity election. Drivers who are constrained below 2 seconds of preview time tend to reduce velocities below freeway levels. With typical response times of 0.7 to 1 second, a 2-second preview gives the driver about 1 second for central processing or decision time.

Obviously car-following performance is affected by several factors. These include driving goals, road curvature, relative velocity, stream speed, whether car-following is elected or imposed, and the length of time in the coupled state. The last condition refers to that spacing and speed condition wherein the following driver must attend to perturbation in the lead car. While no precise value exists, we could argue that at distances under 300 feet and stream speeds approximately 60 mph, the driver is operating at approximately 3 seconds time headway, hence must be sensitive to lead-car velocity behavior. Norman (1942) suggests that car-following involves time spacing of 0.5 to 4 seconds. Overtaking or coupling is considered to begin around 9 seconds, decreasing to 4 seconds. Beyond 10 to 12 seconds it is safe to assume open-road driving exists. Lee (1971) suggests unconstrained flow begins at 500-feet, 6-second headways.

What becomes evident in macro data on car following is the unique capability of drivers to operate at or near unstable flow conditions exhibiting in many cases "negative response times." This develops from anticipation in the detection of perturbations ahead in the stream so that the driver is often acting before the lead car reacts to the perturbation.

Experimental studies in car-following indicate that many performance measures are possible, including:

1. headway variance in time or feet,
2. mean headway in time or feet,
3. relative velocity average,
4. relative velocity variance,

5. the time lag in the velocity profiles of two cars from auto cross-correlation techniques,

6. the ratio of following-car velocity variance to lead-car velocity variance.

Obviously an individual driver car-following strategy might be to maintain low relative velocity at the expense of headway variance or vice versa. Complicating the issue is the fact that many drivers are not able to verbalize their car-following strategy. This lack of a reference car-following strategy and the generally poor psychophysical characteristics of drivers for intervehicular spacing partly explains the rather large headway variations found in experimental car-following. At target headways of 200 feet in stream speeds of 60 mph and small perturbations in lead-car velocity Snider and Ernst (1965) found headway variances to range from 50 to 300 feet^2. While headway variances are somewhat predictable in car-following at a constant distance under small lead-car perturbations, the situation becomes more difficult when the lead-car driver executes sawtooth-type transient velocity profiles. In this case the following driver will frequently not readjust to the original target headways but rather assume headway distances anywhere from 50 to 300 percent of the original target headway. Whether this constitutes a lack of skill or whether drivers in fact adjust their target headways after a maneuver is a moot question at this time.

Table 2 depicts typical car following performance from experimental studies, using the same subjects described in Table 1.

Table 2 Steady-State Car-Following Performance Headway—Relative Velocity Variability[a]

	60 mph	
Target Headway	H_T = 100 feet	H_T = 500 feet
Average σ_H^2	170 feet^2	900 feet^2
Average σ_{RV}^2	1 mph^2	4 mph^2

H_T = Target Headway; σ_H^2 = Headway Variance; σ_{RV}^2 = Relative Velocity Variance.

[a] From Ernst and Rockwell (1966).

In general, it was found that no single measure of car-following performance is adequate to describe car-following skill. Driver strategies tend to vary over time. In enforced car-following with instructions to maintain a constant headway under small lead-car perturbations, we can expect headway variances to be 50 to 300 percent of the mean headway obtained with $\approx$ 200 percent being the median figure.

Again we must be careful in using any of the above measures in describing skill since drivers will often relax such measures if the situation does not demand it. In effect, drivers appear to apply skill in driving situations only to the extent to which such skill is necessary.

DRIVER JUDGMENT

The measurement of judgment in driving is a difficult task because decisions cannot be adequately evaluated without knowing the alternative courses of action open to the driver and his motivation behind a given decision. Field observation of elected spacing, passing, and so on, suffer from this problem. Experimental studies provide better control of contributing variables but can produce bias.

Judgments must be classified into the three following categories:

1. emergency decisions—one-time situations requiring unique, often rapid decision-making and response, such as to an object on roadway. Simulation of these events lack the realism of real-world threat and after the first exposure the situation is no longer unique. Field studies, in addition to being dangerous, again limit unbiased data to one exposure.
2. decisions whether or not to engage in driving. These cover situations where the driver may be tired, drinking, or aware of vehicle defects. Such decisions are also unique and not easily researchable although obviously perhaps the key to good driver judgment.
3. operational decisions, including routine decisions as to headway election,* speed selection, passing decisions, and merging decisions. These decisions are amenable to observation and research and are important because they dictate the level of subsequent skill required of the driver to execute the decision and maintain a given performance. It is apparent then that skill and judgment are highly interrelated.

Two areas of such operational decisions are reported below—car-following strategy and passing decision.

DRIVER JUDGMENT IN CAR-FOLLOWING AS REFLECTED IN HEADWAY ELECTION

Elected headways represent an interesting part of driver judgment. When headways are expressed in time it is found that both large intra-

* Headway election—driver statagem for maintenance of headway.

subject and intersubject variability exists. With aerial photogrammetry Lee (1971) found that on expressways under free flow, the minimum mean time headway was approximately 2 seconds for densities from 35 to 100 vehicles/miles. At higher densities the average time headway actually increases. Greenshields (1935) reported that accidents were related to the mix of speeds and headways in driving. It is easy to visualize this since the interaction of two cars of different speeds encourages decision-making, such as passing, and hence increases the probability of errors. Differences in speed and headway also result in flow perturbations. Intrasubject variability is somewhat easier to explain since it is known that merely changing instructions will produce different headways, for example, normal car-following results in approximately 3 to 4 seconds of time headway. "Following so as not to lose the lead car" might increase this to 4 to 6 seconds. "Following at minimum safe distance" is in the order of 1 to 2 seconds and following with preparation to pass may be down in the region of 0.5 to 1 second. In any event, there is little data to suggest that drivers follow a National Safety Council rule of one car length for each 10 mph, probably because of the perceptual difficulties described earlier and partly because, where they have the option, most drivers refuse to car-follow in low traffic density. Rockwell and Snider (1967) in studying truck drivers were unable to get the drivers to car-follow even when deliberately impeded by unmarked research vehicles. In general, drivers will prefer more than 4 seconds as compared to the National Safety Council rule of approximately 1.5 seconds. On the other hand, in high-density urban expressway traffic, drivers are forced to operate below the National Safety Council rule because of system constraints. In general, drivers do not elect to car-follow and will usually attempt to either pass or fall back beyond a 4-second time headway.

Intrasubject variability in headway election is influenced by several factors. Forbes (1959) found in tunnel operation that right curves, downgrades, and low illumination levels all tended to increase elected headways in the Holland and Lincoln tunnels. Tunnel operation, which reduces the field of vision, typically results in larger headways at equivalent speeds or reduced speeds at equivalent headways.

As indicated earlier, while the headway variance figures might be suggestive that the driver is not precise in car-following, it is well to note that operant skill is a function of the demand placed upon the driver. Large variation in headway in a two-car case might be acceptable if the platoon is two cars. If *n* cars are involved, the drivers compensate by reduced inter- and intradriver variability. Thus, the interesting feature in car-following is the adaptability of the driver's strategy and corresponding faster response times. This adaptability exceeds any automatic system that could be practically designed today. In effect, the driver makes up for poor highway and vehicle design and crowded traffic conditions. It is only when flow patterns become unstable that the driver falls victim to the system.

As Herman, et al. (1959) demonstrated, with *n* cars in a chain at conservative initial headways, normal velocities, and attentive short response time drivers, it is possible that a flow disturbance caused by the platoon leader* can cause a chain reaction in which the drivers back in the platoon have little or no hope of accident avoidance. In this instance, no amount of skill can offset system instability. It is in these situations that driver-aided systems might be used to supplement sensory and decision-making abilities.

DRIVING SKILL AND JUDGMENT IN OVERTAKING AND PASSING

In discussing the two-car interface in driving, we can conveniently separate out three phases: overtaking, car-following, and passing. Overtaking covers the transition from open-road to car-following, that is, from large time headways down to the region of 3 to 4 seconds when the following-car driver becomes affected by the perturbations of lead-car velocity. Passing involves elements of car-following in terms of the actual intervehicular dynamics before the decision to pass (called the prepass headway). Passing also includes intervehicular dynamics associated with oncoming cars (in the case of the undivided highway) and associated elements of the pass, such as, speed and safety margin.

For a comprehensive review of two-lane rural overtaking and passing, the reader is referred to *Overtaking and Passing on Two-Lane Rural Highways*, Franklin Institute (1967). For two-lane highways the elements in the overtaking and passing situation include:

1. distance required to pass,
2. the time required to pass,
3. the prepass headway and stream speed,
4. the postpass headway and stream speed,
5. passing reaction time,
6. available time and distance to execute a pass,
7. the safety margin or that interval of time between the time the passing car regains the right-hand lane and the time when the oncoming car arrives,
8. passing threshold—the minimum separation between a lead and oncoming car that a driver will accept for passing.

* Platoon leader—the first car in a platoon.

Several types of passes are also recognized: the flying pass where no deceleration is required of the passing vehicle; and the acceleration pass, that is, a pass which is made from the car-following mode in which the following car must accelerate in order to execute the pass. Passing return may be elected or forced by low safety margins.

Passing times from Matson and Forbes (1938), Prisk (1941), and Crawford (1963) for different overtaking car speeds are summarized in Table 3. As can be noted, passing times increase with stream speeds and are longer for flying passes since prepass headways are longer for the flying pass as opposed to the acceleration pass. These prepass distances reported by Forbes and Matson (1938) are surprisingly small; 40 feet for an acceleration pass and 70 feet for a flying pass. These result in time headway in the neighborhood of 0.5 to 1 second in the prepass condition. As expected, acceleration prepass headways varied with speeds. Longer time headways exist for slow overtaken car speeds, gradually shortening to approximately 1 second as this overtaken car speed increases. That overtaken car speed does not affect the prepass headway for the flying pass suggests that drivers lack sensitivity to closing relative velocities in this situation.

Crawford (1963) found driver response time to be minimum during acceleration passes near the passing threshold (that is, the minimum time to accept the pass) and longer either at more safe or more difficult passes. This is supported by the work of Veliz (1961) who showed that reaction time in simulated industrial tasks is a function of stress; that is, as stress increases, reaction time first decreases and then reaches a point of human disorganization and begins to increase. Psychologists would relate this phenomenon to the arousal hypothesis or the Yerkes-Dodson law.

Forbes and Matson (1939) reported 20 percent of drivers left themselves a safety margin of 1 second or less and 10 percent forced oncoming cars to give way. Safety margins reported by Crawford vary as a function of time available above passing threshold. In general, 10 to 20 percent of passing is executed with safety margins less than 2 seconds suggesting that drivers are poor estimators of closing relative velocities.

It is not known what cues the drivers use in making decisions to pass. Rockwell and Snider (1969) suggest decisions are not based solely on distance and gap size. Drivers make use of visual cues such as vehicle size in the selection of offered gaps. They may well get gross cues regarding closing relative velocity but this has not been clearly demonstrated.

Passing on divided highways represents a less serious problem from a safety point of view and illustrates that the drivers elect different available gaps in lane changing. It has been found that subjects varied con-

Table 3* Passing Times

Type of Pass	Overtaken Car Speed (Medians)[a]		Overtaken Car Speed (Means)[b]					Overtaken Car Speed (Means)[c]			
	30	50	0–19	20–29	30–39	40–49	50–59	25	30	40	50
Accelerative, voluntary	10.0	11.5	8.7	8.8	9.8	10.8	10.5				
Accelerative, forced	8.0	9.5	7.7	8.0	8.8	9.4	8.4	7.8	8.1	8.9	9.6
Flying, voluntary	10.5	12.0	10.0	9.9	11.0	11.9	9.6				
Flying, forced	8.0	10.5	8.1	8.9	9.8	11.8	9.3				

[a] Forbes and Matson (1939); Matson and Forbes (1938).
[b] Prisk (1941).
[c] Crawford (1963).
* From Franklin Institute (1967).

siderably in terms of the gap available in the passing lane but are relatively unaffected by the closing velocities of approaching vehicles. As with any risk study, subjects varied widely. Thresholds varied 70 to 140 feet with test cars speeds at 60 mph and the following approaching car speed at 70 mph.

Perhaps the classic field experiment in overtaking and passing was conducted by Farber (1969). In this case selected vehicle target speeds were first evaluated and these vehicles were subsequently impeded by a test vehicle before a no-passing zone. Upon leaving this zone, the passing behavior—that is, time available, speed, and so forth—of the impeded vehicle was measured. It was found that the probability of a pass increases with distance to the oncoming car and decreases with increasing stream speed. Night passing decisions were more conservative requiring 2800 feet at night compared to 2050 feet in the daytime. If 13 seconds is taken to be a minimum acceptable passing time (8 seconds for passing and 5 seconds safety margin), then on the basis of median speeds encountered, distances are between 1600 and 1800 feet. Forty-two percent of acceptable (safe) night passes were rejected while 25 percent of acceptable nighttime passes were rejected. Mean passing times were of the order of 8 seconds and safety margins varied as a function of passing opportunity distances decreasing to 4 to 5 seconds at distances below 1500 feet. Nighttime visibility conditions did not have a large cautionary effect on passing behavior possibly due to additional cues from headlights in short-sight distance situations.

While more research is needed in the area of passing, evidence to date would suggest that drivers do a remarkably good job in passing decisions especially in view of the fact that their sensory capability in these situations is poor.

SKILL AND JUDGMENT IN NOVICE DRIVERS

Studying the novice driver provides insight into skill and decision-making development. Zell (1969), Harootyan (1969), Vojir (1969), and Mourant and Rockwell (1970a) tested novice high school drivers before, during, and after their driving education program, at 2- to 3-week intervals. It was found that psychophysical performance developed rapidly in training with headway estimation, velocity control, and car-following developing early in training. Typical range tests, for example, rapid deceleration to a fixed point, likewise showed early learning as did cornering and lateral acceleration. Gap acceptance* shows that changes

* Gap acceptance—driver decision making whether to pass on a 2-lane road. The

continue later in training, suggesting that decision-making is later in development. Of particular interest was the fact that eye search and scan patterns continue to develop long after licensing. This will be discussed in more detail below. Much of the skill development depends in large measure upon exposure both as driver and passenger in the family auto environment.

INFORMATION ACQUISITION IN DRIVING AND EYE-MOVEMENT RESEARCH

For years researchers in human factors have attempted to define the driving task and to ascertain the elements of the driving control process in order to develop an understanding of human vehicular control. This understanding is imperative if we hope to design better vehicles and highways around the capabilities and limitations of drivers and to train drivers themselves to effect safer and smoother flow on our highways. The problem has been a difficult one because the input side of the process has been largely unknown. Skill and judgment in driving have been studied without knowing the information acquisition aspects of the task. General conceptualizations, such as information theory and servo theory, have not been altogether convincing because of our lack of knowledge about the information needs and information acquisition characteristics of the driver. Since driving information acquisition is largely a visual process, it was apparent that this sensory mechanism first demanded quantification and analysis. Several years ago the techniques in eye movements began to be applied to the driving task and results, while still exploratory, suggest a new area of research investigation with exciting potential.

The role of vision in driving is believed to constitute over 90 percent of information input to the driver. Regardless of the exact percentage, without a doubt, visual perception is paramount in vehicular control. Unlike motor output, perception is very sensitive to changes in the roadway environment, vehicular design, and particularly to changes in the driver's psychological and physiological state at any given time. Visual processes can be degraded by glare, fog, lack of illumination in the environment, by vehicular design (in terms of tinted glass windshields or "A" pillar location), and by such factors as alcohol, fatigue, and drug usage.

---

gap is the available interval for passing, that is, the time or distance between successive oncoming cars.

Eye-Movement Technique

Eye-movement technique essentially permits determination of foveal fixations in time and space, recording voluntary and/or involuntary saccades. Drift or tremors of the eye are too small and of too short a duration to be captured with the equipment to be described. Pursuit eye movements, however, can be detected and represent one of the unique characteristics of the fatigued driver. Eye movements can also be characterized by amplitude of movement (angular distance between successive fixations) and fixation duration. Most eye movements in driving are less than 6 degrees travel and most eye fixations are between 100 and 350 milliseconds in duration. In driving we can further determine that some 90 percent of the observed fixations fall in a small region, within $\pm$ 4 degrees from the focus of expansion.*

The earliest measurement technique involved direct photographs of the eye, used in aircraft instrument flight operation to record instrument sampling. This method is not too accurate and is not useful if the scene objects change their position in time as with automobile driving. Direct photoelectric methods that measure contrast differences of the sclera and the iris are useful only for static scenes because they suffer in vertical accuracy. Such systems can be used for laboratory confirmation tests of such questions as sign reading time. Mechanical cups or mirrors fastened to the anesthetized eyeball are found in precise laboratory research but not in the harsh realities of the actual driving situation.

One system in use today involves both video and 16-mm motion picture processing and operates on the corneal reflection technique (see Figures 2 and 3). With this method a small collimated beam of light is reflected off the cornea back into a collecting lens and recorded on film or tape. The proper calibration of normal eyes permits accuracies of $\pm$ 1 degree vertically and $\pm$ 0.5 degree horizontally. Subjects must have reasonably round corneas to get a small eyespot. Range of eye travel for useful calibration is $\pm$ 10 degrees from line of sight. Subjects must also not suffer from amblyopic problems.

The key to good and accurate eye-movement research technique is stabilization of the input system relative to the position of the eye. The three-vidicon system has a 54- by 41-degree field of the view and uses only one fiber optic cable to transmit the corneal reflection. The system synchronizes three vidicons—one for the scene, one for recording the corneal reflection, and a third to photograph the eye directly to record

* Focus of expansion—that point in the moving visual field straight ahead of the driver where objects on the roadway appear stationary.

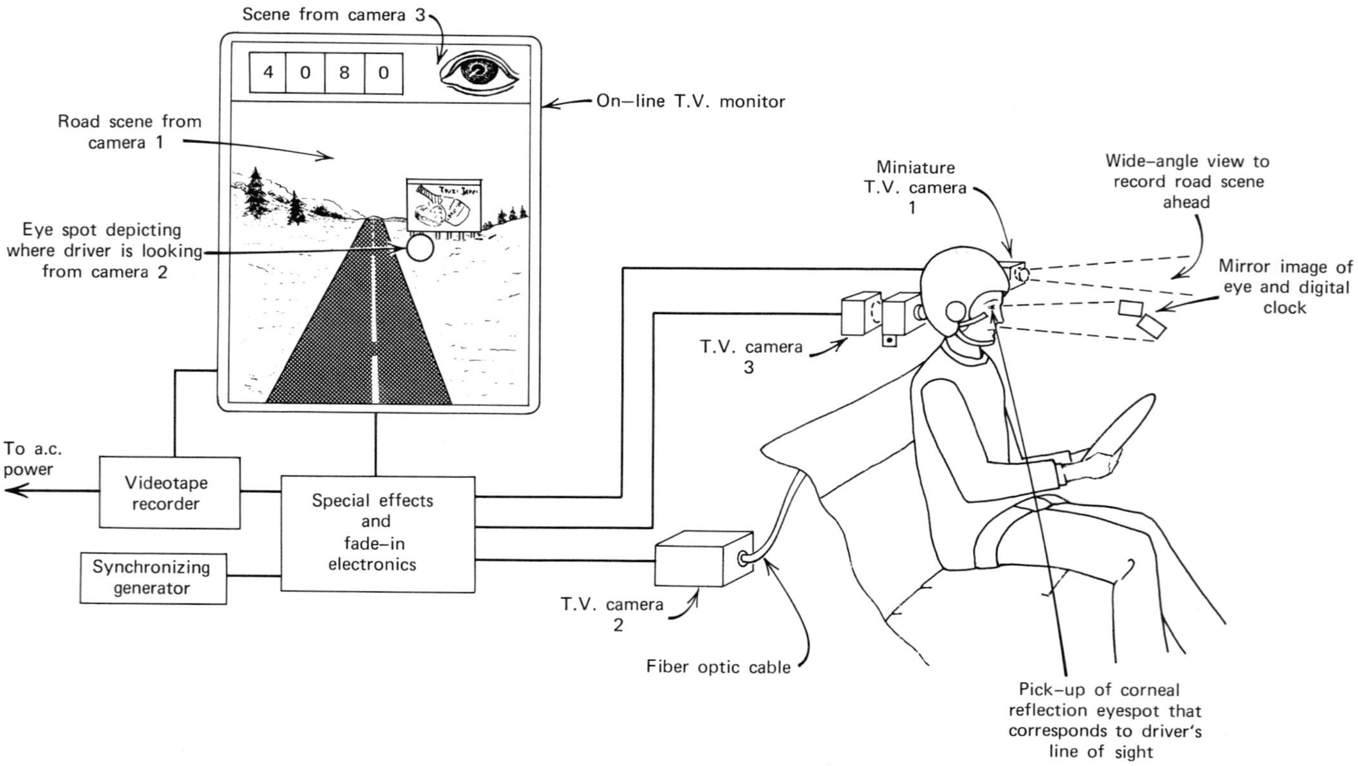

Figure 2. Television eye-movement system for automobile driving.

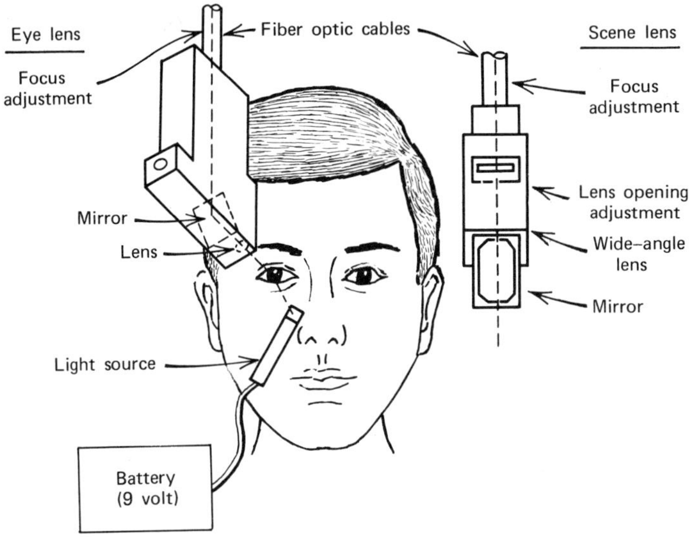

Figure 3*a*. Input system.

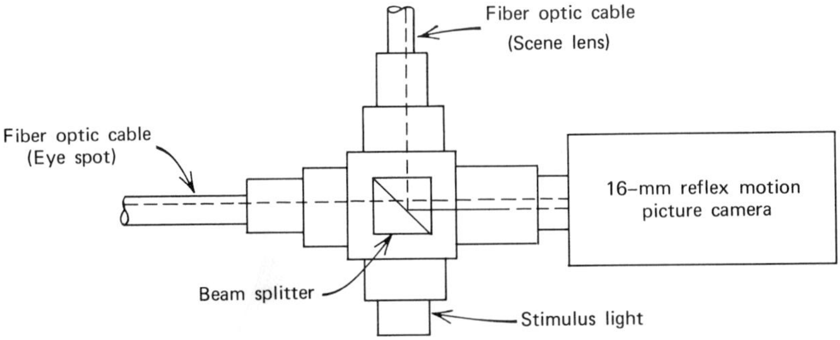

Figure 3*b*. Output system.

mirror and speedometer usage when the eyespot leaves the 35- by 35-degree view forward. Thus we can ascertain the rate the driver is mirror- or instrument-sampling and can also record head movements, blink rates, and time (in 50 millisecond intervals from a digital clock).

Basic analysis formats involve temporal analysis using fixation histograms or fixation aggregation (glimpse) histograms. Eye movements may also be analyzed by spatial density maps, assuming that one understands what a coordinate means in terms of the driving task and environment. Eye movements can be studied as a Markovian process examining transition probabilities, that is, the probability of the eye moving from one spatial segment to another or from one object to another. Eye travel distances can also be used to analyze a particular sample of eye-movement data by recording the distribution of eye travel distances. Object analysis is becoming a common procedure whereby we determine the percent of time that the driver spends on details in the scene such as signs, delineators, or the car ahead. Spatial-temporal analysis, that is, the percent of time the eye spends in a given location, is still probably the basic approach in analysis. In addition, eye-movement results can be identified by the degree and amount of pursuit eye movement in terms of the total visual task.

Eye-Movement Technique Potential

In describing eye-movement research, it is important to point out that use of an eye-marker camera probably has fewer artifacts than any other technique of measurement of driving performance because there are no instructions on how the driver is expected to use his vision. Unlike response time studies, vehicle control studies, or car-following studies, the driver has no indication as to what constitutes "good" performance. Thus the task is essentially instruction free. If we decide to study signs, we never tell the driver that we are interested in sign fixation. It must be admitted, however, that the wearing of this equipment may well influence eye-movement patterns and head movement although recent data have indicated little differences in head movements with and without the head-mounted eye-movement device. The fact that drivers can wear the helmet for 2 and 3 hours and the fact that drivers in fatigue research will actually begin to fall asleep with the device in place would suggest that subjects can adapt reasonably well to the system.

Because the state-of-the-art in eye-movement research is in an embryonic development stage, a few major limitations in interpretation must be faced. First, in most cases the driver has considerable spare visual capacity. Most interstate driving probably requires less than 50 percent of a driver's perceptual capability. Thus, the driver often deliberately samples at repeated intervals completely irrelevant information such as signs which are covered. The second major problem in eye-movement research is the role of peripheral or extra-foveal vision. A fixation may be merely a reference point for organization of peripherally acquired information. Research indicates that extra-foveal vision plays a large part in driving. Indeed it may well be said that driving is largely a dynamic peripheral vision task. Foveal vision is important in terms of its characteristics of finer discrimination (e.g., sign reading) and higher rates of information extraction, such as quick glimpses of oncoming vehicles on undivided highways. It is no surprise that research has found little correlation between visual foveal acuity and accidents because visual acuity may be less important in driving than the detection of movement by peripheral visual processes. Finally, the driver may be looking at an object but he may or may not be processing the information.

Despite these drawbacks, however, there are some interesting and provocative results derived from eye-movement research to date. Eye-movement studies have been shown to be useful as a means of measuring degradation of driving performance as a result of intrasubject factors, such as experience, alcohol, or fatigue, and environmental factors, illumination, traffic load, and so forth.

As proposed by Mourant and Rockwell (1970b), the visual task in driving may be described as the monitoring of the continuous stream of information through which the vehicles travel. At a given instance the foveal region of the eye examines only about a 2-degree circular (diam.) region of the stream. Much more of the information is available to the extra-foveal portions of the eye. There is some evidence (Mackworth, 1965; Sanders, 1966) that the planning of eye movements is partially controlled by information received through the periphery of the eye. For example, a vehicle traveling in an adjacent lane may first be detected peripherally and confirmed foveally. Because the visual function of information seeking plays a basic role in the driving task (Connolly, 1968), several benefits may be realized from describing the search-and-scan behavior of drivers. For example, Walraven and Lazet (1966) have suggested that a record of drivers' eye movements may provide a better method of assessing driving skill than has been available in the past. This assumes that analysis of eye-movement patterns of well-experienced and accident-free drivers will result in the development of criteria for good search and scan patterns. If such criteria were developed, they could be used to assess drivers' visual performance during licensing examinations by objective quantitative measurement. Eye-movement research may also improve the content of driver education programs. Standard methods may be developed to teach good search and scan patterns to inexperienced drivers. Finally the relationships between perceptual load and driving environment may be explored by studying driver eye movements. The effects of various types of highway geometry, traffic conditions, road signs, visual aids, and vehicle designs could be evaluated by recording and analyzing driver eye movements.

Studies of Eye Movements in Driving Degradation Conditions

While intersubject differences in driving eye movements are difficult to analyze because of the varied idiosyncratic perceptual characteristics of drivers, it is possible to use eye-movement techniques to study intrasubject differences as a function of degradation situations such as alcohol, carbon monoxide, and fatigue. Here eye-movement changes can serve as early detectors of subsequent control process degradation.

Belt (1969) examined eye-movement changes as drivers were studied at blood alcohol levels of 0.04, and 0.08 milligrams of alcohol per cubic centimeter of blood. In these cases, eye-movement patterns were dramatically affected. At the 0.04 level, some concentration of eye-movement pattern was apparent. At 0.08, significant perceptual narrowing or tunnel vision was evident. In this case using a concentration index (defined as the percent of time the fixation occurs in a 3- by 3-degree space near the focus of expansion), it was found that in open-road driving the concentration index went from 25 percent in the control case to 40 percent at the 0.08 blood alcohol level. In car-following, one driver elicited almost a complete lack of search outside of the concentration zone. Passing vehicles were always fixated when the driver was sober. However, at 0.08 level the driver made no fixations on passing cars, suggesting the degradation of peripheral detection. Fixation duration tended to increase with increasing alcohol level. Finally, since lateral control was lost twice in these studies at the 0.08 level, it was decided to investigate what eye-movement patterns preceded these conditions. It was found that before loss of control, the driver reverted to his sober sampling techniques. The implication from this study suggests that perceptual narrowing is an adaptive process that the driver needs in order to maintain any semblance of control. Abandoning this compensatory action leads to loss of necessary control cues. It is believed that eye movements will reflect the effects of alcohol long before overt control or measured driving performance degradation is detected.

Kaluger and Smith (1970) employed eye-movement techniques to study the performance of drivers with and without sleep in the previous 24 hours. In the fatigued state, drivers were observed with a large number of fixations in close and to the right of the highway, which the authors interpreted as a foveal compensation to offset diminished peripheral detection capability. In addition, they observed that while no pursuit eye movements were found in the control conditions, subjects exhibited pursuit eye movements almost 5 percent of the time in the sleep-loss condition. Despite the use of this testing equipment, the fatigued driver would frequently doze or close his eyes for 1 to 3 seconds during the test runs.

LEARNING AND SEARCH AND SCAN PATTERNS

Considerable efforts over the past few years have been directed to visual information seeking of novice drivers. Zell (1969) and Mourant and Rockwell (1970a) have discovered significant changes in eye-movement patterns with experience. Most of the differences are reflected in spatial rather than temporal changes. During their training, drivers switch from frantic cue searching, large eye-movement travel distances and fixations on nonrelevant cues, such as lamp poles and guardrails, to alternate sampling near and far. The far fixations are thought to be primarily directional cues while the very near samples (usually less than 1 second ahead of the vehicle) suggest foveal determination of lane position. The experienced drivers concentrate fixation near the focus of expansion and are thought to use peripheral or extra-foveal processes for lane positional feedback (see Figure 4).

In the main, students early in their driving experience fail to adjust their preview sampling as a function of their velocity. Experienced

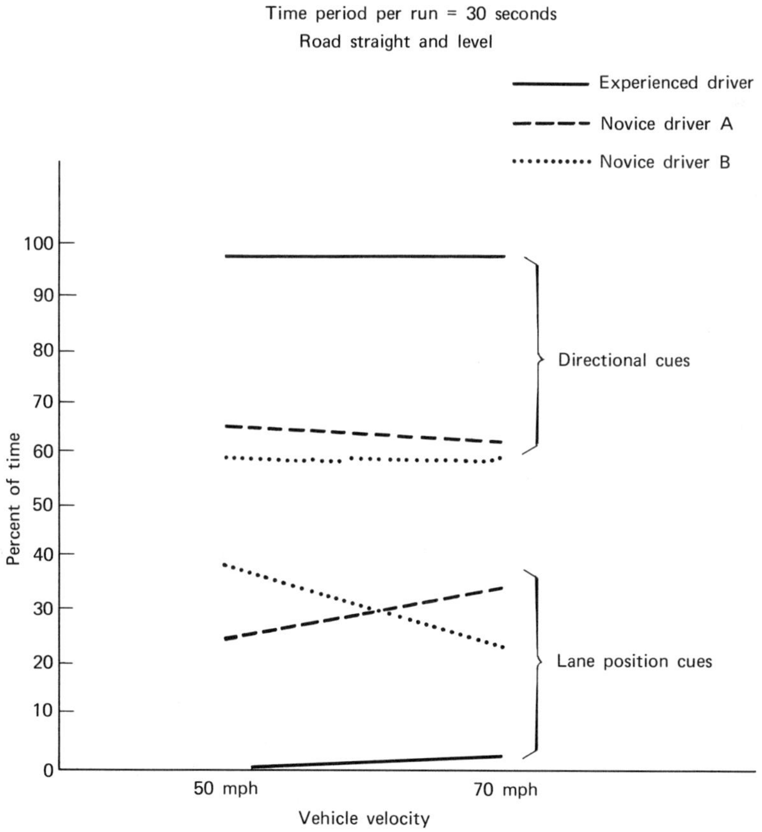

Figure 4. Percent of time sampling for directional and lane position cues as a function of vehicle velocity.

drivers, on the other hand, attempt to maintain a good 2.5 to 3.5 seconds minimum preview time adjusting their forward reference distance with velocity changes. Novice drivers, especially in their early hours of driving, sample close in to the car. This may be due to their inability to make temporal-spatial estimations and good use of peripheral processes.

The potential of eye-movement techniques in understanding the driving phenomena is virtually untapped. Eye-movement research has developed sufficiently over the past four or five years to begin the study of other facets in the driving task. These include the possible effects of carbon monoxide, narcotics, and marihuana on information acquisition, the effect of background and landscaping on curvature search patterning, the effects of driver aided systems (e.g., head-up displays), the effects of glare, rain, and fog on search patterns, and the use of eye-movement patterns for evaluating traffic control devices. While eye-movement research focuses on only one aspect of the total driving task, it is significant that without knowledge of the information-acquisition side of driving, no real development in driving theory such as information processing, anticipation, and learning can be developed. Any generalized predictive model of driving will have to have quantification of the informational inputs to the driver.

DRIVER AIDING

Driver aiding in control functions is well accepted. For example, power steering and power brakes do much to improve driver performance. Velocity control systems, anti-skid devices, and speed limit warning devices are all examples of systems that supplement the driver's sensory, decision-making, and control functions. Because of his inherent limitations in intervehicular sensing, efforts have been made to provide the driver with sensory supplementation. Gantzer and Rockwell (1968) presented the driver with both headway and relative velocity information and established headway and relative velocity bandwidths within which the driver was to operate. If the driver nulled the red and green lights on the dashboard, he was confident that he was in "the safe operating zone." Using target headways of 70 and 170 feet and average stream speeds of 60 mph, Gantzer was able to show that the driver indeed could drive with less headway variance and relative velocity variance under this aided system. The headway variance improvement was in the order of 100 percent at the 170 feet target headways but was substantially less at the 70 feet target headway. It was hypothesized that at short target headways the driver is less interested in using sensory supplementation information and more dependent upon his own perception. Interestingly enough, psychophysically at 70 feet and 70 mph the driver is able to detect very small changes in spacing ($\approx$ 10 ft). While there are some improvements in individual subject performance from aiding studies, the most striking feature of the data is that the intersubject differences become smaller, that is, there is a homogenizing effect with aiding systems that makes the drivers perform more alike. This has obvious implications in terms of improved stability of traffic flow patterns.

There is little question that providing the driver with accurate relative velocity and headway information would improve car-following performance. The basic technological problem is whether we could develop a passive system in automobiles that would sense spacing and relative velocity reliably and economically.

While open-road longitudinal performance can be aided by velocity control systems, and experimental headway and relative velocity aiding can provide improvement in car-following, the ability of aided systems to assist the driver in lateral control remains suspect today. This is because no method for measuring lateral placement along the highways has been reliably demonstrated and, further, the response time characteristics of such a sensing and warning system would be such that by the time the information on lateral deviation from the path is detected by the sensor, it would be of little or no use to the driver. It may well be that systems design must evolve from the current system into a semi-automated lateral control system in which vehicles are controlled down highways following centerline guidewires embedded in the highway pavement.

HEAD-UP DISPLAY AIDING IN DRIVING

Head-up type displays are so named because the operator does not have to lower his head to look at instruments or displays located inside the vehicle. This concept was first applied in aircraft but has recently been adopted for use in automobiles.

In early 1968, the Bureau of Public Roads contracted with the Kollsman Instrument Corporation to conduct a feasibility study and build and test a feasibility model of a Route Guidance Head-Up Display. The Head-up Display (HUD) was to be installed in an automobile for presentation of route guidance directional symbols to the driver as a subsystem of the Bureau's Experimental Route Guidance System (ERGS). This study demonstrated that the HUD concept could be applied to automobiles and that it was both technically and economically feasible to do so (Benzinger and Bell, 1969).

In 1969, Robbins (1969) adopted the HUD principle as a method of aiding the automobile driver in the close-interval car-following situation. In previous experiments conducted by Gantzer and Rockwell (1968) the driver was presented with discrete headway and/or relative velocity information via color coded lights on the instrument panel but the results indicated that the drivers became more reluctant to look down at the display to get the information as the car-following distance decreased. The HUD was considered to be a possible solution to this problem since the same information could be presented to the driver.

Within the context of driver aiding, it becomes evident that any additional information presented to the driver must not act as a distraction to the primary task of longitudinal and lateral control. Since it takes about 0.7 second to get information from instrument panel displays, novel techniques to display information on the windshield have been investigated. These would present information focused at infinity which the driver could look through while he undergoes his normal search and scan patterns. At the same time there would be no need for accommodation.

The results of using the HUD to present the information were very similar to the results of using the dashboard display. The headway variance was significantly reduced and the relative velocity variance increased somewhat, as a result of the drivers making speed changes in response to HUD information that would have gone undetected without the aiding. It was also determined that headway information alone, without relative velocity information, produced the best performance.

Unlike the dash-mounted display, however, the HUD has several other effects on the drivers' performance. First, the drivers appeared to be able to receive and use the information even at very short headways. This was also reflected in the fact that the drivers' estimates of the minimum safe distance were consistently revised toward a shorter distance using the HUD. Secondly, the drivers were more alike in their driving performance, as measured by the variance of headway, when using the display than without it. These two results have significance toward achieving a high speed/density traffic condition without risking a further increase in the number of accidents.

Harrass and Mourant (1970) extended HUD application to close-interval car-following using continuous headway information, via a moving reticle that depicted actual headway and desired target headway, computed from stream speed conditions. The results of this experiment showed again a significant reduction in headway variance and a small increase in relative velocity variance. The reduction in intersubject variability was found again but it was a much more pronounced effect with the continuous display. This was probably because there was less interpretation to be made by the subjects using the continuous display. When the discrete green light came on, the subject had to decide, using other information, whether to slowly accelerate back to the desired headway or whether to rapidly accelerate because he was rapidly falling behind. With the continuous display, the driver could get all the information that he needed to make the decision right from the display itself. The continuous display not only told the driver that he was off the desired headway but also told him how much he was off and how fast he was getting farther off because the rate of movement of the marker was actually giving him relative velocity information.

Can the Head-up Display be used to give automobile drivers useful information other than route guidance or car-following information? To answer this question, an experiment was designed to test the effects of giving the driver a "preview" of the road geometry ahead under conditions of reduced visibility, when he is unable to get the information without some kind of aiding. Since the easiest condition of reduced visibility to achieve is darkness, the experiment was conducted at night.

The results of the experiment showed that there was a significant shift in the average lateral acceleration on the curves between the day and night, but the HUD preview information did not cause any change in the mean lateral acceleration at night. Also the variance of the gas pedal position was found to be higher at night without HUD aiding, but the difference was only marginally significant ($p < 0.25$). The HUD preview in this case did have the effect of significantly reducing the variance of the gas pedal position over that of the unaided night condition.

While head-up display technology is still developing, it represents a new approach to the information acquisition issue. Whether such a display will *really* improve driving skill is still open to debate.

SUMMARY

Based on the evidence of driver skill, it is apparent that the driver will not easily be replaced by automated systems. Despite his variability in performance, the driver still can perform complex driving tasks with amazing reliability and safety. Considering the opportunities for accidents, the accident record of the average driver is very commendable. If we were to design a system with the specifications of the diverse skills of the human operator, most systems engineers would quickly concede defeat.

Indeed, contrary to the usual platitude about the "nut that holds the wheel," it can be argued that it is the driver who by his adaptability and skill makes what is often a badly designed car and/or highway system, work safely.

This chapter has attempted to show what can be expected of today's driver in terms of his skill and judgment. Serious questions arise concerning the role of the driver in transportation systems of the future, at least in terms of his role as vehicle controller. For example, can drivers be expected to safely operate on highways with 100-mph speed limits? Has the evolution of driving skill reached the limit and, if so, can aiding be developed to assist him particularly in the areas of information acquisition and decision-making where his limitations seem greatest? It can be argued that at the present time the complexity of the driver-vehicle system will demand further studies of perception and skill of drivers.

REFERENCES

Belt, B. L., Driver Eye Movements as a Function of Low Alcohol Concentrations, Technical Report, Engineering Experiment Station, The Ohio State University, Columbus, Ohio, 1969.

Benzenger, R. W. and Bell, E., Experimental Route Guidance Head-Up Display Research. Paper presented to the Highway Research Board, Washington, D.C., 1969.

Connolly, P. L., Visual Consideration: Man, the Vehicle and the Highway. *Highway Research News,* 30 (Winter, 1968).

Crawford, A., The Overtaking Driver, *Ergonomics,* 6, 2 (1963).

Crossman, E. R. F. W., *Methods and Techniques for Evaluating Motor Vehicle Handling Qualities,* 1967. *Research in Vehicle Handling Properties,* Sec. IV, U.S. Department of Transportation, NHSB, Washington, D.C.

Ernst, R. and Rockwell, T. H., Motion Sensitivity in Driving, EES 202B-4, Engineering Experiment Station, The Ohio State University, Columbus, Ohio, April 1966.

Farber, E., Passing behavior on Public Highways Under Daytime and Nighttime Conditions, *Highway Research Record,* 292 (1969).

Forbes, T. W., Human Factors in Highway Design Operation and Safety Problems, *Human Factors,* **2**, 1 (1959).

Forbes, T. W. and Matson, T. M., Driver Judgments in Passing on the Highway, *Journal of Psychology,* 8 (1939).

Forbes, T. W., Zaborski, H. J., Holshouser, E. L., and Deterline, W. A., Measurement of Driver Reactions to Tunnel Conditions, *Highway Research Board Proceedings,* **37** (1958).

Franklin Institute, *Overtaking and Passing on Two-Lane Rural Highways,* Federal Highway Adm., U.S. Dept. of Transportation, U.S. Gov't Printing Office, Washington, D.C., 1967.

Gantzer, D. and Rockwell, T. H., The Effects of Discrete Headway and Relative Velocity Information on Car-Following Performance, *Ergonomics,* **II**, 1 (1968).

Gordon, D. A., Experimental Isolation of the Driver's Visual Input, *Highway Research Record,* **122** (1966).

Gordon, D. A. and Michaels, R. M., Static and Dynamic Fields in Vehicular Guidance, *Highway Research Record,* **84** (1965), 1–15.

Greenshields, B., Distance and Time Required to Overtake and Pass Cars, *Highway Research Board Proceedings* 15 (1935), p. 332.

Harootyan, L. D., Jr., The Effect of Experience on Longitudinal and Lateral Control Characteristics of Automobile Drivers, Master's Thesis, The Ohio State University, Columbus, Ohio, 1969.

Harrass, J. A. and Mourant, R. R., Continuous Tracking With a Head-Up Presentation in Automobile Driving, presented at the Human Factors Society 14th Annual Meeting, San Francisco, Cal., October 1970.

Herman, R., Montroll, E. W., Potts, R. B., and Rothery, R. W., Traffic Dynamics: Analysis of Stability in Car Following, *Operations Research,* **7** (1959).

Kaluger, N. A. and Smith, G. L., Jr., Driver Eye-Movement Patterns Under Conditions of Prolonged Driving and Sleep Deprivation, *Night Visibility and Driver Behavior, Highway Research Record,* 336 (December 1970).

Lee, J., The Multilinear Speed-Density Relationship and Its Immediate Applications, Ph.D. Dissertation, The Ohio State University, Columbus, Ohio, 1971.

Mackworth, N. H., Visual Noise Causes Tunnel Vision, *Psychonomic Science,* 3 (1965).

Matson, T. M. and Forbes, T. W., Overtaking and Passing Requirements as Determined from a Moving Vehicle, *Highway Research Board Proceedings* 18 (1938).

Matson, T. M., Forbes, T. W., Prisk, C. W., and Crawford, A., (Table 2), Overtaking and Passing on Two-Lane Rural Roads, U.S. Department of Transportation, 1967.

Matanzo, F. and Rockwell, T. H., Driving Performance Under Nighttime Conditions of Visual Degradation, *Human Factors Journal,* **9** (1967).

Mortimer, R. G., Automotive Rear Lighting and Signaling Research, Federal Highway Administration, Department of Transportation, Washington, D.C., 1969.

Mourant, R. R., and Rockwell, T. H., Learning of Visual Patterns by Novice Drivers, *Proceedings Federation Internationale Des Societes D'Ingenieurs Des Technique De L'Automobile,* Brussels, 1970a.

Mourant, R. R. and Rockwell, T. H., Mapping Eye-Movement Patterns to the Visual Scene in Driving: An Exploratory Study, *The Journal of Human Factors,* **12**, 1 (February 1970b).

Mourant, R. R., Rockwell, T. H., and Rackoff, N. J., Drivers' Eye Movements and Visual Workload, *Highway Research Record,* 292 (1969).

Norman, O. K., Results of Highway Capacity Studies, *Public Roads,* 23, **4** (1942).

Prisk, C. W., Passing Practices on Rural Highways, *Highway Research Board Proceedings* (1941).

Robbins, C. K., Head-Up Display (HUD) Aiding in Car Following, Master's Thesis, The Ohio State University, Columbus, Ohio, 1969.

Rockwell, T. H. and Ernst, R., Studies in Car Following, EES-202B-5, Engineering Experiment Station, The Ohio State University, Columbus, Ohio, August 1965.

Rockwell, T. H., Ernst, R. L., and Hanken, A., A Sensitivity Analysis of Empirically Derived Car-Following Models, *Transportation Research,* 2, Pergamon Press, New York, 1968.

Rockwell, T. H. and Snider, J. N., An Investigation of Variability in Driving Performance, RF 1450, Research Foundation, The Ohio State University, Columbus, Ohio, 1967.

Rockwell, T. H. and Snider, J. N., Investigations of Driver Sensory Capability and its Effect on the Driving Task, RF 2091 Final Report, Research Foundation, The Ohio State University, Columbus, Ohio, July 1969.

Safford, R. R., Rockwell, T. H., and Banasik, R. C., The Effects of Automotive Rear Signal System Characteristics on Driving Performance, paper presented to the Highway Research Board Meeting in Washington, D.C., January 1969.

Salvatore, S., Velocity Sensing-Comparison of Field and Laboratory Methods, *Highway Research Record,* 292 (1969).

Sanders, A. F., Peripheral Viewing and Cognitive Organization, *Studies in Perception,* Institute for Perception, Soesterberg, Netherlands, RVO-TNO, 1966.

Sheridan, T. B., The Human Operator in Control Instrumentation, *Progress in Control Engineering,* **1** Academic Press (1962) 141–79.

Silver, C. A. and Farber, E., Driver Judgement in Overtaking Situations, *Highway Research Record,* 247 (1968).

Snider, J. N. and Ernst, R. E., A Study of Driver Variability in Car Following for Open Road, *Highway Research Record,* 84 (1965).

Snider, J. N. and Rockwell, T. H., The Development of an Instrumentation System to Measure True Driving Performance, *Automobilismo e Automobilismo Industriale,* Rome, Italy, January, 1963; *Traffic Safety Research Review,* **7**, 3 (1963).

Veliz, F., An Exploratory Study of Human Motor Performance Under Stress, Master's Thesis, The Ohio State University, Columbus, Ohio, 1961.

Vojir, R. J., Velocity Estimation and Headway Change Detection as a Function of Driving Experience, Master's Thesis, The Ohio State University, Columbus, Ohio, 1969.

Walraven, P. L. and Lazet, A., Perception Research and Human Engineering, in *Studies in Perception,* Institute for Perception, Soesterberg, Netherlands, RVO-TNO, 1966.

Weir, D. H. and McRuer, D. T., *Conceptualization of Overtaking and Passing on Two-Lane Rural Roads,* Vol. III, Driver Control, System Technology, Inc., December 1967.

Wojick and Hulbert, S. F., "The Driving Simulator—A Research Tool,"* *Mathematical Models and Simulation of Automobile Driving,* MIT, September 28, 29, 1967. *Appendix II—"A Summary of Group Discussion on Mathematical Models," edited by Ed Heitzman.

Zell, J. K., Driver Eye-Movements as a Function of Driving Experience Technical Report, IE-16, Engineering Experiment Station, The Ohio State University, Columbus, Ohio, 1969.

VIII

THE DRIVER IN A MILITARY SETTING*

J. E. Uhlaner, A. J. Drucker, and Emma E. Brown

Since 1961 J. E. Uhlaner has been director of the U.S. Army Behavior and Systems Research Laboratory (formerly the Army Behavioral Science Research Laboratory). After obtaining his degrees in psychology—B.S. from the City College of New York, M.S. from Iowa State University, and Ph.D. from New York University—he started his career of over 20 years as an Army scientist.

Dr. Uhlaner has made major research contributions in the fields of screening, selection, classification, and behavioral evaluation. He devised and directed the development of the Armed Forces Qualification Test (AFQT). In recent years he has concentrated on development of a research program of human factors utilization problems in man-machine systems, integrating personnel measurement and experimental approaches. Specifically in the field of driver research he has advocated the consideration of driving problems within a framework of the traffic-way-driver-vehicle system.

His most recent publication in the field of driver research is on the use of tests in driver selection and licensing.

Dr. Uhlaner is a member of the Road User Characteristics Committees of the Highway Research Board, and the APA Committee on Accident Research. He was the instigator of the Annual Human Factors Workshop now sponsored by the Highway Research Board. Dr. Uhlaner was the 1969–70 president of the Division of Military Psychology of the American Psychological Association. He is a fellow of the APA and five of its divisions, of the Human Factors Society, of the Iowa and the Washington academies of science and a member of the Operations Research Society of America,

* The opinions expressed in this chapter are those of the authors and do not necessarily represent the viewpoint of the Behavior and Systems Research Laboratory or of the Army.

Psychonomic Society, Psychometric Society, and the International Association of Applied Psychology.

Arthur J. Drucker obtained his B.S. in 1942 from the University of Rochester, his M.S. in 1947 from Purdue University, and his Ph.D. in 1949 from Purdue. He was assistant director of the Division of Educational Reference, Purdue University from 1949 to 1951, and concurrently was associate editor of the Purdue Opinion Panel and assistant professor in tests and measurements and attitude measurement. He joined the U.S. Army Behavior and Systems Research Laboratory in 1951 and served as a research psychologist, contract research officer, chief of the leadership and personality research unit and assistant director for operations, his current position.

Dr. Drucker is a fellow in the Division of Industrial Psychology, American Psychological Association, as well as in the Division of Military Psychology. He is a member of several regional psychological associations and of the Human Factors Society. He has published and presented at various professional psychological organizations more than 15 papers and research reports, including previous coauthorship with Dr. Uhlaner on papers on driving and measurement. He has contributed chapters to books on industrial relations and attitude and opinion measurement.

Emma Brown has been with the Behavior and Systems Research Laboratory since 1942 as a research psychologist, serving in the past 10 years as assistant for reports. Her earlier work with the organization was in personnel measurement for selection and classification, where she contributed to the improvement of methods and techniques of personnel management. She has authored or coauthored a number of reports in this area. She is one of the authors of *Marginal Man and Military Service—A Review,* the product of a four-man working group that, in 1965, analyzed past research studies and programs dealing with marginal manpower in the military sector, as a basis for planning subsequent manpower programs.

She received her B.A. and M.A. degrees from the University of Colorado in 1924 and 1927 in the fields of languages and linguistics. She is a member of the American Psychological Association, the District of Columbia Psychological Association, and the Federal Editors Association.

Wherever there are roads, vehicles, drivers, there are traffic problems. So far, no method of assuring even a reasonably accident-proof system has been devised. Can the public obtain from the military motor vehicle operator program some idealized solution that may be applied to public driving? The services place heavy reliance upon an effective driving program, as accidents and ineffective driving cause delays, inconvenience, loss of manpower and man-day effort, and can even result in missed tactical objectives. Let us examine some records.

Half the hospitalized Army casualties during the Korean conflict were the results, not of enemy action, but of accidents—and 70 percent of the accident cases had been injured in land-operated vehicles (McFarland, 1952). In the Navy and Marine Corps, motor vehicle accidents were reported in a 1953 and 1954 summary as the leading cause of death (U.S. Department of the Navy, 1954). The Air Force also has cited its toll from motor vehicle accidents as the leading cause of death, injury, and noneffectiveness (Armstrong, 1953). This service attributes an average of 60,000 lost man-days over the last 10 years to motor vehicle accidents (U.S. Air Force, 1969). Army figures for fiscal year 1969 show a total of 8271 accidents, a worldwide rate of 6.8 accidents per million miles of travel (U.S. Department of the Army, 1969). The number of accidents was about equally divided between the continental United States and overseas (excluding Vietnam as atypical), but the overseas rate was 9.1 per million miles of travel, the rate within the United States 5.5. Clearly, the relatively rigorous driver selection and training programs of the services have not eliminated motor vehicle accidents.

While these rates do suggest a better record than civilian figures—a countrywide rate of 14.6 accidents per million miles of motor vehicle mileage (National Safety Council, 1969)—the record should be a lot better. Military driving *is* the source of persistent concern among those whose responsibility it is to see that the wheeled vehicles of the armed forces are operated safely and in effective support of military objectives.

Our purpose in this chapter is to examine implications of past and ongoing research dealing with problems of motor vehicle operation in the services and to point to those that may generalize to civilian driving.

SPECIAL NATURE OF MILITARY DRIVING

Military driving, in contrast to civilian, is done in a highly regulated environment, with servicewide and local post regulations providing the framework. Courses of action open to the military driver are defined much more narrowly than in state and local civilian traffic systems.

A driver licensed by the armed services may be assigned either to a full-time driving job, or may have to drive as an incidental requirement in his main assignment. He is usually assigned to a motor pool in which personnel bear a stated relationship—hierarchical in a measure—to each other. He may or may not have a regularly assigned vehicle, but usually he is limited by his service permit to vehicles of certain types. In the continental United States, for the most part, he drives his vehicle over well-marked routes within a limited area, somewhat analogous to the routes pursued by a truck driver or chauffeur on a regular run. His driving is usually limited to daytime hours. He takes orders from a motor pool supervisor or dispatcher.

Maneuvers or assignments abroad may be something else again. The military driver may be required to remain at the wheel for long hours traversing unfamiliar roads, perhaps crossing untracked fields or shell-pocked terrain. He may have to accommodate to unfamiliar driving practices and regulations. In tactical driving, he faces blackout conditions, mined roads, sniper fire, or direct attack.

Motor vehicle operator programs in the armed services lean heavily, but not exclusively, on research. For the scientific investigator attempting to improve the safety record of service drivers, the special environment in which the military driver operates calls for a flexible approach.

Drivers for military assignment can be selected from a large number of potential motor vehicle operators. This favorable selection ratio permits selection tests of moderate validity to exclude a greater proportion of potentially unsafe or ineffective drivers than would be acceptable in a local or state licensing procedure. By the very nature of the objectives, selection procedures have a better prospect of improving the safety performance of drivers in the military setting than do licensing procedures in a civilian traffic system.

Accident records have come to be regarded as unstable criteria for studies of civilian drivers—so goes the consensus. There is no reason to expect accident statistics to be more stable in the military environment. Indeed, they may well be less stable because of a heavy penalty system. The services remove a driver from driving duty as soon as he has accumulated a total of 12 points for traffic violations. The driver is assessed an immediate 12 points for major violations, including driving under the influence of intoxicating liquor, leaving the scene of an accident involving death or personal injury, negligent homicide, and using an automobile to commit a felony. Two lesser violations usually are sufficient to warrant revocation of permit. Also, driving conditions from pool to pool vary greatly in the vehicles used, mission, supervision, climate, terrain, density of traffic, and night versus day driving. Accident rates are thus contaminated with factors that are not subject to the controls essential to experimentation.

On the other hand, the military driver's job offers other good possibilities for measuring the performance of numbers of drivers under fairly uniform conditions—route limitations, similar driving hours, and regulatory procedures imposed. There is thus opportunity to gauge the effect of alternative management policies and operating procedures.

MILITARY DRIVER MANAGEMENT

All the armed services have driver management programs aimed at safety and at the effective utilization of motor vehicle and driver resources. The regulation governing motor vehicle traffic supervision for the Departments of the Army, the Navy, the Air Force, and the Defense Supply Agency (Military Police, 1962) states as a guiding philosophy that traffic accidents are preventable, and that "the intentional or unintentional, yet unsafe acts of vehicle drivers are primarily responsible for the high death, injury, and property damage rates experienced in vehicle accidents throughout the nation." Each service has instituted a system of motor vehicle management which includes screening and selection of drivers, driver training and remedial retraining, organization and administration of motor pools or facilities, traffic regulations and enforcement procedures, and administration of the traffic point system for motor vehicle violations.

SCREENING AND SELECTION OF DRIVERS

The Army

Since the U.S. Army has the largest driving program in the world—and the greatest number of drivers*—a description of its driver selection program will provide a somewhat detailed view of the motor vehicle operations in a military setting.

The Army is concerned with selection of personnel whose chief duty is driving and with licensing for all jobs in which driving is required. In licensing, management concentrates on eliminating only the obviously unqualified; in selection, it seeks to identify only the best. Licensing procedures are designed to assure that the individual has the minimum knowledge and skill and is physically able to drive. They do not assure that he will drive responsibly, although they may attempt to detect attitudes grossly incompatible with responsible driving.

Here is a brief review of the development of the screening and selection procedures currently in use by the Army. The senior author devoted a number of years to the direction of research activities to develop devices for the selection and licensing of Army motor vehicle operators (Uhlaner, 1956). First, hundreds of existing tests were sifted, since the literature seemed to hold many promising leads. Many of these leads

* The Annual Report for fiscal year 1969 (U.S. Department of the Army, 1969) gives a figure of 775,000 wheeled vehicles designed for over-the-road purposes and a total mileage of 1,210,221,000 for the Army.

were examined as possible bases for research hypotheses, but most of the early hypotheses were ultimately rejected. For many years an assumption had existed among driver officials and researchers that visual and psychophysical measures were among the most effective predictors of efficient and safe driving. Close examination of findings available at the start of the Army research did not bear out this hypothesis (DeSilva and Robinson, 1939; Goldstein, Van Steenberg, and Birnbaum, 1952). Admittedly, in the Army setting, this hypothesis had less chance of being substantiated than in civilian driving, since military personnel have already met minimum physical, visual, and psychophysical requirements for admission to the military ranks. Hence, such measures as field of vision, eye dominance, visual acuity, reaction time, depth perception, peripheral vision, auditory acuity, resistance to glare, and strength of grip could not be expected to differentiate as significantly among Army driver applicants as among civilians. Yet a better screening and selection system was needed. New measures were therefore sought to select from the military manpower available those Army personnel who were most likely to be—or to become—safe and efficient drivers. Emphasis was placed on development of measures of driving information, emergency driver information, personality characteristics, attitudes, biographical information, and specially tailored psychological measures (Uhlaner, Van Steenberg, and Goldstein, 1951).

In the light of the shortcomings of accident records as criteria against which to check the effectiveness of instruments for the selection of safe drivers, the decision was made to explore the possibility of assessing the driving behavior of Army drivers on the basis of the observations and pooled judgments of their supervisors and associates. In view of the generally high interrelationships between ratings and checklist scores, and for practical considerations, it was decided to develop a criterion measure of simple rating scales and a driving habit checklist. The four scales included in the final criterion instrument were:

1. How often does he have near-accidents?
2. How well does he react to sudden changes of traffic conditions?
3. How much does "temper" or "nerves" affect his driving?
4. How well does he know his own limitations—poor sight, slowness, lack of skill, and so on—and drive according to what he knows he can do?

The raters who supplied ratings on the above scales also indicated, for each of 105 descriptions of unsafe driving habits, how ratable (observable) the behavior was and how important it was to safe driving. Fifteen statements adjudged most ratable and important were selected for the final checklist (Uhlaner, Van Steenberg, and Goldstein, 1952).

As a result of experimentation, six tests were finally selected as most effective. These tests comprise Driver Battery I and Driver Battery II as currently used by the Army.

The predictive test battery finally developed had a reasonable amount of validity for the purpose of selection—in the range of 0.35 to 0.40 (Uhlaner, 1956). It should be stressed that benefits from this validity can be achieved when many more applicants for driving are presented for assignment than will ultimately be accepted. In the Army, this difficulty is only partially overcome by requiring that all replacement stream enlisted personnel processed through reception stations be given a preliminary driver selection battery.

Driver Battery I consists of the following series of written tests to assess driving aptitude and basic knowledge of motor vehicle operation.

Driving Know-How Test. This is a test of knowledge of good driving practices—what a person should know in order to drive safely—how the vehicle works, how to maintain it, how to keep out of trouble in traffic, and rules of the road commonly in effect. The multiple-choice items are similar to the following excerpt:

What is the BEST way to prevent skids in wet weather?
(a) Keep tires inflated properly.
(b) Adjust speed to conditions.
(c) Use brakes lightly.
(d) Stay farther behind other cars than usual.

Where should the driver in the sketch look in order to avoid headlight glare of the oncoming vehicle?

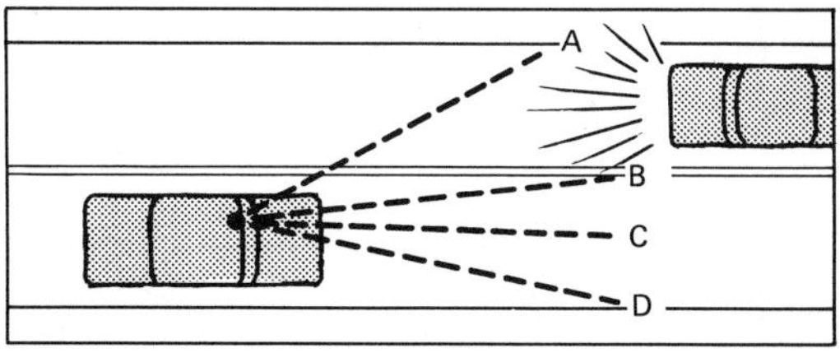

Attention to Detail Test. This is a measure of perception, tapping the ability to focus on detail and to respond quickly and accurately. The examinee is required to count letter C's interspersed among letter O's in page-length lines of capital letters. Here are practice items:

DIRECTIONS

This is a test of your ability to follow instructions in finding an important detail. Look at the sample test below. Each problem looks like a line of O's, but in some lines there are some C's. You are to find the C's in each line and check (√) the number on the right-hand side which tells how many C's you found in that line. You may find no C's, or you may find as many as four C's in a line.

Look at problem 1 from left to right. It contains 3 C's. So the number 3 is checked on the right-hand side of that problem. Now do the rest of the problems on this page in the same way.

1. OOOOOOOOOOOOOOOOOOOCOOOOOOOOOOOOOOOOOOOOOOOOCOOOOOOOOOOOOOOOCOOOO 0 1 2 3 4
2. OOOOOOOOOOOOOOOOOOOOOOOOOOOOCOOOOOOOOOOOOOOOOOOOOOOOOOCOOOOOOOOOO 0 1 2 3 4
3. OOOOOOOOOOOOOOOOOOOOOOOOOOOOOOOOOOOOOOOOOOOOOOOOOOOOOOOOOOOOOOOOO 0 1 2 3 4
4. OOCOOOOOOOOOOOOOOOOOOOOOOOOOOOOOOOOOOOOOOOOOOCOOOOOOOOOOOOOOOOOOO 0 1 2 3 4
5. OOOOOOOOCOOOOOOOOOOOOOOOOOCOOOOOOOOOOOOOOOOOOCOOCOOOOOOOOOOOOOOOO 0 1 2 3 4

Army Self-Description Blank (Transport). A measure of personality and attitudinal factors such as interests, annoyances, likes and dislikes, preferences, driving and mechanical experience:

What kind of vehicle did you first learn to drive?
(a) Dump truck.
(b) Passenger car.
(c) Semi-trailer truck.
(d) Racing car.
(e) Never learned to drive.

Since you learned to drive, how many different makes or models of passenger cars have you driven over 100 miles each?
(a) None.
(b) 1 or 2.
(c) 3 or 4.
(d) 5–9.
(e) 10 or more.

Driver Battery II also consists of three instruments:

Two-Hand Coordination Test. A measure of eye-hand coordination in which the examinee, grasping a stylus—about the size and weight of a chisel—in each hand, taps a succession of circles alternatively with right and left hand. The circles, irregularly spaced, are printed in rows on either side of a large sheet of paper resting on the desk in front of the examinee. Both speed and accuracy count in the score.

Visual Judgment Test. Taps ability to match identical pairs of words, which are presented in progressively smaller type. The early questions look like this:

CUT (A) CAT (B) COT (C) OUT (D) CUT (E) CUP

Answer sheet: A B C D E

The final questions are about this size:

Emergency Judgment Test. Deals with knowledge of solutions to emergency driving problems. Here is Practice Question 1:

The driver of car A should
(a) slow down and drop behind car B.
(b) speed up and get around car B.
(c) swerve to the left.
(d) sound his horn to warn truck C.

A passing score on Driver Battery I is the first step toward obtaining a military driver's license, termed the United States Government Motor Vehicle Operator's Identification Card (SF 46), required for every person operating a motor vehicle for the Army—and required by all the other services as well. Battery I is administered to all personnel as part of reception station processing. It serves as a screen for referring individuals for further testing and licensing for driver assignments or assignments involving driving. Driver Battery II is administered in conjunction with licensing of personnel who have failed to attain a specified score (Army Standard Score of 85) on Battery I. It is administered by driver testing stations or teams that have the primary function of issuing—and renewing or revoking—military permits and the related functions of driver interviewing, counseling, and guidance, and the recording, review and evaluation of driver records.

Psychophysical evaluation measures—visual acuity, field of vision, depth perception, color perception, foot reaction time, and hearing—are administered by means of standard driver testing and training devices. Results are used almost entirely in counseling the driver regarding any deficiencies he may have and demonstrating how he can compensate for them by changes in his driving habits. The driver whose depth perception is poor may be shown how he can make use of cues from the size of objects and buildings and their position in relation to each other. The driver whose reaction time is greatly above the norm can be cautioned not to stop too short if other drivers are behind him. Only if a defect is discovered which is a clear risk in driving are these evaluations reason for rejection.

A road test is an important part of the licensing procedure and includes manipulation of controls, a practice run, check for emergency equipment, a before-operation check, and location of instruments.

In sum, to obtain a permit to drive in the Army—and similar requirements obtain in all the services—the individual must pass Driver Battery I at the reception station; or, if he has failed Battery I or somehow missed taking it, he must pass Driver Battery II at the local installation. He must also qualify on a physical evaluation test and pass the road test.

The Navy

Requirements for civilian drivers employed by the Navy follow Civil Service Commission procedures and include a written test and a road test. Navy organizations select drivers from names submitted from the appropriate register. In addition, the applicant must have a valid state driver's license, required, incidentally, of all drivers in all the services. The Navy then applies standards of its own. After the driver is hired, he is again tested for weaknesses and special training is given to help him overcome any faulty driving habits. This reexamination includes written, road, and obstacle tests, and a complete physical check, as well as psychophysiological measures. Qualified drivers are awarded the Government Motor Vehicle Operator's permit, and the type (or types) of vehicle they are licensed to operate is specified. If a driver is to be required to drive a different type of vehicle, he is put with a qualified driver for training until the tutorial driver is satisfied that the novice driver is competent to operate the new type of vehicle, for which he receives a permit.

For military drivers the procedure, first developed for civilians and then adapted to the military, is much the same. Each Naval activity conducts driver testing and training functions using available Army, Navy, or Air Force facilities.

The Navy has in operation ten mobile vans containing simulators used in training new drivers. After basic training with these simulators, drivers undergo comprehensive motor vehicle operator tests to qualify for their driver's permit.

In a program just getting under way, all men in Navy uniform from admirals on down are given the National Safety Council's Defensive Driving Course. The program will proceed by degrees throughout the service, each group of about 20 trained by Navy or civilian driving instructors providing a cadre of instructors for ensuing courses in which additional drivers—and instructors—will be trained. Topics covered in the first eight hours are: the practice of defensive driving, how to avoid collision with the vehicle behind, how to avoid collision with an oncoming vehicle, how to avoid an intersection collision, the art of passing and being passed, and how to avoid other common types of collision. Individuals planning to teach later classes continue with an Instructor's Course.

The Air Force

The Air Force Motor Vehicle Operator Test (AFMVOT) is a 65-item multiple-choice test on the proper operation of a motor vehicle. It is designed to evaluate the basic knowledge required for successful completion of base motor vehicle operator courses and is the basis for awarding the United States Government Motor Vehicle Operator's Identification Card. The test is administered to United States Air Force personnel who apply for the government license and may be given to United States and foreign civilian personnel employed by the Air Force to determine eligibility to operate Air Force motor vehicles (U.S. Air Force, 1968).

The Air Force Traffic Safety Education Program has adopted an intensive method of instruction consisting of six courses (U.S. Air Force, 1969). The first course is designed to add to the individual's knowledge of safe driving practices, to help him identify driving errors and develop attitudes and techniques to improve his safe driving behavior. The remaining courses are directed mainly at local problems, individual remedial education, and special driving requirements. A two-unit overseas indoctrination course is given to military and civilian personnel newly assigned at an overseas base to familiarize them with traffic practices and conditions not normally encountered in the continental United States.

A Driver Training Test in which individuals record their responses to questions presented on filmstrips is administered as a diagnostic instrument at the beginning of the initial safety course and as an achievement test after completion of the course. Program evaluations are prepared in summary form and reviewed by a group professionally qualified in traffic accident prevention. Program modifications and procedural revisions are recommended to U.S. Air Force Headquarters.

The services thus tend to conduct a coordinated program within the framework of a transportation facility. The transportation officer largely influences the application of the motor vehicle safety program. Problems of human engineering of vehicles and roadways usually involve efforts of the research and development authorities and the Defense Supply Agency.

All the services have come to their present motor vehicle safety procedures through efforts extending far into the past. The Navy has tended to be eclectic. The Air Force has leaned heavily on findings from studies of accidents associated with flying—stellar research conducted by E. L. Thorndike for the School of Aviation Medicine and reported in 1950 (Thorndike, 1950). The report covers the then state of research on accidents in many activities in addition to aviation. Dr. Thorndike's painstaking analysis has been helpful in distinguishing substantiated findings from hypotheses and from mere speculation.

For most investigations into the causes of accidents—and always, so far as we know, in the case of civilian traffic systems—the final aim is to reduce the number and severity of accidents, with resultant saving in human life and productivity. In military driving, safety is not always the foremost aim. Very possibly, when the goal is delivery of cargo, getting a certain number of troops into a prescribed position as quickly as possible, passing certain points undetected by the enemy—in short, the accomplishment of a military objective—safety may be a secondary consideration.

TESTS AND THE DRIVING POPULATION

While use of military tests is not suggested as a screen for civil permits, it seems important to offer some discussion of the significance of selection tests as they relate to possible use in the public licensing of drivers.

Everyone knows someone who should not be allowed behind the

wheel of a vehicle. But on whose say-so should a driver be removed or not allowed there in the first place? And on what basis?

The crux of the matter is the established predictive efficiency of the selection tests, expressed in terms of validity coefficients. As far as safety is concerned, licensing procedures function, not to select the safest drivers, but to disqualify the very poorest and least safe. In this context, the predictive efficiency of even the best tests currently available is so low that a cutoff score selected to reduce accidents by even a small percentage would involve taking off the road a very large number of drivers, many of whom would not have accidents if driving were continued.

To illustrate, assume a liberal estimate of validity of a good selection battery for drivers to be 0.35, using a rating criterion.* But because a rating criterion does not necessarily coincide with actual incidence of accidents, assume the estimate to be a validity coefficient of 0.20. Using this coefficient, public officials would have to take off the road 23 million of the 100 million drivers now on the road in order to reduce the number of accidents to 10 million per year—that is, by one-third (Figure 1). Further, the cost to the public would be a loss of 18 million good drivers who score low on the tests for the benefit of removing 5 million poor drivers.

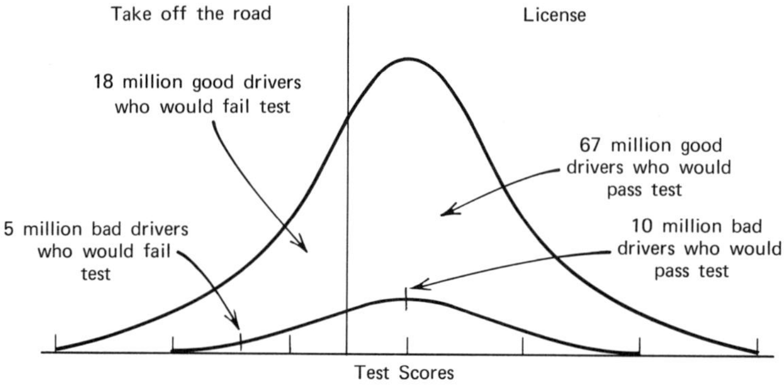

Figure 1. Impact of selection battery for licensing, using validity coefficient of 0.20. Accidents would be reduced by one-third.

* The presentation that follows is adapted, with permission, from a chapter prepared by Dr. Uhlaner and Dr. Drucker, "The Use of Tests in Driver Selection and Licensing" appearing in *Studies in Personnel and Industrial Psychology*, Edwin A. Fleishman, ed., The Dorsey Press, Homewood, Ill. 1967. See also Uhlaner and Drucker (1965).

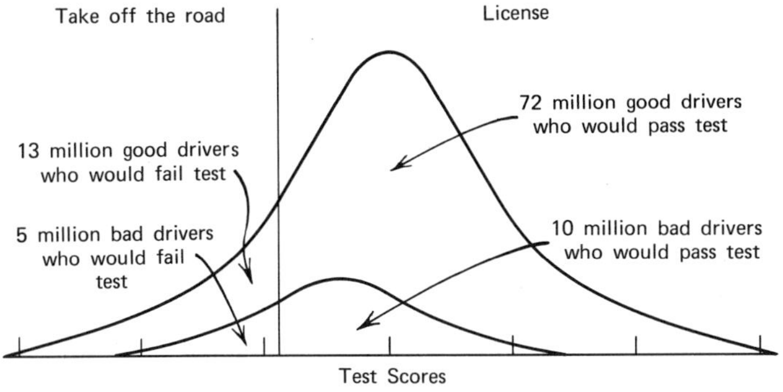

Figure 2. Impact of selection battery for licensing using validity coefficient of 0.35.

If, through the expenditure of funds for additional research effort, we could raise the validity coefficient to 0.35, public officials could reduce the number taken off the road to 18 million to achieve the same reduction to 10 million accidents per year (Figure 2). The loss this time would be 13 million good drivers who score low on the tests.

What would be the impact on accident reduction if public officials would be willing to remove 10 million drivers? Using a validity coefficient of 0.20, we might expect only 2 percent of the 10 million to be bad drivers (Figure 3). With a validity coefficient of 0.35, we might expect 3 percent of the 10 million to be bad drivers (Figure 4). In each case, the increase in validity results in only slight improvement for the research money invested.

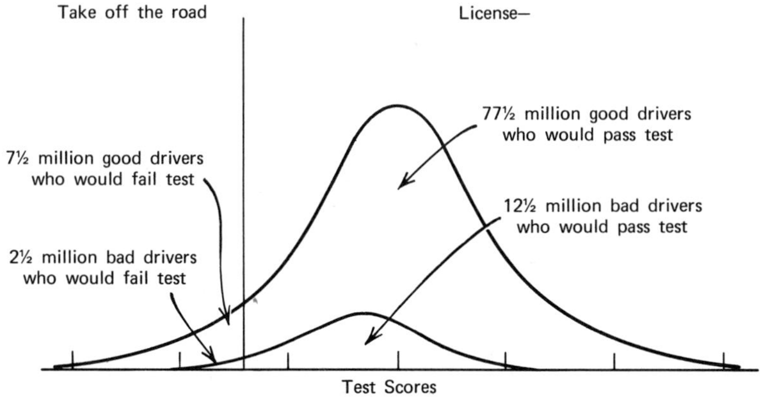

Figure 3. Impact of not licensing lowest 10 percent, with validity coefficient of 0.20.

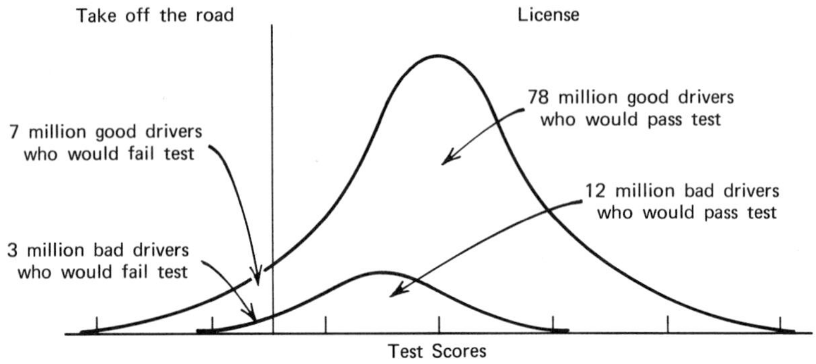

Figure 4. Impact of not licensing lowest 10 percent, with validity coefficient of 0.35.

True, if much higher validity could be achieved, the benefits in reducing accident rates would be much greater. (This exercise is a theoretical one, of course, as such prospects are not in sight.) Assume, for example, a 10 percent point of cut or disqualification and a predictive validity of 0.90. Then about nine-tenths of the drivers removed would be bad drivers and only one-tenth good drivers, and the bad drivers licensed would be reduced to about 6 percent (Table 1). Similarly (Table 2), for a validity coefficient of 0.90, with a goal of reduction of the annual accident rate from 15 to 10 million, virtually all good drivers tested in applying for licenses would receive them. The value in such an exercise is in gaining a greater appreciation of the infeasibility of applying selection procedures in a licensing situation.

Table 1 Effect on Driver Accident Reduction of Removing Bottom 10 Percent Using Selection Tests for Licensing

Validity Coefficient	Total Removed (millions)		Total Licensed (millions)	
	Bad Drivers	Good Drivers	Bad Drivers	Good Drivers
0.10	1.9	8.1	13.1	76.9
0.20	2.4	7.6	12.6	77.4
0.30	3.0	7.0	12.0	78.0
0.40	3.5	6.5	11.5	78.5
0.50	4.2	5.8	10.8	79.2
0.60	5.0	5.0	10.0	80.0
0.70	5.9	4.1	9.1	80.9
0.80	7.1	2.9	7.9	82.1
0.90	9.1	0.9	5.9	84.1

Table 2 Effect on Driver Accident Reduction of Using Selection Tests for Licensing[a]

	Total Removed (millions)		Total Licensed (millions)	
Coefficient	Bad Drivers	Good Drivers	Bad Drivers	Good Drivers
0.10	5.0	23.0	10.0	62.0
0.20	5.0	18.2	10.0	66.8
0.30	5.0	14.0	10.0	71.0
0.40	5.0	11.4	10.0	73.6
0.50	5.0	7.5	10.0	77.5
0.60	5.0	5.1	10.0	79.9
0.70	5.0	3.2	10.0	81.8
0.80	5.0	1.7	10.0	83.3
0.90	5.0	0.6	10.0	84.4

[a] To reduce accident rate from 15 to 10 million.

Grant that with fewer cars on the road, the progression of reduced accidents would not necessarily be a straight line, but might accelerate in curvilinear fashion. This would not alter the conclusion that selection tests by themselves would not reduce our national motor vehicle accident rates *if such devices were to be employed in the practical setting of general licensing.*

One reason for the ineffectiveness of selection tests applied to a licensing situation is the administrative necessity to leave the point of cut at a low level. The value of selection tests is in the selection or screening situation—even with tests having validity coefficients as low as 0.20. Figures 5 and 6 illustrate this point. As the vertical bar is moved

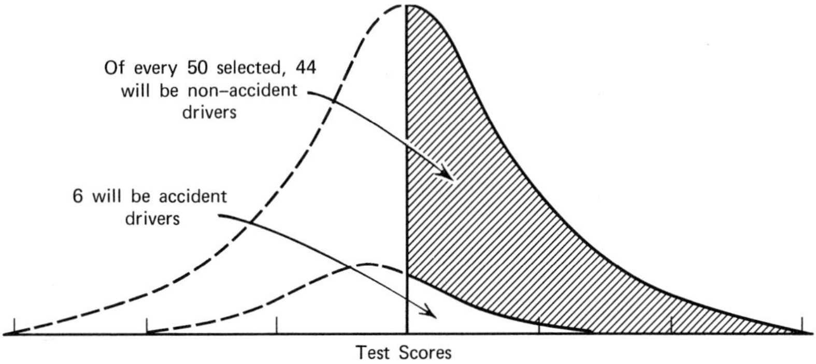

Figure 5. Influence of cutting off bottom 50 percent of selection applicants, given validity coefficient of 0.20.

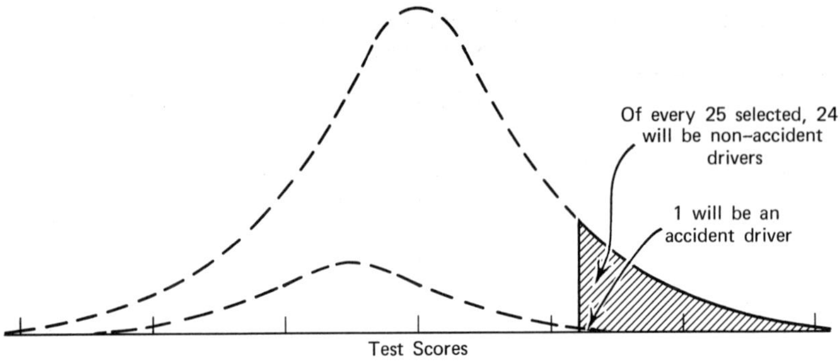

Figure 6. Influence of cutting off bottom 75 percent of selection applicants, given validity coefficient of 0.35.

to the right, indicating a progressively higher cutting score on the test battery, the number of qualified drivers decreases, but the proportion of poor drivers among those selected decreases more rapidly than the proportion of good drivers. If the number of applicants far exceeds the number to be selected, the selection device can save money, equipment, and lives. Tables 3 and 4 give the values for 10, 25, 50, 75, and 90 percent

Table 3 Impact on Accident Reduction of Rejecting Various Proportions of Driver Applicants, Validity Coefficient of 0.20

	Percent Rejected		Percent Selected	
Selection Ratio[a]	Bad Drivers	Good Drivers	Bad Drivers	Good Drivers
10	2.4	7.6	12.6	77.4
25	5.3	19.7	9.7	65.3
50	9.4	40.6	5.6	44.4
75	12.6	62.4	2.4	22.6
90	14.2	75.8	0.8	9.2

[a] Percent to be eliminated.

points of cut. Maximally effective selection is achieved for a validity coefficient of 0.35 when only the top 10 percent is selected—9.7 percent accident-free drivers versus 0.3 percent accident drivers!

RECENT DIRECTIONS IN DRIVING RESEARCH

A review of the many programs of research to investigate psychological factors in motor vehicle operation by the military has led the authors

Table 4 Impact on Accident Reduction of Rejecting Various Proportions of Driver Applicants, Validity Coefficient of 0.35

	Percent Rejected		Percent Selected	
Selection Ratio[a]	Bad Drivers	Good Drivers	Bad Drivers	Good Drivers
10	3.0	7.0	12.0	78.0
25	6.6	18.4	8.4	66.6
50	11.0	39.0	4.0	46.0
75	13.8	61.2	1.2	23.8
90	14.7	75.3	0.3	9.7

[a] Percent to be eliminated.

to the conclusion that only a small part of safe driving variance (10 to 20 percent) can be ascribed to differences in driver skill and safety factors associated with the driver (in which we include training and motivational devices as well as physical and emotional states). Another slice of safe driving variance emanates from the vehicle and its equipment, and the roadways and quality of engineering that has gone into their making. The nature of the traffic system and the degree and character of enforcement applied accounts for additional variance. Add the variability of weather conditions, time of day, seasonal and other factors not readily subject to control. The gain in safety to be attained by improvement in any one of these components is limited, but since the accident problem is multivariate it must be attacked on a total systems front.

Some of the psychological research of special importance to the military driver problem and some research studies of the civilian driver problem seem to the authors to deal with similar aspects of motor vehicle operation: management of motor pools, evaluation of young drivers, evaluation of cab drivers—considered similar to many motor pools—and examination of driving practices.

Management factors related to safe motor vehicle operation were studied in 1951 by Harold A. Edgerton. He examined administrative practices in Army motor vehicle units in relation to the overall safety performance of motor pools (Edgerton, 1951). The study was conducted for the Behavior and Systems Research Laboratory by Richardson, Bellows, and Henry, Incorporated. Dr. Edgerton's analysis reflected personnel selection and assignment policy, vehicle assignment, incentives and disciplinary action, record keeping, and patterns of responsibility. The study extended to motor pools of various types—administrative, tactical, and ordnance, among others, and various possibilities of measuring units were examined. He first identified, through a rating and ranking process, units having high or good all-round safety records and those at the opposite extreme, and then compared contrasting groups of units with respect to administrative practices. Among the numerous conclusions based on the data, we cite the following:

> Motor units rated high in safety operation made greater effort to select men who could perform adequately as dispatchers and gave their dispatchers more responsibilities.
>
> High units did their own driver training more frequently and also extended training to men temporarily assigned to the unit as drivers.
>
> High units showed greater care than low units in assigning each driver to a particular vehicle.

The study did not attempt to establish causal relationships. Its present interest lies in the fact that it embraced the major elements of motor vehicle systems and viewed them together in relation to what we would today term a systems criterion.

Ross McFarland in the early 1950s stated the safety problem in terms of agent, host, and environment and the interactions of the three (McFarland, 1955). A program for accident prevention that he conducted at the Harvard School of Public Health covered a wide range of problems and involved a number of disciplines—physiology, psychiatry, anthropology, psychology, sociology, statistics, and engineering. Some studies explicitly entered the fields of management—those of environmental influences and supervision and leadership, for example—and most were management-oriented. These studies supported the emerging recognition that accidents stem from many and varied factors, some still unidentified, rather than from any one predominant causative factor.

Through simulation techniques, researchers are seeking to reproduce the meaningful factors thought to be significant in the complex environment of the motor vehicle operator. However, measures attained through simulators have tended to emphasize skills rather than factors related to broad safety goals. One exception is a study recently reported by the American Institutes for Research (Edwards, Hahn, and Fleishman, 1969). The investigators compared on-the-road performance of drivers with their performance on simulated driving tasks in a controlled laboratory setting. Included in the study were not only measures of perceptual motor skill, but also biographical factors and official records of accidents and violations over a five-year period.

Data were obtained by pairs of observers who hailed taxis at a given location and gave the drivers a specified routing and destination so that the task was relatively standard. Without letting the driver know he was being observed, each observer independently recorded errors made by the drivers, using a partially precoded checklist. As the cab arrived at the destination, the passengers asked the driver if he was willing to participate in a study of driving simulation, for which he would be paid. Sixty-six percent of the drivers (304) agreed to take the tests. They were then given driving tests on two different simulators and also four perceptual-motor tests. The design enabled the experimenters to examine the relationships among street driving behavior including practices with respect to speed, braking, steering, and turns, background variables and history of accidents and violations, perception and motor skills, and simulator measures.

The investigators reported favorably on the techniques for measuring street driving performance, although they concluded that ride-reride reliability needs to be further determined. The study failed to show any significant correlation with on-street measures for component or total scores on either of the driver simulator-trainers. There was also lack of positive relationship between scores on the two simulators designated as measuring the same driving functions. The perceptual motor tests did not predict on-street driving performance.

A novel approach to the study of the driver's perceptual behavior on the road has been developed under Dr. Thomas H. Rockwell's leadership in the Driving Research Laboratory, Department of Industrial Engineering, the Ohio State University. The experiments studied differences between new and experienced drivers with respect to eye-movement patterns under various driving conditions—open-road driving at 50 and 70 miles per hour—and car-following at various speeds and with long and short headway. Zell, the Ohio State University investigator for this particular experiment, was concerned with the eye as the major source of information the driver acquires concerning the speed of his vehicle, its position on the highway, and its relation to other vehicles (Zell, 1969). His work is a challenge to slogans such as "aim high," or "keep your eyes moving," that have become standard text in many driver training courses—a challenge not because such slogans are necessarily misleading but because they have not rested on empirical findings. It has not as yet been determined that such principles are consistent with the manner in which the "good" driver seeks visual information about his driving environment.

Using an eye-movement recording device linked to a television camera, Zell compared driver eye movements of four new drivers from the time they began driving until after they had received their permanent driver's licenses. Two experienced drivers were studied to provide a norm. Greater differences between novice and experienced drivers were noted in open-road driving than in car-following, a result suggesting that the hazard of a car just ahead forced all drivers to spend more time keeping an eye on the lead car. During the first few months of driving, the new drivers came to fixate less on the right edge of the highway. They still spent more time than the experienced drivers fixating straight ahead and scanning the surrounding visual field. They used their rear mirrors less frequently. They showed less tendency to seek information at varying distances in front of their car when altering the speed of their vehicle. Rate and duration of fixations did not change much during the apprentice period. These results represent trends for four drivers. It was also clear from Zell's individual analyses that the new drivers varied in the method they adopted to obtain more and more information on road and traffic conditions as part of the driving process. Zell suggests that automatic data reduction would make feasible the use of larger samples and larger amounts of data.

Studies such as this bear upon broad aspects of the motor vehicle safety problem—driver education, traffic conditions, stages in acquiring driving skills beyond the minimum required for a license—and highway and road design to make the traffic bed more compatible with human vision capabilities and limitations.

The studies conducted under the direction of Dr. Rockwell at the Ohio State University represent the broader look and model formulation we consider to be the most productive approach. Instrumented vehicles were used to study variability in the performance of both professional and nonprofessional drivers. A model was evolved to explain the driver variability observed, based on the concept of a threshold (Rockwell and Snider, 1965). According to this hypothesis, the driver has a definite sensory threshold for each type of information he uses in controlling the vehicle. When he senses an adverse condition, he controls his vehicle through an appropriate action to suppress or "null out" the condition. In the case of speed, for example, the driver makes corrective changes based on his direct sensing of the difference between the actual and the desired vehicle speed. Rockwell and his associates have applied this "threshold control" model in studying velocity sensing, velocity change detection, acceleration detection, and headway change detection.

From the point of view of these investigators and of the current authors, improvement in motor vehicle operation can best be attained through application of a variety of efforts that include selection and assignment programs, driver training (initial and remedial), human engineering of vehicle and roadway, and management factors such as the organization of the motor vehicle facility, its supervision, and the traffic system. These subsystems have to be viewed as they interact to promote the objectives of the military operation.

CURRENT DEVELOPMENTS

The serious researcher in traffic safety today looking to means of achieving gains in traffic safety sees some avenues less fruitful of meaningful gains and others more promising. He has been compelled by weight of evidence to recognize that limited improvement can be expected from civilian driver licensing programs, particularly when he considers the economic and social impact. In the military sector, however, as among such professional drivers as taximen, truck drivers, and bus drivers, a valid selection procedure (with a validity coefficient of, say, 0.40) can be practically effective in licensing and screening. Where many apply but few are chosen, selection tests have limited, but some, potential. The authors of this chapter have looked at other elements in the traffic system and find that appreciable gains are not likely to be forthcoming through research studies of individual components of the system unless a sophisticated methodology is employed in setting meaningful priorities.

Current direction believed profitable by the authors is toward application of systems psychology methodology to more comprehensive relationships of men and machines—in this case the motor vehicle—within their total environment. As systems-oriented research scientists, we must first look at the kinds and amounts of outputs desired. We can, for example, project the kinds of individuals likely to drive, design equipment and organization, and tailor functions so as to be within the capabilities of the target group of individuals. We can develop programs, devices, aids, to assist in training such individuals. We can systematically evaluate varied driving methods in varying environments.

The complexity of this kind of research effort requires a variety of research methods, including simulation, laboratory experimentation, and field research on an iterative basis. In this problem area, the systems psychological approach is thought to contribute most to the setting of research priorities, and ultimately to products of maximum practical applicability.

One of the most encouraging signs of progress in recent years is the interest and willingness of investigators to examine the problem from a systems point of view. The military man and his weapon (whether simple or complex) and the environment in which he performs his assigned duties are viewed as a manned weapons system. In like manner, the driving process can be considered a man-machine system. Malfunction of this system can occur because of poorly designed and maintained vehicles, poor roads, poorly controlled traffic patterns, or poor driving —or some general environmental condition interacting with one or all of these.

If it can be shown that improvement in any one element of the motor vehicle traffic complex can be expected to yield only slight gain in total performance, studies planned would seem to call for an approach that would deal with the various elements as they contribute to whatever is decided upon as the desired objective. The objective may be safety— the reduction of accidents. It may be efficient transportation. It may be a specified mix of safety and efficiency. D. L. Cooper and R. J. Walinchus of the TRW Systems Group, Houston, Texas, in a paper presented at the 49th Annual Meeting of the Highway Research Board in January 1970, described the evaluation of an urban traffic control system in terms of meeting objectives of (1) maximization of service, (2) optimization of quality of service, and (3) minimization of cost—no explicit mention of safety there.

To illustrate the steps taken in systems psychology methodology, we start with the development of a *systems measurement bed* with built-in weights on objectives established by the organization, military or civilian, responsible for the traffic program. The measurement bed is used to evaluate the adequacy of system performance. A first requirement is a firm understanding of goals and specified desired outcomes. Inputs in such a systems measurement bed reflect the vehicles, the drivers, their preparation and requirements, and driving situations of the kind the user deals with. It provides the structure for formulating and examining hypotheses that need verification and the basis for setting priorities for problems to be attacked intensively.

Next comes a critical examination of the body of theory and knowledge that has accumulated over many years for indications as to which factors appear most likely to affect measurably and meaningfully the output of the system. The aim is to find how much difference each factor makes in the total result in order to establish priorities for further research. The measurement bed is exercised in order to fasten upon the hypotheses that offer the most opportunity for gain—as a means to economy of effort, if you will, whereby time, resources, and lives, can be saved.

Illustrative of factors that should be examined critically in building the driving systems measurement bed are:

Individual differences before driver training.
Individual differences after driver training.

Kind and amount of driver training provided.
Relevant experience before driver training.
Driver experience after training.
Effect of human engineering products.
Environment in which the vehicle is operated.
Differences in control of traffic flow, laws, enforcement procedures.
Alcohol, drugs, fatigue and other influences modifying behavior and judgment.

As relationships are established, research priorities can be modified. Unproductive avenues can be eliminated or given the amount of attention dictated by their contribution to the desired outcome. Likely trade-offs can be clarified through study of conditions or situations that can compensate for inadequacies of driving skill or judgment. Human engineering products can be identified as related to safe or efficient operation or to comfort or appearance. Traffic patterns can be designed to compensate for driver and equipment inadequacies.

Application of the systems concept and methodology to motor vehicle operation would require a huge effort and expenditure of resources. But the lesson of past efforts, productive as they have been of a vast store of knowledge, is that anything less than a holistic attack on the problem would yield very little gain in the safety or efficiency of operation in the complex of motor vehicle systems.

REFERENCES

Armstrong, H. G., Accidents Rank Number 1 in the Air Force as Cause of Death. *U.S. Air Force Medical Service Digest,* 4 (1953).

DeSilva, H. R. and Robinson, P., Some Psychological Factors in Accident Repeater Drivers, *Journal of Abnormal and Social Psychology,* 34 (1939), 124–128.

Edgerton, Harold A. (RBH), Personnel Management Factors in Vehicle Safety, *BESRL Technical Research Report 911,* May 1951.

Edwards, Dorothy S., Hahn, Clifford P., and Fleishman, Edwin A., Evaluation of Laboratory Methods for the Study of Driver Behavior: The Relation Between Simulator and Street Performance, American Institutes for Research, Washington, D.C., May 1969.

Goldstein, L. G., Van Steenberg, N. J., and Birnbaum, A. H., Evaluation of Instruments to Select Safe Drivers, *BESRL Technical Research Report 962,* July 1952.

McFarland, R. A., Human Variables in the Design and Operation of Highway Transport Equipment, Preprint 717, Society of Automotive Engineers, New York, 1952.

McFarland, Ross A., Human Variables in Motor Vehicle Accidents, a Review of the Literature, Harvard School of Public Health, Boston, Mass., 1955.

Military Police, Section I. para 3, DSAR 5720.1, AR 190-5, OPNAVINST 11200.5, AFR 125-14, MCO 5110.1 Military Police: Motor Vehicle Traffic Supervision,

20 December 1962.
National Safety Council, *Accident Facts,* National Safety Council, Chicago, Ill., 1969.
Rockwell, Thomas H. and Snider, John N., An Investigation of Variability in Driving Performance on the Highway, Systems Research Group, Department of Industrial Engineering, The Ohio State University, Columbus, Ohio, September 1965.
Thorndike, R. L., Human Factors in Accidents, American Institute(s) for Research, Pittsburgh, Pa., 1950.
Uhlaner, J. E., Tests for Selecting Drivers, presented at meeting of the Eastern Psychological Association, March 1956.
Uhlaner, J. E. and Drucker, A. J., Selection Tests—Dubious Aid in Driver Licensing, *Highway Research Record,* **84** (1965), 51–53.
Uhlaner, J. E., Van Steenberg, N. J., and Goldstein, L. G., The Construction of Experimental Group Tests for the Prediction of Safe Driving, *BESRL Research Memorandum 51-40,* 1951.
Uhlaner, J. E., Van Steenberg, N. J., and Goldstein, L. G., Development of Criteria of Safe Motor Vehicle Operation, *Highway Research Board Bulletin* **60** (1952), 1–16.
U.S. Air Force, *Air Force Manual* AFM 35-8, Military Personnel: Air Force Military Personnel Testing Manual, 7 May 1968.
U.S. Air Force, AF Regulation 50-24, Training: Traffic Safety Education, 27 August 1969.
U.S. Department of the Army, Deputy Chief of Staff for Personnel, Safety Division, Department of the Army, U.S. Army Safety Program Annual Report for Fiscal Year 1969.
U.S. Department of the Navy, Injuries and Deaths Due to Motor Vehicle Accidents. Navy and Marine Corps, 1953, Medical Statistics Division, Bureau of Medicine and Surgery, Department of the Navy, Washington, D.C., 1954.
Zell, John K., Driver eye movements as a function of driving experience, Technical Report 1E-16, Engineering Experiment Station, The Ohio State University, Columbus, Ohio, June 1969.

IX

HUMAN FACTORS IN VEHICLE DESIGN

Rudolf Mortimer

Rudolf G. Mortimer is research psychologist at the Highway Safety Research Institute, University of Michigan. He received a Ph.D. from Purdue University, and his B.A. and M.A. from New York University.

He has carried out research in vehicle headlighting, rear lighting and signaling, and vehicle ride while employed as a senior research psychologist at the Research Laboratories, General Motors Corporation. At HSRI he has conducted research in vehicle lighting, braking and handling, driver eye movements, rear visibility, and alcoholism as related to traffic safety.

He is a member of the American Psychological Association, Human Factors Society, Ergonomics Research Society, and the American Association for Automotive Medicine.

Drivers of motor vehicles have anthropometric, sensory, perceptual, motor, judgmental, and other attributes that need to be considered by vehicle designers in order to provide compatible vehicular characteristics. This cannot be done out of the context of the overall highway system in which the vehicle operates. The geometry of roads, the location of traffic controls and signs, and the variety of driving environments are some factors affecting the performance of the driver and the design of the vehicle. In addition, social, aesthetic, legal,* economic and collision protection considerations influence the vehicle design, but are not included in this discussion. This chapter emphasizes knowledge, practice

* The U.S. Motor Vehicle Safety Standards relevant to pre-crash safety are shown in Table 4.

and research in the driver-vehicle system for improved performance and safer transportation.

ANTHROPOMETRY

Information concerned with limb dimensions, movement, and force capabilities of males and females is summarized by Damon, Stoudt, and McFarland (1966) and for the United States civilian population by Stoudt et al. (1965). The correlations among anthropometric variables are low (Hertzberg, 1966) so that the "average man" physically (Kyropoulos and Roe, 1968) does not exist any more than he does psychologically, complicating the layout of the driving compartment.

The Driver's Workspace

The design of the driver's workspace normally proceeds from his seated location. The H-point, approximately the hip joint, is a driver reference used with two manikins (SAE J-826, 1962). The two-dimensional manikin is intended to be laid over full-scale drawings during design.

The three-dimensional manikin is used to evaluate a mock-up or actual vehicle. The device is made of metal and plastic to represent the stature and weight distribution of a 50th percentile male. When the manikin is in place on the seat, it is possible to determine the spatial location of the H-point, which can then serve as a frame of reference for other relationships between the occupant and the vehicle structure. The important angular relations of the body, such as the back, thigh, knee, and foot angles, can be read from the device. Driver anthropometric data can then be used to locate control and display surfaces and determine seating adjustments.

Seat Dimensions

Based on the anthropometrics of the European driving population, Black (1966) recommended the "driving chair" to have the following dimensions: seat height, 16 inches; pad depth, 17.5 inches; pad angle, 6 degrees; back height, 20 inches; pad back angle, 105 degrees. Damon et al. (1962) suggest the following: seat height, 10–14.5 inches; seat pan depth, 18 inches; seat pan angle, 7 degrees downward slope from fore to aft; seat back height, 18–21 inches; seat back width, 20 inches; seat pan width, 18 inches; seat back angle, 112 degrees; and a fore and aft adjustment of about 8 inches, with a vertical height adjustment of about 4.5 inches. These recommendations are based on dimensions of the

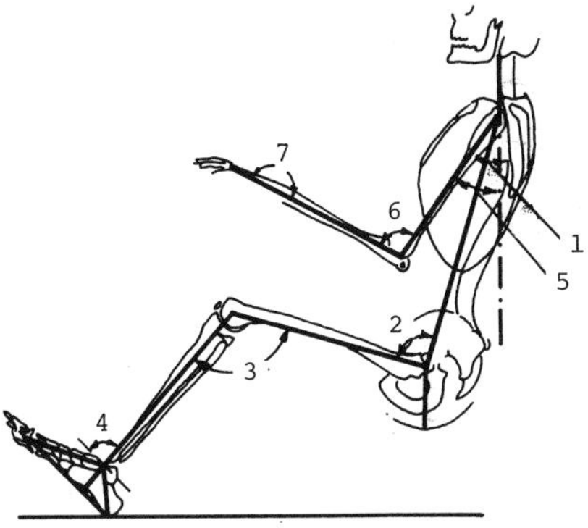

Figure 1. Important joint angles affecting comfort. (From R. Rebiffé, *Proceedings: Institute of Mechanical Engineers* [London], 1966.)

United States civilian population and are similar to those proposed by Black (1966).

Seat Comfort, Health, Performance Effects

The comfort of the seated operator depends to a great extent on the inclination angles of the various joints of the body (Figure 1; Rebiffé, 1966). The comfort limits of these angles are indicated in Table 1. An actual driver package is shown in Figure 2 for the 1965 Ford Mustang

Table 1 Joint Comfort Angles[a]

$20° < 1 < 30°$
$95° < 2 < 120°$
$95° < 3 < 135°$
$90° < 4 < 110°$
10°[b]– $20° < 5 < 45°$[c]
$80° < 6 < 120°$
$170° < 7 < 190°$

[a] Refers to angles shown in Figure 1.
[b] Depending on seat back.
[c] With hand supported.
Source: Rebiffé, 1966.

(Olsen, 1965). Most of the joint angles are close to the comfort recommendations made by Rebiffé.

Wachsler and Learner (1961) found that ratings of seat comfort after five minutes of sitting are as reliable as those obtained after four or

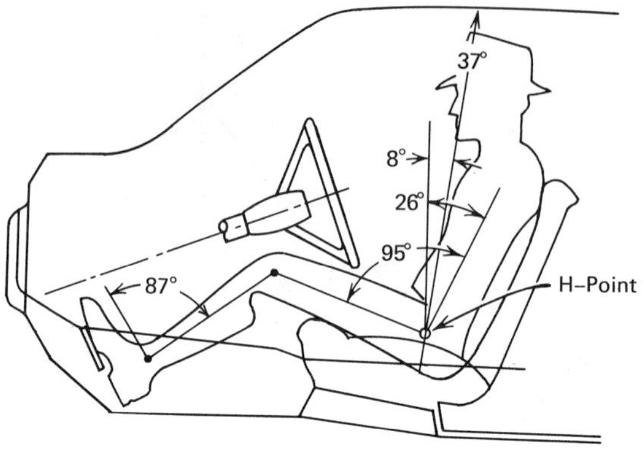

Figure 2. Driver package: 1965 Ford Mustang. (From F. G. Olsen, Society of Automotive Engineers, Rept. 650463, 1965.)

more hours; and that overall seat comfort is rated principally on the basis of sensations produced in the back and buttocks. Rieck (1969) reported that subjective feelings of comfort did not correlate with the number of movements made per unit time while sitting. Thus, fidgeting was not related to discomfort.

A method of "fitting trials" developed by Jones (1961) was used by Dutch (1965) to obtain comfort-distance relationships for seats and controls. For example, car seat heights may be systematically raised or lowered in 1-inch increments, after each of which the subject is asked to rotate the steering wheel 180 degrees and to indicate whether or not the movement could be executed in comfort. In this way the maximum and minimum seat heights that are rated as being just within the comfort range can be obtained, and the midpoint of this range approximately defines, for that particular individual, an optimum comfort distance. Ascending and descending trials are run as in the conventional method of limits. Using this technique Dutch (1965) found values for a number of seat dimensions that would fit 98 percent of British males and females. Jones (1969) found the results to agree with earlier recommendations made by Domey and McFarland (1963).

INFORMATION DISPLAY

Automotive displays provide vehicle-state cues such as the speed, or feedback to the driver of his own actions such as turn signal operation. Displays are provided for: (1) check, (2) qualitative, and (3) quantitative reading.

Figure 3. Variation in passenger car displays.

Currently Used Displays and Their Design

Speedometers have either a round or horizontal scale with a moving pointer. Odometers are counters indicating to the nearest mile or tenth of a mile. The other principal display found in all vehicles is the fuel level indicator. Other displays, some of which are now mandatory, are for level of brake fluid, headlamp beam, turn and hazard warning signal, engine indicators, and so forth. Display configurations vary widely (Figure 3).

BASIC DESIGN FACTORS

The nature of the display will be influenced by its function. Check-indicating, warning light/sound, displays are those used to monitor system malfunctions to which the driver's attention should be rapidly drawn, and to indicate normal or abnormal operation of other systems.

Qualitative displays are suitable for use where precise indication of a value being measured is not essential, it being desired only to indicate the approximate operating range of a particular component. It is good practice to indicate acceptable operating conditions in the same way in each gauge and to locate them in clusters to facilitate rapid reading.

The speedometer is the only safety-related display that warrants quantitative reading. Since speed limits are generally in 5-mph increments, the speedometer should be designed to provide drivers with reading accuracy to these limits. Dials should be graduated in 1, 2, 5, or multiples of 10 scale values (Loucks, 1944; Morgan et al., 1963). Speedometers should be calibrated with principal scale markers at every 10 mph and with scale units at every 5 mph. Current practice seems to use this rule. A number of speed display designs may be used, including circular and horizontal scales with moving pointers and the open-window, moving-scale type that has been found to be highly effective for rapid and precise reading (Sleight, 1948). Digital instruments may also be suitable (Grether, 1949).

Sensory Modes

Because the primary information processing task involved in vehicle control depends on visual inputs, it would be expedient to provide secondary information, such as that provided by the in-vehicle instrumentation, by other sensory modes whenever possible. Auditory and tactile stimuli may be suitable. Certain warning displays may best be presented auditorily.

Drivers carry out instrument-reading tasks on a selective, self-paced basis with other tasks and, therefore, the use of many qualitative or quantitative displays in the vehicle may not be detrimental under most situations. This question, however, should be evaluated by research upon the effects of various forms of instrumentation displays on the driver's time-sharing behavior. An early study by Fitts and Jones (1947) was concerned with this type of behavior in aviation. Similar studies should be conducted in automobiles to evaluate instrumentation format, design, location, and spacing.

Instrument Legibility

There is a great deal of information available concerning the effects on instrument legibility of instrument size, legend stroke and width relationships, major and minor scale markers, numbering of scale markers, and so on, and can be readily obtained from human engineering data sources (Morgan et al., 1963; McCormick, 1964).

Instruments that are recessed into the panel are reduced in illumination in daytime, which may cause difficulty in reading them. Adequate contrast ratios must be used between scale markers, their background, and the pointer. Design ground rules for these contrast ratios need to be developed by analysis and research.

Panel Layout

The layout of instrument panels is dependent on the frequency of use and importance, the visual and other sensory mode constraints of drivers, and impact protection. Some displays are utilized when the vehicle is in motion and others when it is at a standstill. For example, the speedometer is important only when the vehicle is moving, whereas an indicator showing that the parking brake is applied should be prominent when the vehicle is at a standstill.

Warning/check lights should be color coded and located close to the driver's line of forward vision. Red should be reserved for vehicle malfunctions that require immediate attention, such as loss of brake line pressure. Amber should be used for less serious conditions, such as generator malfunction; and green-blue for driver-actuated control feedback, such as the headlight beam indicator. It would be expected that color coding using driver stereotypes would be readily learned.

A general rule regarding the location of displays is to group together the ones that indicate similar functions, such as engine condition (oil pressure, oil temperature, water temperature) or vehicle velocity (speedometer, tachometer). Much information is already available for design and location of displays and is interpreted in a recent report by Woodson et al., (1969).

Head-Up Displays

A relatively new aviation concept applicable to motor vehicles utilizes the projection of displays onto the windshield to reduce reading time. Research is required to determine the characteristics of such a display that are compatible with other aspects of driving.

VEHICLE CONTROLS

The primary vehicle controls are the steering wheel, throttle (accelerator), and brake. Secondary controls, which are not used to modulate vehicle motion, consist of the transmission selector, parking brake, radio and heater controls, seat adjusters, window cranks, light switches, and the like.

Energetic and Informational Properties of Controls

A distinction has been made by Black (1966) between the energetic, force-displacement properties of a control and the informational, feedback characteristics.

The energetic properties of a control relate to the amount and direction of force and displacement required to operate it. The forces must be within the limitations of the driving population. The energy expenditure required to operate a control depends on the direction of motion, the size and shape of the control surface, the limbs with which it is operated, the location relative to the body, the speed demands of successful operation, and the displacement. Therefore, control design must take into account the dexterity of the operator, reach, and force capability. Automotive controls are designed for operation by either one hand or both, or by the feet, usually one foot at a time. For example, the throttle must provide a comfortable position for the foot to allow the driver to maintain a fixed setting in turnpike cruising, and for controlled modulation of speed in dense traffic or winding roads. The throttle should be located so that, in its undeflected position, the ankle angle is approximately 90 degrees. Foot support is obtained by a restoring force of 6.5 to 9 pounds (Dupuis, 1957; Chaillet, 1966; Morgan et al., 1963). Studies concerned with response time, effort, and accuracy recommend that the pedal should rotate about a point at the heel of the foot (Barnes et al., 1942; Trumbo and Schneider, 1963; Ensdorff, 1964). Maximum angular displacement of the pedal should be about 20 degrees (Dupuis, 1957; Chaillet, 1966) and the extent of the displacement at the ball of the foot should be 1.5 to 2 inches (Dupuis, 1957; Chaillet, 1966; Morgan et al., 1963). Further data would be useful of desirable relations between pedal displacement and vehicle performance.

Data for the location and dimensions of the clutch and service brake pedal were derived in an HSRI (1967) report. The principal difference between these controls lies in the relative duration for which they are used and the safety implications.

A study by Stoudt et al. (1969) measured brake pedal force and steering wheel torque for females seated on a car seat. Mortimer and Segel (1970) measured foot force for females and males. They used a hard seat and obtained the cumulative percentage distributions of maximum force shown in Figure 4, for the first trial with the right foot. The 5th percentile female was capable of exerting only about 70 pounds while the corresponding figure for males was 140 pounds. On a second trial, with exhortation by the experimenters, these values increased by about 30 pounds. The data are valuable for design of foot-operated controls, such as the service brake.

Control Location Factors

Control location is affected by the reach of drivers and their ability to apply forces and torques in specific locations. Some controls are used when the vehicle is at a standstill and others when it is in motion. Therefore, other aspects of driving, with which a particular control operation must be shared, have to be considered. In addition, there may be other controls that interfere with adequate reach, grasp, or force exertion upon a specific control. Thus, overall control layout must be taken into account and the design may not proceed successfully on the basis of the requirements of an individual control. Standardization of location is desirable to allow control positions to be learned and minimize operation time.

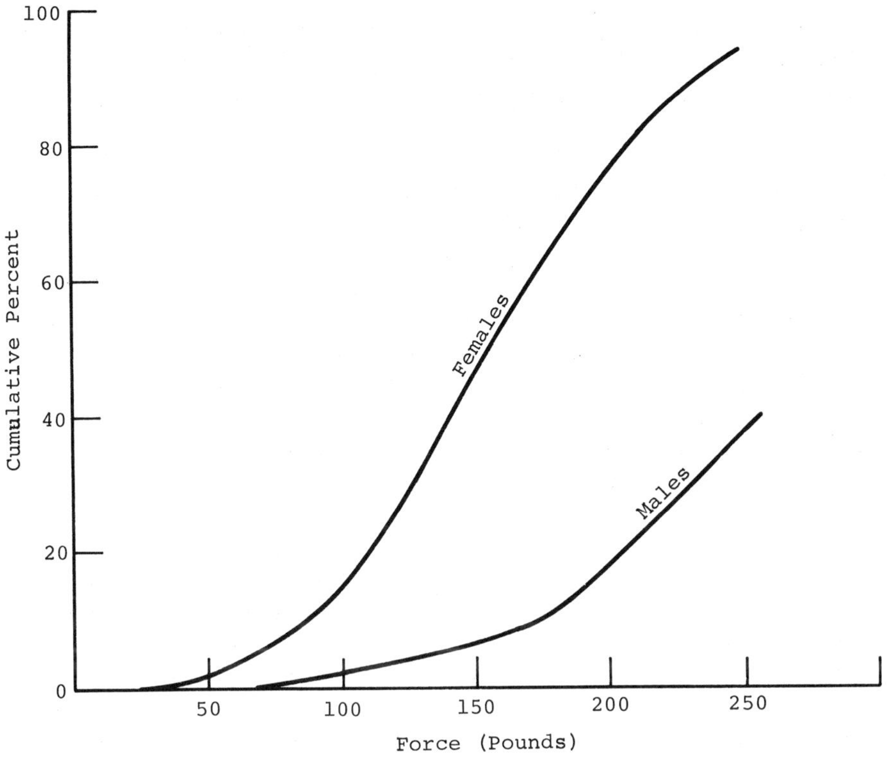

Figure 4. Cumulative maximum foot force distribution for male and female drivers. (From R. G. Mortimer and L. Segel, U.S. Dept. of Transportation, Final Rept., Contract FH-11-6952, 1970.)

Secondary-Control Coding

The informational property of a control is enhanced by visual and kinesthetic coding techniques. In addition, numerous controls are linked to displays and must be considered with them to optimize control-display relationships. All controls should have various types of coding to accomplish different objectives.

Control function should be readily identified by drivers. Standardization of location should not be relied on as the only code for control identification. Controls should be labeled either by symbol or legend. Shape coding could also be used. Control coding also refers to indicating the status of a particular control during and after manipulation. A common technique used to accomplish this during manipulation is the use of detents in rotary or push-pull controls. However, following activation the status of some types of controls (e.g., push-pull light switches) is difficult to identify. Pointers, signal lights, and other methods should be used for monitoring the status of safety-related secondary controls.

Primary-Control Feedback Modes

Steering wheel displacement and torque provide cues which the driver reevaluates by the motion of the vehicle. Similarly, braking is modulated by foot force and displacement which, once a model of the vehicle response is learned, results in accurate brake deceleration (Spurr, 1965). This is the precognitive, open-loop aspect of driver behavior which, with the feed forward element of pursuit control (Weir and McRuer, 1968) contributes to stable steering and braking output. Kinesthetic cues are initially used in control operation with loop closure obtained by visual, vestibular, kinesthetic, and proprioceptive cues resulting from vehicle motion.

Control Gain

The relationship between the control inputs of the driver and the dynamic response of the vehicle is important for safe vehicle operation. The psychophysical parameters have not been clearly defined for the steering (lateral) control or the throttle and brake (longitudinal) controls, and are discussed later. The input-output relationships for secondary controls are much simpler. Their operation hinges principally upon the requirement that they do not exceed the force limitations of the operator.

VISIBILITY

Visibility depends on the absence of obstructions caused by the vehicle structure and other occupants, and the position of the eyes of the driver in the vehicle.

A study of the location of drivers' eyes based upon a sample of thirty seated, male drivers was carried out by the Road Research Laboratory in England (1963). It was found that 95 percent of the eyes of these drivers were located in a rectangle having a length of 7 inches and a height of 4 inches. These differences in eye location can have a drastic effect on the driver's field of view. A tall driver may have visibility upward curtailed by the upper edge of the windshield as well as by obstructions caused by the rearview mirror; while the short driver may have good visibility upward, in which important signals such as traffic lights are located, with forward visibility impeded by the steering wheel and the hood.

An extensive study was carried out in the United States (Meldrum, 1965) in which 2300 drivers were randomly chosen, seated in three standard vehicles, and photographed from the front and side. The frequency of eye locations was described by the "eyellipse," which is used in design to ascertain driver eye locations (SAE J-941, 1965).

When a vehicle mock-up is available it is desirable to measure the visibility. General Motors Corporation (1968) uses a panoramic camera to evaluate forward visibility, and the windshield-wiped area. Rear visibility of mirrors is evaluated by positioning two high-intensity bulbs at the eye positions of drivers. The light is reflected in rearview mirrors illuminating a graduated screen behind the car from which the field of view is obtained.

Visibility Requirements

It is difficult to state what the extent of the driver's visual field should be, if not 360 degrees. One way by which it could be estimated is on the basis of simple analyses of driving in compliance with roadway geometry, the avoidance of objects such as pedestrians and other vehicles, and information gathering from road signs and traffic signals. Experimental methods are also needed. There are no data available showing the effects on accidents of changes in drivers' visual fields.

Visual Cues for Steering Control

Gordon (1966) utilized a head-mounted camera aligned with a small tube in front of one of the driver's eyes, the other eye being covered. The driver steered the car along a slightly winding road. The film record showed that drivers utilized the edges of the road and the center line as principal cues for vehicle control.

These data have since been extended by recording eye fixations by corneal reflection techniques with superimposition of the eye movements upon the roadway scene. Data have been obtained (Rockwell, 1968) of the frequency and time durations of fixations on various aspects of the road, signs, traffic signals, and other vehicles. An attempt has also been made (Kondo and Ajimine, 1968) to measure the driver's visual inputs for tracking and to establish relationships with vehicle dynamic response.

The studies carried out by Rockwell (1968) and Gordon (1966) were concerned mostly with the use of foveal vision. Foveal vision is essential to predict required inputs of steering, acceleration, or braking for collision avoidance and tracking. The importance of preview can be determined both experimentally (Sheridan, 1967) and by analytical considerations based on vehicle speed and driver perceptual-motor response lags. It is hypothesized that preview information obtained by central vision seeks out the vehicle heading and path angle and their derivatives (McRuer and Weir, 1969). Peripheral vision was reported to be used in locating the vehicle in the lane (Mortimer, 1967), although Fry (1967) feels that perspective cues are most important for lane placement. A study by Senders (1967), using a moveable vizor over the eyes, has shown that drivers sample visual information at intervals and durations dependent upon the criticality of the driving condition, and showed that there is a great deal of redundancy in normal driving. It is obvious that redundancy decreases markedly when the potential for an accident or loss of control becomes great. The fact that Senders was able to obscure vision of his subjects for significant proportions of the driving time also shows the value of kinesthetic, vestibular, and proprioceptive cues for vehicle steering.

In steering it is probable that drivers use the vehicle structure as a frame of reference. It is interesting to speculate, therefore, whether drivers of vehicles that provide reduced hood reference cues, such as van types and cab-over-engine trucks, may be at a disadvantage in some driving maneuvers. There is some indication (Kao and Nagamachi, 1968) that the hood provides a reference for slow-speed maneuvering, but it is questionable that it plays a significant role at highway speeds. For this reason it may be supposed that a main source of vehicle reference is provided by windshield pillars and other vehicle structures within the driver's peripheral field of view. Furthermore, the driver may have a learned frame of reference of his orientation within the vehicle, determined by his posture in the driving seat, by which he can detect headway and course angles.

Steering is a similar task to tracking in walking. During walking the human is continually monitoring his location and requires preview in order to avoid obstacles and to stay on course. Since it may be simpler to carry out initial investigations to determine how people track in walking, it may be fruitful to study the cues used in this task before tackling the more complex instrumentation problem encountered in carrying out analogous research in driving.

Obstructions in the Forward Field

Obstructions 180 degrees to the front of the driver should not obscure visibility of important objects in the forward field of view or impair the ability of the driver to carry out certan maneuvers, such as turning through large angles. The principal obstructions are passengers, the interior mirror, vent panes, and windshield pillars.

The windshield pillar should not be so wide that it produces a zone in which visibility is obscured to both eyes. Pillar obscuration in European small- and medium-sized cars was about 6 degrees and in large cars 3 degrees (Road Research Laboratory, 1963). The difference is probably mostly attributable to the distance of the pillar from the eyellipse. This matter is dealt with in detail by Devlin and Roe (1968) who show the extent of pillar obscuration as a function of pillar location and pillar-eye distance. The data are shown in Figure 5, which is based upon an average interpupillary distance of 2.5 inches. Other obstructions can be treated in a similar way.

Windshield Characteristics

In modern vehicles the trend has been toward increased inclination of the windshield from the vertical. This increases refractive errors, reduces transmission, and increases reflections from inside the vehicle, particularly at night. Tinted windshields have been found to cause small reduc-

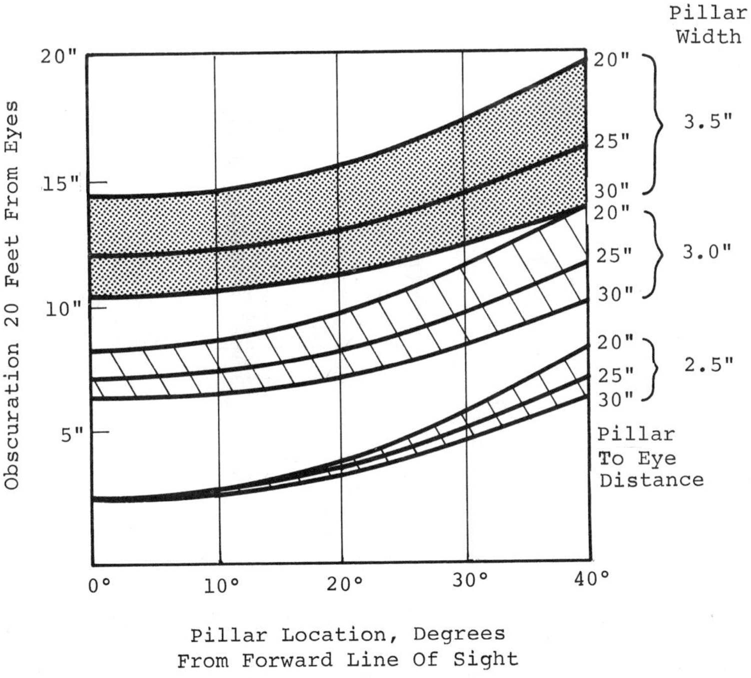

Figure 5. The magnitude of pillar obscuration affected by pillar location, width, and distance from the driver's eyes. (From W. A. Devlin and R. W. Roe, Society of Automotive Engineers, Rept. 680105, 1968.)

tions in night visibility (Doane and Rassweiler, 1955; Blackwell, 1954). The selective spectral transmission of tinted windshields may also impair identification of vehicle taillights, traffic signals, and other colored lights.

Rear Visibility Requirements

The rear visual field can be defined as 180 degrees to the back of the driver. Federal Motor Vehicle Safety Standard-111, "Rear View Mirrors," calls for two mirrors on United States automobiles. The inside rearview mirror must provide a horizontal field of view of not less than 20 degrees and a vertical angle sufficient to provide a view of the road not further than 200 feet behind the vehicle and continuing to the horizon. The outside rearview mirror, on the driver's side, should provide a horizontal field of 10 degrees (SAE J-834, 1967). These minimum standards are shown in Figure 6 for a fixed driver head position (Devlin and Pajas, 1968; Marcus, 1968). Blind areas exist on the right and left side in which a car or motorcycle may be hidden. This condition is particularly hazardous for lane changing and passing. Kelley and Prosin (1969) measured eye fixations of drivers using a wide-angle, experimental mirror. They concluded that 100 degrees of rear visibility are needed.

It is possible to increase the rear field of view by using a convex mirror, by increasing mirror size, and by locating the mirror close to the driver's eyes. Walraven and Michon (1969) found that mirrors

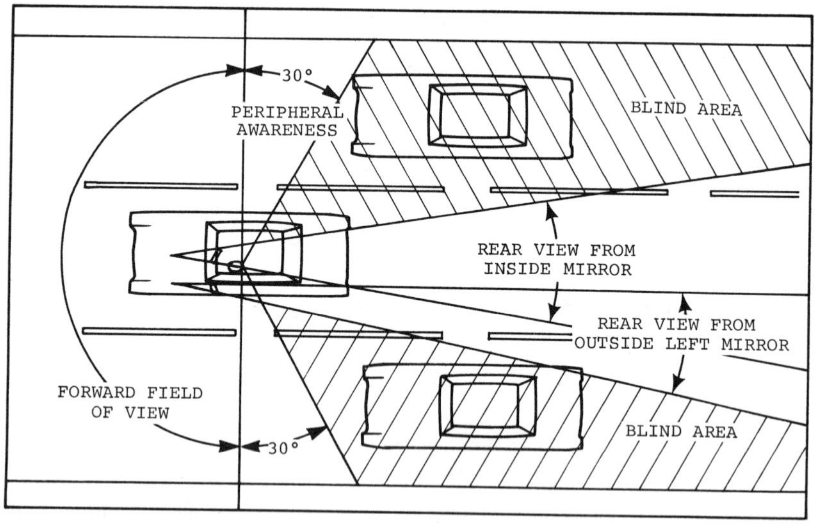

Figure 6. Blind spots in rear visibility. (Adapted from W. A. Devlin and M. R. Pajas, and K. H. Marcus, Society of Automotive Engineers, Repts. 680106 and 680404, 1968.)

located less than 30 degrees from the forward line of sight provide improved detection of signals given to the rear of the vehicle. The study was concerned with the location of exterior mirrors, but similar findings have been reported for the interior mirror (Morrow and Salik, 1962). However, a plane exterior mirror located at 30 degrees or less from the forward line of sight would have to be mounted on the fenders of American automobiles and, therefore, would probably be a considerable distance away from the eyes of the driver. Since a large eye-mirror distance reduces the visual field, practice in the United States is to place the outside mirror on the driver's door. However, such a location requires eye and head rotation to utilize the mirror, which diverts the driver's attention from the forward field of view.

In order to obtain the same or a larger visual field than at present, from a plane mirror mounted on the fenders, will require that the mirror be 9 to 12 inches wide, dependent upon the distance from the driver's eyes. This could obstruct forward visibility. A solution is to use a convex mirror, which provides a virtual image between the mirror and its center of curvature (Sears, 1949). Thus, if a convex mirror with small radius of curvature is close to the driver's eyes, he will need to accommodate to the image. Mean accommodation time has been found to be 0.11 to 0.15 seconds for young and old observers, respectively (Jani and Menzes, 1962), in a test using a 41-inch radius convex mirror positioned 19 inches from the eyes. Such a short distance would not be used for outside convex mirrors mounted on vehicle fenders and, therefore, accommodation times would be lower.

Convex mirrors minify the image of the object in such a way that size constancy may incline drivers to underestimate the distance of objects seen as images in the mirror. This is particularly true for radii less than 30 inches (Hanson et al., 1969; Walraven and Michon, 1969).

Convex mirrors have been used in some European countries for a number of years and offer the most immediately practical means of enlarging the rear field of view. It is important to learn more about the ability of drivers to use such a mirror in passing and lane changing. One study (Mortimer, 1969a) found that drivers could safely change lanes with left and right, fender-mounted convex mirrors of 30 inches and 48 inches radius, and they reached earlier decisions than by using a plane mirror of the same size in the same location. Walraven and Michon (1969) found that drivers with no previous experience with convex mirrors made more conservative lane change judgments with exterior mirrors of 24-inch and 48-inch radius than with a plane mirror. Drivers who had used convex mirrors before made the same lane change judgments with plane and convex mirrors. These data suggest that convex mirrors may be suitable. Ultimately, it may be possible to develop wide-angle periscopic mirror systems (Marcus, 1968), which could be the most effective solution (Kelley and Proslin, 1969) to the rear visibility problem.

Consideration also needs to be given to the reflective properties of mirrors for adequate visibility and to minimize glare effects at night. Some data (Mortimer, 1969a) show that subjects rated plane mirrors of up to 40 percent reflectance as not causing unacceptable glare by reflection of low-beam headlights. Therefore, the use of 4 percent reflectivity for the "night" position of day-night mirrors is lower than necessary.

VISIBILITY AND TRAFFIC ACCIDENTS

A recent study (Barnoski et al., 1969) attempted to establish a relationship between fields of view from motor vehicles and safety. The required visual field was derived by analysis of driving situations and target locations. Estimates were made of the relative importance of sectors in the driver's visual field on the basis of the frequency per mile with which targets (e.g., pedestrians, other vehicles) occur in each sector and the probability and severity of accidents with each type of target. It was reported that the forward field of 180 degrees of visibility was 90 percent of the required field. A zone of 50 feet about the driver accounted for 57 percent of the required visibility, and 21 percent were in the front and rear $\pm$ 8 degrees azimuth, respectively.

VEHICLE LIGHTING

Vehicle lighting has two major components: display lighting and lighting for illumination, marking, and signaling.

Display Lighting

Warning lights must be visible in daytime and at night. In daytime they can be shrouded from direct sunlight but may require intensities that are too bright for use at night. At night the driver's visual adaptation level is determined by the moonlight, street lighting, and the light returned from headlights. In these conditions the driver will be adapted to about 0.1 to 4 foot-lamberts (Schmidt, 1961). At these levels instrumentation lighting need not be very intense. It is usual to provide a rheostat by which the driver can control instrument illumination to account for variations in drivers' dark adaptation, brightness contrast thresholds, and the ambient lighting at night. Techniques used to illuminate instruments include direct illumination, back lighting, and the use of electroluminescent panels. The wavelength of the illuminant is not critical for mesopic visual adaptation, but it must be compatible with the color scheme used on the instrument dial, markers, and pointers.

Vehicle Marking and Signaling

The first stoplight appeared on an automobile in 1906 (Kilgour, 1962). Since that time turn, back-up, and hazard warning signals have been added. On United States automobiles the rear presence lamps also provide the turn signal and the stop signal. Stop signals are indicated by an increase in intensity of the presence lights, with a minimum signal-presence light intensity ratio of 5:1. Turn signals are indicated by an increase in intensity of the presence lamp on the turning side, which is flashed at 1 to 2 cps. Other techniques may be employed by which to code stop and turn signals.

A study concerned with this problem (Mortimer, 1969b) used a static outdoor simulation of night driving. Various rear lighting configurations were displayed on the rear of a vehicle to subjects seated in an automobile 300 feet behind the test car. The method was similar to that used in other field lighting tests (Gibbs, 1952; Mortimer and Olson, 1966). The subjects were carrying out a time-shared signal detection task and their reaction times to the turn and stop signals given by the test vehicle were measured. Number coding and color coding reduced reaction time to turn and stop signals compared to the use of flash and intensity coding alone. Tests (Mortimer, 1969c) have also been conducted in night driving to evaluate rear signal systems (Figure 7) mounted on the rear of a test vehicle that was driven in the normal traffic flow on city streets and on an expressway. The geometric mean reaction times to the stop and turn signals and the rank order of the ratings of effectiveness of each system are shown in Table 2 for city driving.

Partial functional separation of lamps, such as by combining presence and turn lamps and separating stop lamps, resulted in improved signal perception as well as subjective opinion. Performance was further enhanced when presence, turn, and stop lamps were separated. Best performance was obtained when complete functional separation was employed with individual color coding for each function.

Studies of color identification (Middleton, 1963; Holmes, 1941; Hill, 1947) have shown that green-blue appears to be satisfactory. Amber is frequently confused with red even at rather close distances (Mortimer, 1969b). Green-blue may be a suitable presence light color so that red could be isolated for the stop signals.

Vehicle rear lighting and signaling research is also concerned with

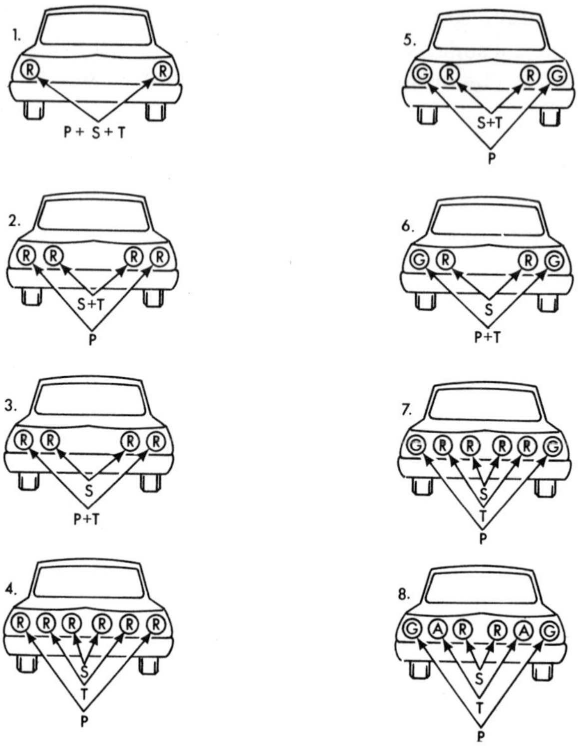

Figure 7. Rear lighting test configurations. P = presence (taillight); S = stop; T = turn; R = red; G = green-blue; A = amber. (From R. G. Mortimer, 1969c.)

Table 2 Geometric Mean Reaction Times (RT) and Subject Rankings of Effectiveness of Rear Signal Systems, in City Driving

	System 1	2	3	4	5	6	7	8
RT	1.309	1.148	1.133	0.896	1.123	1.121	0.900	0.857
Rank	8	5	6.5	3	4	6.5	2	1

determining the form of information that should be displayed by rear lighting and signaling systems. Studies (Nickerson et al., 1968) have indicated that a display providing velocity of the vehicle may be useful. It has also been suggested that deceleration rate (Voevodsky, 1967) should be coded by frequency modulation of the stop signal. A signal occurring as soon as the driver releases the accelerator has been studied

(Mortimer, 1968; Nickerson et al., 1968) and found to be undesirable (Valasek, 1961; Mortimer, 1970).

Table 3 shows that 50 percent of all traffic accidents are "same-direction" collisions and are responsible for 10 percent of fatalities (National Safety Council, 1968). For collisions involving two or more vehicles 62 percent are same-direction types responsible for 23 percent of fatalities. The role of the rear lighting and signaling system in affecting this accident picture cannot be directly determined from available data, but there can be little question that an improvement in intervehicular communication should be an aid in reducing accidents and improving traffic flow.

Table 3 Percent of Accidents Involving Like-Oriented Vehicles in 1967

Accident	All	Rural	Urban	All 2-Car	Rural 2-Car	Urban 2-Car
All types	50.0	36.4	55.4	62.3	60.8	64.7
Fatal	9.8	9.3	10.8	23.2	21.3	26.6

HEADLIGHTING

Vehicles were equipped with oil and acetylene lamps before electric lighting was introduced in 1910. Incandescent bulbs used with parabolic reflectors provided a beam of concentrated light which was glaring to approaching drivers. Combined with increasing density of traffic there was a need to design a meeting beam. For this reason vehicles were equipped with two beams, a main or driving beam and a meeting or low beam. In the United States a two-filament bulb was used, one for each of the beams, with switching between the filaments to produce the main or low beam. Early lamps used separate lenses, reflectors, and bulbs so that the focusing of the lamp was not very reliable. In addition, the reflector would deteriorate because of the entry of moisture and dirt. In the United States and England the sealed beam lamp was introduced in order to overcome this problem. European practice continued to favor a separate bulb, but the reflector was sealed to the lens and the bulb inserted through the back of the reflector.

In 1957 the United States quad-lamp headlighting system was introduced. In this system (SAE J-579a, 1965), the outside or upper headlamps are type-2 units and contain two filaments. The on-focus filament is in use in both of these lamps to provide the low beam. On switching to the high beam the off-focus filament in the type-2 units is energized and the second pair of headlights, the type-1 lamps, having a single filament, on-focus, are turned on. The principal advantage of this system is that it enables both the low beam and the high beam to utilize filaments that are on-focus, thus providing good light output and light control.

Headlamp Visibility Testing Procedures

Testing procedures for evaluation of vehicle headlighting systems use static and dynamic methods. In a static method the vehicle carrying the test headlamps is positioned on a test track and the observer locates targets. These are pedestrian dummies with the reflectance of dark clothing or smaller objects, normally a black board 16 inches square, with a reflectance of about 7 percent. Targets are located at the road edges and centerline. Assessments are made of the number of targets that can be seen at each distance and location.

Dynamic visibility tests have also been used (Roper and Meese, 1964; Hemion, 1968; Webster and Yeatman, 1968). In these tests subjects drive the test vehicle while another vehicle is used to simulate an approaching car. The subject is instructed to depress a switch as soon as he can see a target or note its orientation. The distance at which each target becomes visible is measured. When a two-car meeting situation is simulated the distance between the two vehicles is measured, so that it is possible to obtain the target visibility distance as a function of the separation distance between the cars.

The Compromise: Illumination and Glare

The principal problem facing headlamp designers is to provide adequate roadway and target illumination without causing excessive discomfort and disability glare.

Fundamental relationships between target illumination and glare have been established (Stiles, 1929; Holladay, 1927). The Stiles-Holladay relation states that

$$\text{glare disability} = \frac{Kg}{d^2\theta^2}$$

where g = glaring intensity
d = distance between glare source and the eye of the observer
θ = angle between line of fixation and glare source
K = constant

As two vehicles with headlights of uniform beam intensity approach each other in a nighttime meeting situation on a straight road, disability would increase due to the decrease in d while θ remains fairly constant. Before the meeting point the angle (θ) between the headlights and the forward line of vision of the drivers begins to increase at a rapid rate, which will offset the effect of the shorter distance and reduce the glare disability. If θ can be maintained large, the effect of the glaring intensity will be reduced. For this reason nighttime visibility can be demonstrated to be much less affected by approaching traffic on divided highways (Roper and Meese, 1964; Webster and Yeatman, 1968).

In practice, meeting beams are designed to provide asymmetric intensity distributions so that maximum illumination is placed on the lane being traveled by the vehicle and to the right, with reduced intensities on the left lane and in the potential locations of the eyes of approaching drivers, compatible with road geometry.

The use of the Stiles-Holladay equation in making analytical comparisons between headlamp systems is demonstrated in the work of Jehu (1955). As a start, measurements were made to obtain the relationship between glaring intensity, intensity toward the test object, and the seeing distance. The data obtained in one such test are shown in Figure 8. Having established this relationship Jehu incorporated the Stiles-Holladay formula to determine visibility distances for headlamp beams of known candlepower distribution and for known target and approaching vehicle positions.

European and United States Beams

The European beam initially was a symmetrical beam having a sharp vertical cutoff so as to provide little light in the eyes of the approaching driver. The modern version of this beam is asymmetrical with a sharp

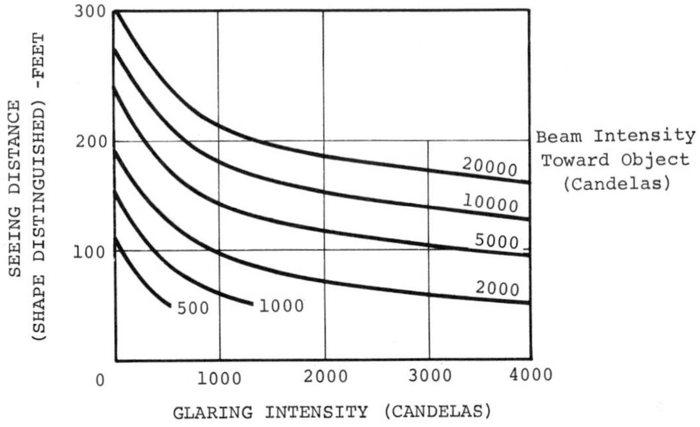

Figure 8. The visibility of 7 percent reflectance target affected by beam intensity and glaring intensity. (From *Research on Road Safety,* 1963, by permission of the Director of Road Research and the Controller, H. M. Stationary Office: Crown Copyright.)

vertical cutoff on the left and a lance of light aimed toward the right. The intensities to which approaching drivers are exposed are low, but the sharp cutoff means that illumination is curtailed above the road with loss of visual context. The system depends on precise aiming, which can be disturbed by pitching of the vehicle. The United States and United Kingdom meeting beam provides a more gradual decrease of intensity above the horizontal axis of the lamp, resulting in greater glaring intensities. Advantages claimed for this system are a more gradual and uniform decrease in illumination of the roadway, better visibility of high-mounted signs and contextual stimuli, and utilization of most of the light provided by the filament.

Yellow versus White Headlights

In France headlights emit a yellow light. This has been attributed to reducing glare effects. Also, it has been suggested that amber will give better illumination in fog.

In tests conducted at the Road Research Laboratory (1963) seeing distances were measured for yellow and white headlights having the same beam pattern and intensity. A small advantage was found in the meeting situation for the yellow beam. Another test measured driver opinions of discomfort glare from approaching headlights and of preference for the light from their own headlamps. All subjects preferred to drive with white lights and less than half preferred the glare car to have yellow lights.

In practice, the fitting of an amber lens or filter will reduce headlight output by about 20 percent and this loss would tend to offset any possible gains that may exist in visibility for a yellow light. Fog penetration is not expected to be better (Middleton, 1963). There may be an affective benefit to amber that has not been explored and visual adaptation may be less reduced in a meeting than for white lights (Peskin and Bjornstad, 1948).

Illumination Requirements in Night Driving

In 1975 approximately 28 percent of driving in the United States is projected to occur on freeway or interstate roads, 30 percent on urban streets, and about 32 percent on rural, main, and local roads (Jensen and Ruby, 1968). Because these roadways have significantly different lighting requirements it was proposed (Mortimer, 1969d) that the vehicle lighting system should be designed for those conditions.

At present the low beam is normally used in all of these conditions when another vehicle is met (Hare and Henion, 1969). The low beam does not provide a safe sight-stopping distance for speeds in excess of about 50 mph, which will frequently be exceeded on rural roads and almost always on freeways and interstate roads. It is also questionable whether the low beam is the appropriate beam distribution for use in city streets with luminaires. Recommendations have been made in England for the use of a so-called dim-dip system in city driving (Jehu, 1965).

The most complex situation arises on two-lane rural roads because the lateral distance between meeting vehicles is quite small. For this condition a beam providing more light than the present low beam on the right side of the road should increase visibility. This can be accomplished by the use of greater intensities in the important "½°D–2°R" (SAE J-579a, 1965) test point (Roper and Meese, 1964).

There is little question that considerable visibility improvements can be obtained on high-speed divided highways (Meese, 1966).

Polarized Headlighting

A number of studies of polarized headlights (Land, 1948) have recently been conducted with promising results (Hemion, 1969; Webster and Yeatman, 1968; Johansson and Rumar, 1968). Polarizers, usually aligned at 45 degrees to the horizontal, and an analyzer aligned at the same angle, are used. When another vehicle approaches there is a 90-degree phase difference between light from the headlamps and the light that is passed by the analyzer. As a result glare is eliminated. Headlights of approximately four times the intensity of normal headlights are required to provide the same visibility because of the losses in the polarizer and analyzer. However, visibility will be only slightly reduced when meeting another vehicle. Some technical problems must be resolved before the method is feasible.

Recent Developments in Headlighting

An adaptive headlamp is under development (Hicks, 1970) in which a photocell detects an approaching vehicle and drives a servo to move gates across the beam to block light causing glare. A turnpike beam has also been introduced. Lights of this type must be so designed to minimize the glare to approaching drivers on curved sections of highways and to avoid undue glare created by reflection in rear view mirrors. A combination of changes in highways (e.g., median screens), fixed lighting, signposting, rear view mirrors, and headlamp beams will yield the greatest benefits.

RIDE AND HANDLING

There appears to be no simple way in which the ride and handling properties of vehicle and driver combinations can be separated into two distinct phenomena. Ride is the sensation of the vehicle occupants resulting from vertical, roll and pitch motions of the vehicle. Handling is classically concerned with driver-vehicle lateral control. Although loss of control is a frequent cause of single and multivehicle collisions (Grime, 1963), the roles of ride and handling are not known.

VEHICLE RIDE

Comfort

Most studies of vehicle ride were concerned with the effect of vertical vibration spectra on thresholds of perception of movement, discomfort, and intolerance. The complexity of this endeavor is indicated by the biomechanics involved in vibration. The human body can be considered to be a system of masses, elasticities, and dampers and of various sensory receptors. Vibration inputs at the wheels of an automotive vehicle are transmitted through its structure and the seat and reach the driver through points of contact with the seat, the floor pan, and the controls. The stimuli excite various receptors of the body for translation by the central nervous system into ride sensations.

The natural frequency of the spine and the internal organs is approximately 5 cps, and that of the chest 3 cps (Coermann, 1963). Sensitivity for vertical inputs is greatest in the frequency range 4 to 7 cps (Pradko, Lee, and Kaluza, 1966). Ride studies have been carried out using simulators, vibrating platforms, and vehicles (Versace, 1963; Van Deusen, 1963; Bauer, 1963) using various psychophysical techniques.

Versace (1963) has reported a vehicle study using a cross-modality approach. Subjects were driven over various road surfaces and matched the ride sensation with the loudness of a tone whose intensity they could control. Twenty-one roadway sections were used with four subjects. The physical measurement of ride was provided by locating accelerometers in the hips and head of an anthropometric dummy seated in the vehicle and driven over the test course. The accelerations were recorded on magnetic tape and averaged for each roadway section over a long time constant. A correlation of 0.84 was found between a composite of the transverse and longitudinal mean-square jerk and subjects' output as measured by the intensity of the auditory tone. Magnitude of vertical acceleration, and its derivative (jerk), provided nearly as good a relationship with the psychological rating.

In another study, using ratings of truck ride, drivers could reliably discriminate trucks having different ride characteristics (O'Hagen, 1969). Inter-rater reliability was 0.96 for the eight evaluators. Subjects rated the vehicles in terms of the vertical, longitudinal, lateral and pitch motions, and overall. The vertical component most affected the overall ride ratings, but the ratings also depended on the other motions. The method would be useful to vehicle manufacturers since it provided an indication of which component of the motion related to objectionable ride sensations and could point the way for design improvements.

Health

The problem of ride in affecting safe operation of the vehicle and the health of the operator is more applicable to truck operations than passenger vehicles. In a study reported by Fishbein and Salter (1950) it was found that a large number of cases involving spinal disorders existed in this sample of truck drivers. It is difficult to assess whether these problems were aggravated or caused by the driver's occupation. Another study reported by McFarland and Mosley (1954) also showed that back problems were found in 52 percent of a sample of long-distance truck drivers.

Performance

The safety implications of vehicle ride, particularly that of trucks, may be assessed on the basis of the effect upon driver performance. Some data have been obtained in aircraft simulations of low-altitude, high-speed, terrain-following to measure the effect of long-term vibration upon pilot performance. Hornick and Leffritz (1966) found that vibration levels of up to 0.20 rms g vertically were tolerable by their subjects over a period of 4 hours, but that performance did degrade in tracking and vigilance tasks. These data have been confirmed by Holland (1967). It would appear valuable to measure ride motion inputs to truck drivers from a variety of truck types in order to obtain a better understanding of the nature of the physical, input variables.

Vehicle Handling

Vehicle handling refers to the lateral control response of the driver-vehicle combination. More inclusively, handling should be concerned not only with lateral but also with longitudinal control. There is interaction between the lateral and longitudinal vehicle response and, therefore, the analysis becomes particularly complicated in emergency, accident-avoidance situations since the directional control properties of a vehicle are modified in braking or accelerating. In addition, the response of the driver becomes potentially more complicated to predict because of driver differences although it may be expected that his response repertoire under extreme conditions becomes limited.

Vehicle Dynamics

Early descriptions of open-loop vehicle directional response were concerned primarily with "oversteer" and "understeer" characteristics. A single degree of freedom model was reported by Schilling (1953) in which yaw velocity was predicted from steering angle. This analysis was increased in sophistication by some simplifying assumptions and also due to improved knowledge of tire characteristics (Segel, 1956; Witcomb and Milliken, 1956; Nordeen and Cortese, 1963; Bidwell, 1964). At the present time vehicle dynamics has reached considerable sophistication and is a tool used in vehicle design (Nordeen, 1965).

Driver-Vehicle Lateral Control

While a good deal is known of the dynamic response of the vehicle in linear regions, much less is known of the driver-vehicle combination and its effect on vehicle handling. A variable stability vehicle for handling research was constructed by Cornell Aeronautical Laboratories for General Motors Research Laboratories (Segel and Bundorf, 1965) in which a number of dynamic response properties could be altered, as well as the steering wheel torque, which is a source of direct feedback to the driver. However, most handling tests have been conducted with conventional automobiles in which changes to the suspension, steering, or tires have been systematically introduced (Shoemaker and Dell' Amico, 1966; Hoffman and Joubert, 1968; Olson and Thompson, 1969) to produce changes in vehicle transient and steady-state response. The tests usually involve having the driver maneuver the vehicle through a sine, random, or step function course outlined by traffic pylons. Performance is measured by the number of traffic cones that are touched during a run. Wind gust, road disturbances, and novel controls have also been evaluated in handling tests.

Because of the complexity and costs of handling research, little is known of the interaction among vehicle directional response properties that produce good handling. Most manufacturers still rely largely on "seat of the pants" handling ratings of experienced test drivers (Versace and Forbes, 1968), a procedure successfully applied to aircraft (Cooper, 1957). It has been found useful (Chikamori, 1969) in evaluating some automobile suspension parameters in the design process.

Much of the experimental open- and closed-loop work has been conducted at low lateral accelerations in which linear theory holds. Drivers often exceed 0.3 *g* lateral acceleration levels in normal driving (Ritchie et al., 1968) and in emergency, accident-avoidance situations; and it follows that this is where more study is needed. The use of simulators for vehicle handling research does not appear feasible at this time, although some promising results have been obtained (Crossman, 1966). The economic, experimental, and hazard problems of vehicle handling research and the inadequacies of simulators make it highly desirable to achieve analytic simulations of the driver-vehicle system. Unfortunately, the same factors make the goal elusive. Early driver models have taken much from aircraft manual-control research (McRuer and Krendel, 1957), although the relationship between piloting and driving is probably weak. Sheridan (1966) has conducted simulation studies of preview control as is involved in obstacle avoidance. Weir and McRuer (1967; 1969) utilize a manual control viewpoint to identify good, closed-loop driving structures to identify the perceptual cues used for lateral control. More empirical studies are needed to provide input data for model development.

Driver-Vehicle Longitudinal Control

Research in longitudinal control is much more feasible and at least as important for safety as lateral control. It has already been suggested that throttle pedal gain characteristics should be evaluated. More important are brake control gain characteristics. In one study a variable-braking system vehicle was constructed (Mortimer and Segel, 1970). The principal independent variables in the test were the deceleration/pedal force gain (the relationship between vehicle deceleration [g] and force [lbs] applied on the brake pedal [0.065–0.005 g/lb]), pedal displacement (2.5 inches, 0.0 inches), and tire-road friction coefficient. The test was conducted on a skid pad at 50 and 35 mph. The driver tried to bring the vehicle to a stop in minimum distance within a shallow sine wave course marked by traffic cones (Figure 9). Runs were made on dry asphalt, wet asphalt, and wet painted asphalt giving sliding wheel friction coefficients of approximately 0.82, 0.66, and 0.20.

The results showed that on the 0.20 friction surface, drivers had longest stopping distances, many wheel lockups, and long durations per lockup, with high gain brakes. On the 0.82 friction level high deceleration/pedal force gain gave low stopping distances, but highest frequency and duration of wheel lockup. Intermediate gains of 0.021 to 0.012 g/lb provided, overall, the most compatible performance on all three friction levels. There was little benefit of pedal displacement. Subjective data corroborated the performance measures. These findings support those reported by Brigham (1968) in another dynamic brake test. Human factors research in driver-vehicle control can provide useful information having direct safety relevance. More research needs to be done to measure driver inputs and to structure criteria for vehicle handling performance. Federal standards in many of these areas have been set up as indicated in Table 4.

Figure 9. Braking test trial in the dry lane. (From R. G. Mortimer and L. Segel, U.S. Dept. of Transportation, Final Rept., Contract FH-11-6952, 1970.)

Table 4 U.S. Department of Transportation Motor Vehicle Safety Standards Dealing with Human and Vehicle Pre-Crash Factors (1969)

Standard Number	Abbreviated Title
101	Control location and identification
102	Transmission shift lever sequence, starter interlock and transmission braking effect
103	Windshield defrosting and defogging systems
104	Windshield wiping and washing systems
105	Service, emergency, and parking brake systems
107	Reflecting surfaces
108	Lamps, reflective devices
111	Rear view mirrors
202	Head restraints
205	Glazing materials
208	Seat belt installations
209	Seat belt assemblies

REFERENCES

Adrian, W., The Principles of Disability and Discomfort Glare, First Annual Symposium on Visibility and the Driving Task, Texas A & M Univ., May 1968, 75–95.

Barnes, R. M., Hardaway, H., and Podolsky, O., Which Pedal is Best?, in *Factory Management and Maintenance,* McGraw-Hill, New York, 1942.

Bauer, H. J., Discussion of J. Versace's "Measurement of Ride Comfort," SAE Annual Meeting (January 1963).

Bidwell, J. B., Vehicle Directional Control Behavior Described in More Precise Terms, *SAE Journal* (1964).

Black, S., *Man and Motor Cars,* Norton, New York, 1966.

Blackwell, H. R., Visual Detection at Low Luminance Through Optical Filters, *Highway Research Board Bulletin,* **89** (1954), 43–61.

Brigham, F. R., A Human Factors Study of Vehicle Braking Systems, University of Birmingham, M.S. Thesis, 1968.

Chaillet, R. F., Human Factors Engineering Design Standard for Wheeled Vehicles, Human Engineering Lab, Aberdeen Proving Grounds, Rept. AD-646681, 1966.

Chikamori, S., An Evaluation Method of Car Handling by Six Suspension Parameters, SAE of Japan, Safety Research Tour in the U.S., 1969.

Coermann, R. R., Mechanical Impedance of the Human Body in the Sitting and Standing Position at Low Frequencies, in *Human Vibration Research,* S. Lippert, ed., Pergamon Press, New York, 1963.

Cooper, G. E., Understanding and Interpreting Pilot Opinion, *Aeronautical Engineering Review,* 1957, 47–51.

Crossman, R. F. W., Szostak, H., and Cesa, T. L., Steering Performance of Automobile Drivers in Real and Contact-Analog Simulated Tasks, Annual Meeting, Human Factors Society, 1966.

Damon, A., Stoudt, H. W., and McFarland, R., *The Human Body in Equipment Design,* Harvard University Press, Cambridge, Mass., 1966.

Devlin, W. A. and Roe, R. W., The Eyellipse and Considerations in the Driver's Forward Field of View, SAE, Rept. 680105, 1968.

Doane, H. C. and Rassweiler, G. M., Cooperative Road Tests of Night Visibility Through Head-Absorbing Glass. *Highway Research Board,* **127** (1955), 23–44.

Domey, R. G. and McFarland, R. A., The Operator and Vehicle Design, in *Human Factors in Technology,* Bennet et al., eds., McGraw-Hill, New York, 1963.

Dupuis, H., Biomechanics of the Driver's Area. *VDI—Berichte Bd.,* **25** (1957), 1–15.

Dutch, W. G., Interior Dimensions of Small Cars Determined by the Method of Fitting Trials, M.Sc. Dissertation, University of Manchester, 1965.

Ensdorff, J., Optimal Design for a Foot Activated Lever Mechanism, M.S. Thesis, Texas Technological College, 1964.

Fishbein, W. I. and Salter, L. C., The Relationship Between Truck and Tractor Driving and Disorders of the Spine and Supporting Structures. *Industrial Medicine and Surgery,* **19**, 9 (1950), 444–445.

Fitts, P. M. and Jones, M. L., Analysis of Factors Contributing to 460 "Pilot Error" Experiences in Operating Aircraft Controls, WPAFB, AMRL, Rept. T-SEAA-694-12, 1947.

Fry, G. A., Measurement, Specification, and Prediction of Transient States of Adaptation, *Illuminating Engineering,* **59** (1964), 453–460.

Fry, G. A., The Use of the Eyes in Steering a Car on Straight and Curved Roads, Annual Meeting, Optical Society of America, Detroit, Mich., 1967.

General Motors Corp., Automobile Safety Seminar, Proceedings of a Symposium, July 1968.

Gibbs, C. B., Car Turning Signals and Delays in Responding to Visual Information. MRC, Applied Psychology Research Unit, Rept. 176/52, 1952.

Gordon, D. A., Experimental Isolation of the Driver's Visual Input. *Public Roads,* **33**, 12 (1966), 266–273.

Grether, W. F., Instrument Reading I: The Design of Long Scale Indicators for Speed and Accuracy of Quantitative Readings, *Journal of Applied Psychology,* **33** (1949), 363–372.

Grime, G., The Importance of Loss of Direction or Loss of Control in Car Accidents, *Proceedings of the Institute of Mechanical Engineers* (*London*), 1963, 1–7.

Hanson, J. A., Ronco, P. G., and Crook, M. N., Rear View Displays in Motor Vehicles, Tufts University, Institute for Psychological Research, 1969.

Hare, C. T. and Hemion, R. H., Headlamp Beam Usage on U.S. Highways, Southwest Research Institute, Rept. AR-666, 1968.

Hartmann, E., Glare Experiments on German Highways, Symposium: Royal Traffic Safety Board (Stockholm), 1963.

Hemion, R. H., Disability Glare Effects During a Transfer to Polarized Headlights, Southwest Research Institute, Rept. AR-672, 1969.

Hicks, H. V., A Fresh Approach to an Idea for Seeing at Night, Society of Automotive Engineers, Rept. 700088, 1970.

Highway Safety Research Institute, Basic Vehicle Handling Properties, Phase I, Final Rept., Contract FH-11-6528, U.S. Department of Transportation, Highway Safety Research Institute, University of Michigan, 1967.

Hill, N. E. G., The Recognition of Colored Light Signals Which Are Near the Limit of Visibility, *Proceedings of the Physics Society* (*London*), **59** (1947), 574–650.

Hoffman, E. R. and Joubert, P. N., The Effect of Changes in Some Vehicle Handling Variables on Driver Steering Performance, *Human Factors,* **8**, 3 (1966), 245–263.

Hoffman, E. R. and Joubert, P. N., Just Noticeable Differences in Some Vehicle Handling Variables, *Human Factors,* **10**, 3 (1968), 263–272.

Holladay, L. L., Action of a Light Source in the Field of View on Lowering Visibility, *Journal of the Optical Society of America,* **14**, 1 (1927), 1–9.

Holland, C. L., Performance Effects of Long Term Random Vertical Vibration, *Human Factors,* **9**, 2 (1967), 93–104.

Holmes, J. G., The Recognition of Colored Light Signals, *Illuminating Engineering Society* (*London*), **6** (1941), 71–97.

Hornick, R. J. and Lefritz, N. M., A Study and Review of Human Response to Prolonged Random Vibration, *Human Factors,* **8**, 6 (1966), 481–492.

Jani, S. N. and Menezes, D. F., A Comparison of Seeing Times Using Plane and Convex Mirrors, *British Journal of Physiological Optics,* 1962, 19, 1–7.

Jehu, V. J., A Comparison of Some Common Headlamp Beams for Vehicles Meeting on a Straight Road, *Transactions of the Illuminating Engineering Society* (*London*), **20**, 2 (1955), 60–77.

Jehu, V. J., Vehicle Front Lights, *Traffic Engineering and Control,* **7**, 7 (1965), 450–453.

Jensen, L. L. and Ruby, W. J., Motor Vehicle Accident Data, Automobile Safety Research Office, Ford Motor Co., Rept. S-68-15, 1968.

Johansson, G. and Rumar, K., A New System with Polarized Headlights, Upsaala University, Rept. 64, 1968.

Jones, J. C., Seating in the Lecture Theater: Theoretical Considerations and Practical

Problems, in *Modern Lecture Theaters,* C. J. Duncan, ed., Oriel Press, Newcastle-upon-Tyne, 1961.

Jones, J. C., Methods and Results of Seating Research, *Ergonomics,* **12**, 2 (1969), 171–181.

Kao, H. S. R. and Nagamachi, N., Visual-Manual Feedback Mechanisms in Human Vehicular Performance, *Ergonomics,* **12**, 5 (1969), 741–751.

Kelley, C. R. and Prosin, D. J., Motor Vehicle Rear Vision, Final Rept., Contract FH-11-6951, U.S. Department of Transportation, Dunlap and Assoc., Inc., 1969.

Kilgour, T. R., Cooperative Research in Vehicle Lighting, *Traffic Quarterly,* **16** (1962), 43–50.

Kondo, M. and Ajimine, A., Driver's Sight Point and Dynamics of the Driver-Vehicle System Related to It, SAE, Rept. 680104, 1968.

Land, E. H., The Polarized Headlight System, *Highway Research Board Bulletin,* **11** (1948), 1–19.

Loucks, R. B., Legibility of Aircraft Instrument Dials: The Relative Legibility of Manifold Pressure Indicator Dials. USAFB, School of Aviation Medicine, Project 325, Rept. 1, 1944.

Marcus, K. H., Periscopic Rear Vision in Automobiles, SAE, Rept. 680404, 1968.

McCormick, E. J., *Human Engineering,* McGraw-Hill, New York, 1964.

McFarland, R. A., The Role of Human Engineering in Highway Safety, in *Human Factors in Technology,* Bennet et al., eds., McGraw-Hill, New York, 1963.

McFarland, R. A. and Moseley, A. L., *Human Factors in Highway Transport Safety,* Harvard School of Public Health, 1954.

McRuer, D. and Weir, D. H., Theory of Manual Control, *Ergonomics,* **12**, 4 (1969), 599–634.

Meese, G. E., Headlights and Highways, Highway Research Board, Night Visibility Committee, 1966.

Meldrum, J. F., Automobile Driver Eye Position, SAE, Rept. 650464, 1966.

Middleton, W. E. K., *Vision Through the Atmosphere,* University of Toronto, 1963.

Morgan, C. T., Cook, J. S., Chapanis, A., and Lund, M. W., eds, *Human Engineering Guide to Equipment Design,* McGraw-Hill, New York, 1963.

Morrow, I. R. V. and Salik, G., Vision in Rear View Mirrors, *The Optician,* **144** (1962), 340–345.

Mortimer, R. G., Psychological Considerations in the Design of an Automobile Rear Lighting System. *Traffic Safety Research Review,* **12**, 1 (1968), 13–16.

Mortimer, R. G., Technical Committees Examine Plane and Curved Rear View Mirrors, *SAE Journal,* **77**, 11 (1969), 48–49. (a)

Mortimer, R. G., Research in Automotive Rear Lighting and Signaling Systems, General Motors Corp., Engr. Pub. No. 3303, 1969. (b)

Mortimer, R. G., Dynamic Evaluation of Automobile Rear Lighting Configurations. Highway Research Board, 48th Annual Meeting, Washington, D.C., 1969. (c)

Mortimer, R. G., Requirements for Automobile Exterior Lighting, Annual Meeting, Armed Forces-NRC Committee on Vision, Washington, D.C., 1969. (d)

Mortimer, R. G., Automotive Rear Lighting and Signaling Research, Final Report, Contract FH-11-6936, U.S. Department of Transportation, Highway Safety Research Institute, University of Michigan, 1970.

Mortimer, R. G. and Olson, P. L., Variables Influencing the Attention-Getting Quality of Automobile Front Turn Signals, *Traffic Safety Research Review,* **10**, 3 (1966), 83–88.

Mortimer, R. G. and Segel, L., Brake Force Requirements, Final Rept., Contract

FH-11-6952, U.S. Depart. of Transp., Highway Safety Research Institute, University of Michigan, 1970.

National Safety Council, *Accident Facts,* Chicago, Ill., 1968.

Nickerson, R. F., Barron, F., Collins, A. M., and Crothers, C. G., Investigation of Some of the Problems of Vehicle Rear Lighting, Final Rept., Contract FH-11-6558, U.S. Department of Transportation, Bolt, Beranck and Newman, Inc., 1968.

Nordeen, D. L., Vehicle Handling: Its Dependence Upon Vehicle Parameters, General Motors Corp., Rept. GMR-432, 1965.

Nordeen, D. L. and Cortese, A. D., Force and Moment Characteristics of Rolling Tires, SAE Mtg., Montreal, 1963.

O'Hagan, J. T., Subjective Truck Ride Evaluation by a Qualitative Scale, SAE, Rept. 690098, 1969.

Olsen, F. G., Comfort Packages for Diverse Passenger Car Objectives, SAE, Rept. 650463, 1965.

Olson, P. L. and Thompson, R. R., The Effect of Variable Ratio Steering Gears on Driver Preference and Performance, Annual Meeting, Human Factors Society, 1969.

Pradko, F., Lee, R., and Kaluza, V., Theory of Human Vibration Response, Annual Meeting, American Society of Mechanical Engineers, 1966.

Peskin, J. C. and Bjornstad, J., The Effect of Different Wavelengths of Light on Visual Sensitivity. USAF, WPAFB, Rept. MCREXD 694-93A, 1948.

Rebiffé, R., An Ergonomic Study of the Arrangement of the Driving Position in Motor Cars, *Proceedings of the Symposium of the Institute of Mechanical Engineers (London)* (1966), 26–33.

Rieck, A. Von, Über die Messung des Sitzkomforts von Autositzen, *Ergonomics,* **12**, 2 (1969), 206–211.

Ritchie, M., McCoy, W. K., and Welde, W., A Study of the Relation Between Forward Velocity and Lateral Acceleration in Curves During Normal Driving, *Human Factors,* **10**, 3 (1968), 255–258.

Road Research Laboratory, *Research on Road Safety,* H. M. Stationery Office, London, 1963.

Rockwell, T. H., Visual Factors in Automobile Driving, Symposium: Visibility in the Driving Task, Texas A & M University, 1968.

Roper, V. J. and Meese, G., More Light on the Headlighting Problem, Annual Meeting, Highway Research Board, 1964.

SAE, J-826, Manikins for Use in Defining Vehicle Seating Accommodation, Recommended Practice, 1965.

SAE, J-579a, Sealed Beam Headlamp Units for Motor Vehicles, Recommended Practice, 1965.

SAE, J-894, Passenger Car Rear Vision, Recommended Practice, 1967.

SAE, J-941, Passenger Car Driver's Eye Range, Recommended Practice, 1967.

Schilling, R., Directional Control of Automobiles, *Industrial Mathematics,* **4** (1953), 64–77.

Schmidt, I., Are Meaningful Night Vision Tests for Drivers Feasible? *American Journal of Optometry,* **38** (1961), 295–348.

Schober, H. A. W., Influence of Disability Glare on Highway Visibility in Fatigued and Normal Observers, *Illuminating Engineering,* **60** (1965), 414–418.

Sears, F. W., *Optics.* Addison-Wesley, Cambridge, Mass., 1949.

Segel, L., Research in the Fundamentals of Automobile Control and Stability, SAE, Rept. 769, 1956.

Segel, L. and Bundorf, R. T., The Variable-Stability Automobile, SAE, Rept. SP-275, 1965.

Sheridan, T. B., Three Models of Preview Control, *IEEE Transactions on Human Factors in Electronics,* **7** (1966), 91–102.

Shoemaker, N. E., Dell'Amico, F., and Chwalek, R. J., Pilot Experiment on Driver Task Performance with Fixed and Variable Steering Ratio, SAE, Rept. 670508, 1967.

Sleight, R. B., The Effect of Instrument Dial Shape on Legibility, *Journal of Applied Psychology,* **32** (1948), 170–188.

Spurr, R. T., Subjective Assessment of Braking Performance, *Automobile Engineer,* **55** (1965), 393–395.

Stiles, W. F., The Effect of Glare on the Brightness Difference Threshold, *Proceedings of the Royal Society,* Rept. B-104, 1929, 322–350.

Stoudt, H. W., Crowley, T. J., Gruber, B., and McFarland, R. A., Vehicle Handling: Force Capabilities for Braking and Steering, Final Rept., Contract FH-11-6910, U.S. Department of Transportation, School of Public Health, Harvard University, 1969.

Stoudt, H. W., Damon, A., McFarland, R. A., and Roberts, J., National Health Survey, Weight, Height and Selected Body Dimensions of Adults, United States, 1960–1962, U.S. Public Health Service, Washington, D.C., 1965.

Trumbo, D. M. and Schneider, M., Operation Time as a Function of Foot Pedal Design, *Journal of Engineering Psychology,* 4 (1963), 139–143.

Valasek, V. R., Engineering Report: Deceleration Communication System, General Motors Corp., Guidelamp Division, 1961.

Van Deusen, B. D., Ride Evaluation, *Automobile Engineering* (Dec. 1963), 532–535.

Versace, J., Measurement of Ride Comfort, Annual Meeting, SAE, Detroit, Mich., 1963.

Versace, J. and Forbes, L. M., Research Requirements for Determining Car Handling Characteristics, Annual Meeting, Highway Research Board, Washington, D.C., 1968.

Voevodsky, J., Inferences from Visual Perception and Reaction Time to Requisites for a Collision-Preventing Cyberlite Stop Lamp. *Proceedings of the National Academy of Sciences,* **57**, 3 (1967), 688–695.

Wachsler, R. A. and Learner, D. B., An Analysis of Some Factors Influencing Seat Comfort, Research Laboratories, General Motors Corp., Rept. GMR-327, 1961.

Walraven, P. L. and Michon, J. A., The Influence of Some Side Mirror Parameters on the Decisions of Drivers, *SAE,* Rept. 690270, 1969.

Webster, L. A. and Yeatman, F. R., An Investigation of Headlight Glare as Related to Lateral Separation of Vehicles, University of Illinois, Engineering Experimental Station, Bulletin 496, 1968.

Weir, D. H. and McRuer, D., Driver Control During Overtaking and Passing, System Technology, Inc., Rept. 1-193, 1967.

Weir, D. H. and McRuer, D. T., A Theory for Driver Steering Control of Motor Vehicles, *Highway Research Record,* **247** (1968), 7–28.

Whitcomb, D. W. and Milliken, W. F., Design Implications of a General Theory of Automobile Stability and Control, *Proceedings of the Institute of Mechanical Engineers (London)*, 1956.

Woodson, W. E., Conover, D. W., Miller, G. E., and Shelby, P. H., Instrument and Control Location, Accessibility and Identification, Final Rept., Contract FH-11-6907, U.S. Department of Transportation, Man Factors, Inc., 1969.

X

THE PEDESTRIAN

Robert B. Sleight

Robert B. Sleight received the Ph.D. degree from Purdue University in 1949 with major study in industrial and experimental psychology. He has served on the faculty of the Johns Hopkins University as a research psychologist and assistant professor and at the Naval Research Laboratory in Washington, D.C., as a research scientist.

As a naval aviator in World War II, Dr. Sleight flew high-performance aircraft and subsequently earned commercial and instructor pilot ratings.

Dr. Sleight has been president of the Century Research Corporation since 1952. In recent years he has been especially concerned with the application of the methods and principles of human factors engineering to the design of aviation and electronic equipment.

In the area of highway research, Dr. Sleight has been an active member for a number of years of the Highway Research Board Committee on Road User Characteristics and is now chairman of its Committee on the Pedestrian. He has numerous publications on various phases of human factors and of highway and safety research.

He is a fellow of the Human Factors Society, the American Psychological Association, and the American Association for the Advancement of Science. Other organizational affiliations include: Aerospace Medical Association, American Institute of Aeronautics and Astronautics, American Ordnance Association, International Association of Applied Psychology, and Society of the Sigma Xi.

A pedestrian is anyone afoot. In the context of transportation rather than recreational walking, we give most attention to the person afoot in relation to the motor vehicle. Frequently this is exemplified by the pedestrian-vehicle conflict, because an average man of 160 pounds cannot compete with the typical motor vehicle weighing about two tons. There must be separation. Then, too, our greatest concern is with the pedestrian in urban areas; and hopefully, in the years to come, cities will be built with the pedestrian considered as a significant element in all planning and construction.

To do this much will be needed by way of quantification of all aspects of the pedestrian and the entire environment of which he is a part. The quantitative knowledge that exists today, along with what we know about the pertinent goals and aspirations of man in relation to his walking environment, form the essence of this chapter.

The facilities that can be and have been provided to aid man in coping with the task of walking come in for discussion. The minimum facility needed for walking is a surface of small slant, of sufficient smoothness, and yet with adequate friction to permit the walker to accomplish his goal of locomotion. The more sophisticated (or "modern") facilities include stairways, ramps, platforms, concourses, escalators, elevators, corridors, doorways, and moving sidewalks.

Like the goals of most transportation facilities that will see use rather than disuse, those for the walking man must have an adequate degree of the following:

Convenience
Comfort
Capacity
Continuity
Speed
Economy

When we have succeeded in specifying in precise man-machine terms the relation between these facilities, the user, and the total environment wherein both exist, then we will have attained our goal of efficient human movement afoot.

SERIOUSNESS OF THE PROBLEM

There can be nothing as permanent as death, so let us look at the place of pedestrians in transportation-related fatalities. The pie graph in Figure 1 shows that, in a recent year, about 16 percent of the deaths were pedestrians. The actual figure in 1968 was 9800. There seems little likelihood of a radical change in this trend, inasmuch as there were 9400 deaths in 1967. In addition, there are well over half a million pedestrians seriously injured each year.

If we combine all non-motor vehicle deaths, we have a total of under 5800 fatalities, which is 1000 less than the pedestrian deaths.

Certainly, any death, injury, or property damage due to whatever

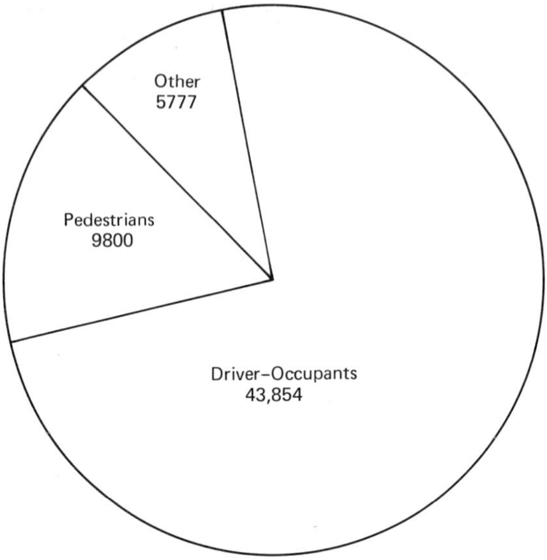

Figure 1. Fatalities in transportation accidents in 1968; a total of 59,431. (Source, National Transportation Safety Board, 1968.)

cause is undesirable and unwanted, but the magnitude of the pedestrian situation deserves full analytical research and remedial attention.

Since 1960, the consistency of the pedestrian fatality rate is either alarming or gratifying, depending on one's perspective. Figure 2 shows how the almost straight-line plot of fatalities for the pedestrian contrasts sharply with the steeply rising curve for other motor vehicle deaths.

It is not known if there has been an increase in pedestrian exposure in recent years, but logically we would expect that general population growth, and especially the increase in urbanization, would have increased the number of people subject to pedestrian accidents.

HAZARDS OF URBAN CONGESTION

The rates of pedestrian collisions in the urban situation, where death and injury rates are high, are shown in Table 1. It is alarming that over one-half of the motor vehicle-related deaths in our largest cities and one-third in our middle-sized cities are pedestrian casualties. These facts cry out for our attention.

The general statements are disturbing, but the specific statistics on the occurrence of death and injury, as stated for 18 representative cities in

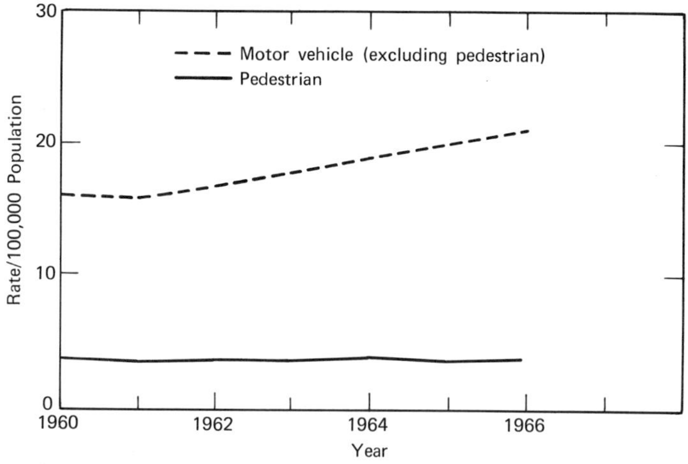

Figure 2. Pedestrian mortality from traffic accidents, United States, 1958–66. (Courtesy, Metropolitan Life Insurance Co., 1969.)

Table 1 Pedestrian Deaths and Injuries in Relation to Population[a]

Population of Municipality	Death Rate (per 100,000)	Percentage[b]	Injury Rate (per 100,000)	Percentage[b]
Over 1,000,000	5.9	52	204	11
500,000–1,000,000	5.0	35	120	8
200,000–500,000	4.5	30	105	8
100,000–200,000	3.9	32	81	7
50,000–100,000	3.2	32	76	7

[a] *Source:* American Automobile Association, 1967 data.
[b] Percent of total traffic cases.

Table 2, can give us little solace. Here we note a range of cases from about one every two days to nearly 11 per day.

We can only wonder about the callousness of a philosophy which says that some risk is necessary to attain the *mobility* that represents *progress.* No matter how "realistic," "hardened," or "practical" we may be in outlook, such death and injury figures as shown in Table 1 cannot be judged as acceptable. Thus, there was good reason that the Highway Safety Act of 1966 (Public Law 89-564, Section 402) stated, as part of the highway safety program that each state shall promulgate standards so as ". . . to improve pedestrian performance"; and that the *Pedestrian Safety Manual* delineates the program's purpose as follows:

Table 2 Pedestrian Deaths and Injuries in Representative United States Cities

State	City	Population[a]	Deaths[b]	Injuries[b]	Combined	Incidents/ Day (Average)
Arizona	Phoenix	505,666	32	337	369	1.0
California	Los Angeles	2,479,015	174	3716	3890	10.6
Connecticut	New Haven	152,048	6	250	256	.7
Florida	St. Petersburg	181,298	11	129	140	.4
Indiana	Indianapolis	491,360	21	787	808	2.2
Iowa	Des Moines	206,739	6	137	143	.4
Louisiana	New Orleans	627,525	36	894	930	2.5
Massachusetts	Boston	697,197	34	694	728	2.0
Michigan	Detroit	1,670,144	103	2837	2940	8.0
Missouri	St. Louis	750,026	52[c]	1533[c]	1585	4.3
New York	Rochester	305,849	15	598	613	1.6
Ohio	Cleveland	810,858	53	1305	1358	3.8
Oklahoma	Tulsa	261,685	19	167	186	.5
Oregon	Portland	372,676	23[c]	478[c]	501	1.4
Washington	Seattle	557,087	35	607	642	1.8
Wisconsin	Milwaukee	741,324	31	1181	1512	4.1

[a] 1960 or later.
[b] 1967 data except "c" which is from 1966.
Source: American Automobile Association. 1968.

". . . expose the seriousness of the pedestrian safety problem;

"emphasize the need to recognize pedestrian safety as an important factor in community planning and all aspects of highway transportation;

"define programs and policies which State and local governments should initiate to increase pedestrian safety;

"provide data to assist States and their political subdivisions in organizing programs and policies for compliance with Highway Safety Standard 14, Pedestrian Safety" (U.S. Department of Transportation, 1968).

VULNERABILITY OF THE YOUNG

Young pedestrians are particularly vulnerable in vehicle-person collisions. Typical statistics are shown in Table 3. For 1968 we note that very young children (i.e., primary grade level) have three times the death and injury occurrence as those about twice this age. There must be appreciable maturation and/or learning between the ages of six and eleven, for we see a steady decrease in accidents during these years.

The extensive school safety education programs presumably contribute

Table 3 Distribution of Deaths and Injuries by Age of Child Pedestrians

	Fatalities		Injuries		Combined	
Age	Number	Percent	Number	Percent	Number	Percent
5	59	26.8	1669	16.6	1718	18.8
6	34	15.5	1731	17.4	1765	17.3
7	39	17.7	1533	15.3	1572	15.4
8	23	10.5	1239	12.4	1262	12.4
9	13	5.9	938	9.4	951	9.3
10	12	5.5	719	7.2	731	7.2
11	9	4.1	568	5.7	577	5.7
12	8	3.6	596	6.0	604	5.9
13	13	5.9	500	5.0	513	5.0
14	10	4.5	499	5.0	509	5.0
Total	220	100.0	9982	100.0	10,202	100.0

After American Automobile Association, 1968.

to this learning, or the sheer perceptual task of judging motion relationships, for example, safe gap acceptance, may be learned the hard way by some. The prospects for teaching the skill of pedestrian movement through fail-safe techniques, such as with simulators, may warrant study.

Certainly we should not expect panaceas solely with the protective aspects of school safety programs, such as those where guards or patrols are provided. Only one of every four children killed in traffic accidents and one of every five injured was in the process of going to or from school. We must also give attention elsewhere.

RISK FOR ELDERLY PEDESTRIANS

Many elderly are active, highly mobile citizens; many are gainfully employed. But the facts of lessened perceptual ability and decreasing agility cannot be ignored. These are accompanied by a lessened ability to withstand the onslaught of a fast-moving vehicle; the elderly are especially vulnerable to serious, even fatal, injury when involved in a collision with a car.

A study of the elderly was done in St. Petersburg, Florida, where a large number are known to live on a part-time or full-time basis. There are estimated to be about three times as many elderly (i.e., over 65 years of age) people in this city as the national average. Shown graphically in Figure 3 is the accident experience in this city. Notice that although the elderly make up less than 30 percent of the urban population, they

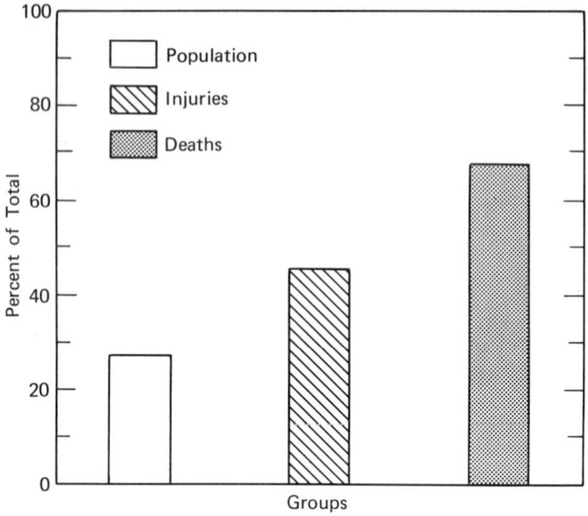

Figure 3. Disproportionate casualties of elderly in St. Petersburg, Florida, 1958–1963. (After Yaksich, 1964.)

experience nearly 70 percent of the deaths, and one-half of the injuries.

Some provision is made for the protection of the elderly who, although in many cases not truly handicapped, frequently have hearing and vision inadequacies. Not enough has been done, though, by way of underpasses, escalators, and general separation, as is desirable. One can appreciate that these facilities cost money, which means increased taxes. Inasmuch as many of the elderly are in a low-tax status but have relatively great political power (a typically high percentage are registered and active voters), it is surprising that they do not take a leadership role and insist that pedestrian facilities be provided.

SCOPE OF PEDESTRIAN BEHAVIOR

The scope of any topic in this age of the information explosion is expansive and impressive. The many headings of this chapter show that it would take a most comprehensive dissertation to critique the extant knowledge and to demonstrate the gaps. A listing of the subtopics, nevertheless, may be of use to the serious student who has occasion to work in the field; in the present discussion, it will be possible to cover only a selected representation of the entire topic. Since there are few bibliographic compilations, students will be able to survey the field only by searching the scattered literature, which will be found to be truly multidisciplinary in nature. Those areas most prominently represented are the fields of engineering, planning, and human behavior.

Below are shown many of the topical headings for pedestrian research.

Accidents	Handicapped	Safety zone
Amenities	Hitchhiking	School crossings
Barriers	Intersections	Sidewalks
Blind	Jaywalking	Signals
Bridges	Legislation	Stairways
Characteristics	Lighting	Subways
Crossings	Malls	Traffic
Crosswalks	Markings of streets	Traffic control
Enforcement	Movement	Traffic delays
Escalators	Overpasses	Tunnels
Facilities	Pedestrian protection	Vehicle conflicts
Footbridges	Prevention	Visibility
Footpaths	Safety education	Walking
Guardrails	Safety measures	Walk signals

INFORMATION SOURCES

The American Automobile Association has taken a leading role in the accumulation of statistics on pedestrian-vehicle collisions and, in addition, has publicized preventive measures. Some of the publications of this organization have been prepared in readily usable form as a Pedestrian Safety Program Series. These have included No. 1, "Older Adult Pedestrian Safety," No. 2, "Pedestrian Control Through Legislation and Enforcement," and No. 3, "The Young Pedestrian."

In addition, many agencies such as municipal and state safety and motor vehicle organizations keep up-to-date statistics on traffic accidents (including pedestrian) and publish them in the public interest. Such statistics do not of themselves necessarily lead to corrective action; rather it sometimes seems that they dull the public into a feeling that any action will be futile, in the face of the apparent inevitability of accidental injury and death.

The annual Pedestrian Safety Inventory of the American Automobile Association and its associational awards to cities and states is another illustration of a continuing effort to publicize the problems of pedestrian safety. In this inventory and "contest" over one-half of the states and about 1900 cities participate.

REASONS FOR PEDESTRIANS

We all remember the old vaudeville joke: "Why did the chicken cross the road?" The answer, of course, amid guffaws, is: "To get to the other side." To understand why people cross the road, or walk in general, may help us to plan pedestrian facilities and procedures, particularly in urban areas. Along with many other factors of "pedestrianization," this one has had minimal analytical study. There seem to be two main purposes for walking in the highly congested downtown portions of today's cities: business and shopping. The city planner who understands and provides for both kinds of trips will be contributing to the safety, comfort, and convenience of his clientele, the walker. One way is to provide sufficient walking surface, usually by means of sidewalks. Other intriguing possibilities are malls or other pedestrian precincts.

We should give some thought to another aspect of why we have pedestrians. The reason reminds one of the story about why Robin Hood stole from the rich—"the poor didn't have any money." Believe it or not, many people today do not have cars. Besides those who cannot afford cars, there are the very young and the very old and others who for various reasons are not capable of driving, or are not permitted to do so, so must move about by public transit and/or on their own legs.

There are at least three other groups who must be classified as pedestrians. First, there are the young, who use relatively open spaces of the roadway for games and play. Second, there are others (not necessarily the young or the elderly) who use the roadway for recreational walking and jogging; in an age when many people live in apartments and work at sedentary jobs, they need to walk or run for health and physical fitness. The third group is highly correlated with the main purpose of the highway; these are people who are afoot principally because of some unreliability in the system, such as the breakdown of their automobile, or perhaps damage to the roadway itself.

For the welfare of all of these road users, it seems reasonable to expect that the roadway should be designed to either (a) accept them for pleasant or beneficial use or (b) provide for fail-safe (emergency) use.

There is a relative paucity of objective information* in the field of pedestrian handling (including safety). There certainly is a need to

* An interesting fact (which we might term evidence of this paucity) is that the 1960 *Highway Engineering Handbook*, an authoritative document of 1555 pages, devotes only one-quarter page to the pedestrian.

determine the causes of pedestrian accidents and what can be done to reduce their occurrence and severity.

PEDESTRIAN STUDIES

Campaign Effectiveness

A frequent answer to reducing pedestrian-vehicle collisions is the institution of a campaign against them. Usually notice is given by a high police officer that the citizenry can expect intensive enforcement of appropriate laws; and then there is often a period of intensive publicizing, through various media, as well as the visible presence of patrolmen.

Such was the case in an experimental situation established in a city known to have a large retirement population. The main unsafe behavior campaigned against was jaywalking. The primary target was the elderly pedestrian who is statistically overrepresented in pedestrian accidents. The curves in Figure 4 show the results of the "safety" campaign, with particular attention to the "presence" of the police for the *before*, *during*, and *after* periods of the campaign. The *before* and *after* percentage of legal crossings improved from 61 to 73 percent where there were policemen for the extreme periods of March (*before*) and October (*after*). Where policemen were absent, the same periods yielded 49 and 50 percent. The most intensive campaigning—during June—yielded 93 percent for the location with enforcement and 75 percent without enforcement. It is apparent that the "safety campaign" or "crackdown" effects lessen as a function of time and require periodic reinforcement.

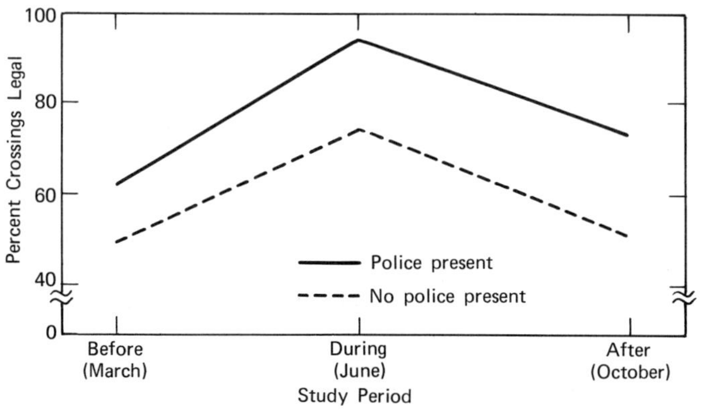

Figure 4. Effect of safety campaign on legal crossings by elderly pedestrians. (After Weiner, 1968.)

Walking Behavior

It may be well to give special attention to that walking behavior classed as walking for pleasure. This recreational activity exceeds all others, except for driving for pleasure, according to a comprehensive study reported by the Outdoor Recreation Resources Review Commissions in 1962. The distribution of this activity is shown in Figure 5. Here we see that in terms of days of participation per year per person, on the average the young (teen group) and the elderly were most active.

As part of an investigation of the behavior of pedestrians at crossings, a Swedish study found that the average adult and elderly person moved at the rate of about 1.4 meters per second, or 4.5 feet per second, as shown in Figure 6. However, many elderly walked more rapidly or more slowly than did typical adults. Most children consistently moved considerably more rapidly, half of them having a rate of movement of about 1.6 meters. Although traffic engineers and others have used frequently a speed around 4 feet per second in their planning, there would be safety justification for use of speeds around 3 to 3.25 in order to safeguard the relatively slow walkers.

For men walking across streets alone, Weiner (1968) found an average rate of 4.22 feet per second; for women the rate was 3.70. When walking among others the rate for men was reduced to 3.83 and for women to 3.63.

In calculating the movement of people using stairways or ramps with particular slants, it is useful to have a measure of the horizontal and

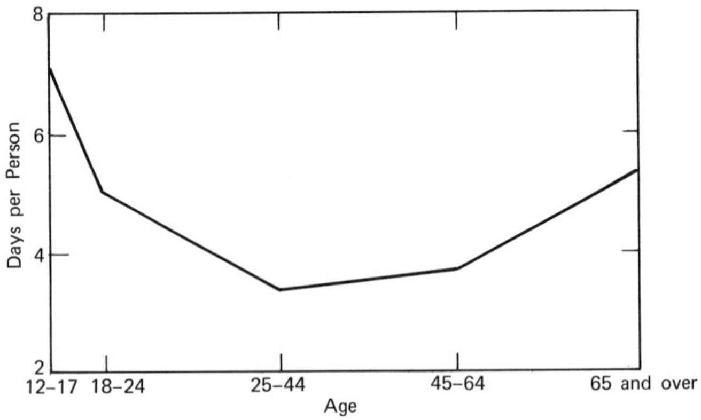

Figure 5. Participation in walking for pleasure in the United States. (From Outdoor Recreation Resources Review Commission, 1962.)

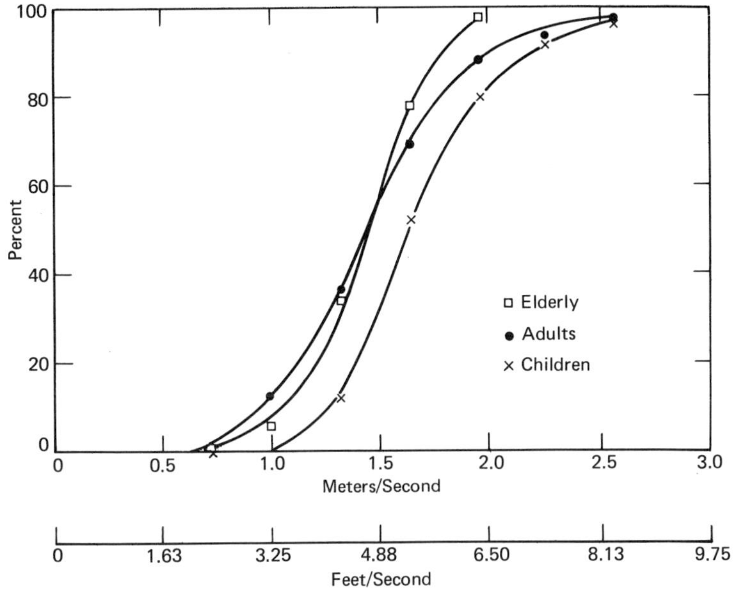

Figure 6. Typical speed of pedestrian movement at crossings. (After Sjostedt.)

vertical distance covered during walking. The relationships relative to a 3-mph horizontal walking speed are shown in Figure 7. The walking speed of 3 mph is equivalent to about 4.4 feet per second, which is close to the speed of the average walker but again does not provide for the slower elderly and the slowing effect of congested walking.

Figure 8 shows the percentage of people of various socioeconomic circumstances who walk various distances to bus stops in residential areas of a large city (Washington, D.C.). For the combined groups, that is, those in both high and low socioeconomic groups, we note that about 55 percent walk one-eighth of a mile, while 14 percent walk about one-quarter of a mile. The high socioeconomic group consistently walks shorter distances than the low group. In this study, we note a lack of much useful data, in spite of its obvious implications for transit and other planning. Future studies should consider fully the environment of the walker and other factors.

One study did look into a variation on this theme of training pedestrians to be good walkers; it dealt with the feasibility of using an automobile simulator to teach drivers how to react when faced with sudden pedestrian emergencies (Barrett, Kobayashi, and Fox, 1968).

When driving was at 20 mph in typical lighting in a large city, it

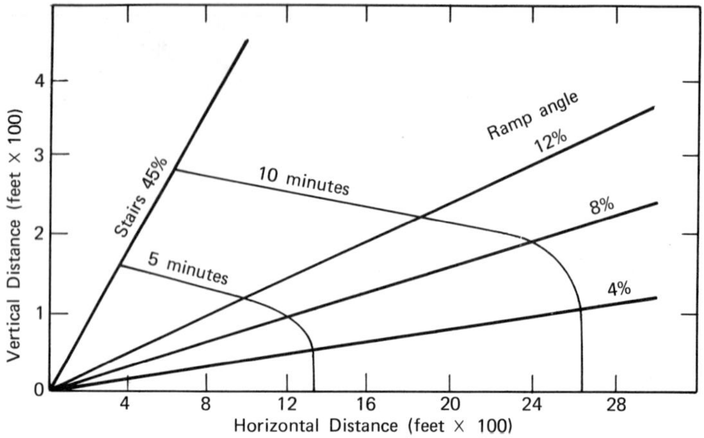

Figure 7. Walking time in relation to ramp angle and horizontal and vertical distance moved. (After *Traffic Engineering Handbook,* 1965.)

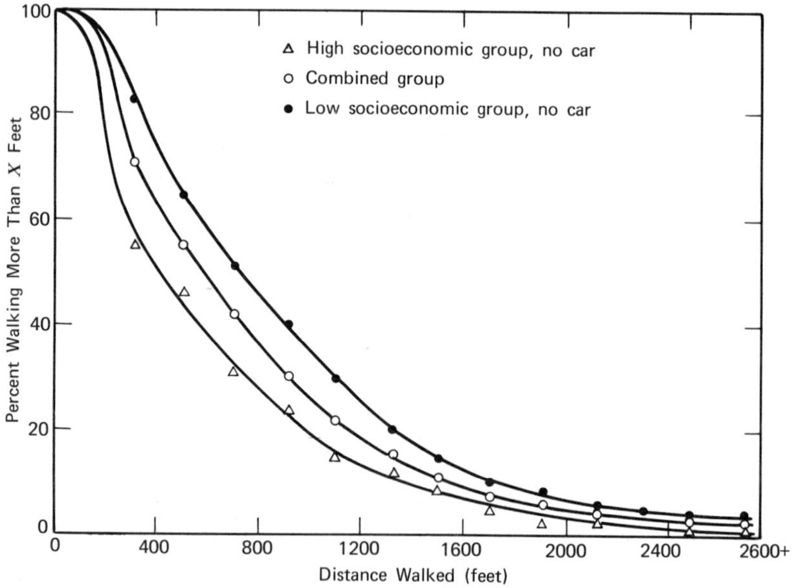

Figure 8. Walking distance for various bus users in Washington, D.C. (After Petersen, 1968.)

was determined that the so-called threshold gap (defined as the gap accepted by 50 percent of the pedestrians and on the basis of which they crossed the roadway) was found to be 84 feet. The distribution of gaps accepted is shown by the curve in Figure 9.

Visibility of the Pedestrian

In one respect the pedestrian in any roadway traffic environment may be likened to the small private plane flying in an air environment populated by larger and much faster aircraft. The "see-and-be-seen" principle, requiring both vigilant observation and small aircraft conspicuity, is a necessary ingredient for collision avoidance. In the case of the pedestrian, it is the pedestrian's conspicuity, or his visibility to the oncoming motorist, that is an essential ingredient for pedestrian safety.

Most studies and handbooks devoted either in whole or in part to pedestrian characteristics and measures for pedestrian safety in motor traffic environments give little or no attention to the important role of pedestrian conspicuity. The *Traffic Engineering Handbook* (Institute of Traffic Engineers, 1965), for example, devotes a 33-page chapter to "The Pedestrian" without once mentioning the visibility of the pedestrian as a safety factor. Special illumination provisions for pedestrian underpasses are included, but for other than traffic safety reasons.

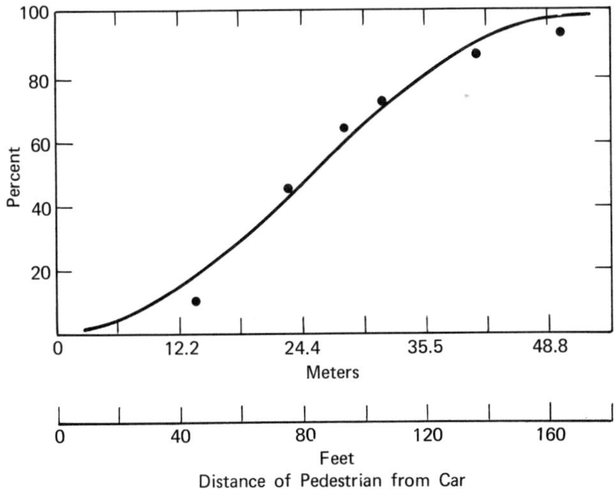

Figure 9. Percent of pedestrians accepting gaps of given size in crossing. (After Jacobs, 1968.)

Although the causes and cures relating to pedestrian casualties are somewhat different in daylight than under twilight and night conditions, it is well known that two main factors can influence the visibility of the pedestrian: the lighting of that pedestrian, and the visual contrast of the pedestrian with his background.

There is statistical evidence that the accident rate per million vehicle-miles is much higher during hours of darkness than during daylight; for fatal and serious accidents it is 2½ to 3 times as high. Another study (Hazlett and Allen, 1968) points out that while overall pedestrian deaths represent slightly less than 20 percent of all motor vehicle fatalities, a three-year study of 12 United States cities with populations of more than 500,000 found that 50 percent of the total nighttime traffic fatalities were pedestrian deaths.

In daylight the contrast of the pedestrian with his background is a very important adjunct to his visibility. In bright sunlight, color contrasts can be the most pronounced, while in the shade of trees and buildings and under unfavorable weather conditions, the advantage of such contrast is considerably less, although still very important. The visibility of the high-reflectance orange belts, shoulder harnesses, and sometimes gauntlets and hats, worn by school safety patrol personnel and some police has been observed by nearly everybody, principally during daylight hours.

The study by Hazlett and Allen (1968), previously mentioned, is particularly directed at the effects of clothing, reflectorization, and driver intoxication on the ability to see a pedestrian at night. In connection with a table showing that the calculated "critical visibility distance" associated with vehicle speed will vary progressively from 45 feet at 20 mph to 450 feet at 80 mph, the authors present a table showing the percentage of simulated pedestrians wearing black, grey, or white clothing, or grey clothing with a strip of silver reflectorized tape (1 inch by 11 inches) placed horizontally 15 inches from the ground, that were safely visible at distances greater than the critical visibility distances associated with speeds of 20, 30, 40, 50, 60, 70, and 80 mph. An abbreviated presentation of a part of their experimental results is shown in Table 4. From these data it is quite evident that the lighter the color of a pedestrian's clothing at night, the more visible he is when illuminated by a headlight beam, and that when reflectorized he would always be visible at distances greater than the normal vehicle's stopping distance at speeds up to 80 mph.

Alcohol and Other Incapacitating Factors

In April 1969, the U.S. Department of Transportation released a report, "Alcohol Safety," prepared by the Highway Safety Research In-

Table 4 Percentage of Simulated Pedestrians Safely Visible at Distances Greater than the Critical Visibility Distances

	Miles per Hour			
Simulated Pedestrians	*20*	*40*	*60*	*80*
Black	86.4	45.4	0	0
Grey	100	47.2	5.5	0
White	100	100	97.2	52.7
Reflectorized	100	100	100	100

After Hazlett and Allen, 1968.

stitute of the University of Michigan. A major finding of this analytical study included the statement the "the over-involvement of drinking drivers and drinking pedestrians in the population of crash-involved persons has been reported and corroborated in an extensive body of domestic and international literature." The report mentions the review of data on the 177 traffic fatalities that occurred in a certain Michigan county during the last six months of 1967. These fatalities consisted of 84 drivers, 38 passengers, and 53 pedestrians 16 years or older. The pedestrians were characterized as having less alcohol involvement than drivers. Advanced age was considered to be a greater factor in pedestrian fatalities.

A newspaper item from Chicago, reported in *The Evening Star* of Washington, D.C. on August 27, 1969, stated that a survey showed that 23 of 100 adult pedestrians killed in accidents in 1968 had been drinking.

A news release from the Insurance Institute for Highway Safety, Washington, D.C., on July 11, 1969, announced that a pilot project to increase public understanding of the role of abusive alcohol use in highway losses would be carried out by the Virginia Association of Insurance Agents. The Institute president indicated that the pilot project would make use of such basic information sources as the Department of Transportation's 1968 Report to Congress on Alcohol and Highway Safety. He quoted a conclusion of that report, that "the use of alcohol by drivers and pedestrians leads to some 25,000 deaths and a total of at least 800,000 crashes in the United States each year."

A special study by the National Transportation Safety Board, adopted on February 20, 1969, was entitled "Alcohol Problems and Transportation Safety: The Need for Coordinated Efforts." A paragraph from the special study is devoted to the relationship between pedestrian fatalities and blood-alcohol percentages.

"Pedestrian fatalities also show a great involvement of alcohol. In different studies, about 45 percent to 75 percent of such 'adult' fatalities have measurable blood-alcohol; *of those with alcohol*, 58 percent to 85 percent have levels of .10 percent and higher, and 44 percent to 69 percent have .15 percent and higher. Of the total "adult" pedestrian fatalities in these studies, 33 percent to 43 percent have blood-alcohol levels of .10 percent and higher, compared with only 9 percent for noninvolved pedestrians who were sampled while using the streets at similar times and places. Again, a great overrepresentation of heavy drinkers among the fatalities is evident. These percentages are probably underestimates because the groups included some persons as young as 10 years of age."

That there has been a relative dearth of research on the role of alcohol in highway safety problems was also pointed out in the Department of Transportation's 1968 *Report to Congress on Alcohol and Highway Safety*. The summary chapter of the *Report* states:

"It is only during recent years that the complexities of the overall problem have begun to be identified by the few research workers concerned with field. Less than a score of qualified research scientists are now known to be at work on this serious problem either in the United States or elsewhere in the world. This is in sharp contrast to the thousands of research workers studying traditional social and medical problems."

Besides the fact that many pedestrians will have their senses and response capabilities dulled and slowed by alcohol or other depressants, there is the real possibility that for other reasons they may not be in optimum reacting condition; for example, there are physical sickness, fatigue, inattention, and mental problems. These conditions can range from a simple headache to slowed reaction caused by physiological fatigue or boredom and on to the extremes of a pedestrian who is marginally or highly suicidal, or a driver with malicious or murderous intent. Not to be ignored are the pedestrians who walk provocatively, even challenging the motorist to come close to hitting them. When these human incapacities of the motor vehicle operator and the pedestrian coexist, it is apparent that a lethal situation may result, especially if such factors as adverse weather and poor mechanical condition of the vehicle should also be present.

For only one of these conditions, namely physical and mental fatigue caused by continuous hours of vehicle operation, we can see a measurable difference in ability as a function of driving time. Long-distance drivers were tested for speed of reaction. It was shown that when rested (before driving), they could turn a clock off in less than .150 second;

after one to nearly ten hours, the average time was about .153 second, but for those who had driven over ten hours, the time for reaction was nearly .160 second (Jones, 1941).

Related to the fatigue condition is one which has been hypothesized by Eysenck (1964) concerning short periods of inactivity. He believes that ". . . involuntary rest pauses account for a great number of accidents which we tend to find inexplicable." Furthermore, he sees some evidence that "general fatigue, as well as the consumption of depressant drugs such as alcohol, increase the number and length of these involuntary rest pauses. . . ." He also sees another facet of driver and pedestrian personality involved; he says: "the perception of danger and the judgment regarding the margin of safety required before one will act in a hazardous situation appear to be basic factors in an individual's safety behavior."

Some groups may come in for special attention in the practical aspects of expedient handling of pedestrians in the traffic situation. Such a group is the blind. They are special only in the sense that they may have a longer term of continuously diminished capability to perceive. We remember the apt description of the extremely inebriated, namely, "blind drunk." The demand-type switch, which can be activated to obtain the right-of-way for the sighted pedestrian, will generally be used by the blind person if it is available. In some installations an auditory signal is provided to indicate to the blind that a traffic light is authorizing their movements across a street. Here we see an instance where a signal, designed for the handicapped, has merit for the sighted as well. In a traffic situation, as in the employment situation, certain aids for the blind can be used beneficially by the sighted. The human factors principle of redundancy of information derived from use of multiple perceptual modes usually has merit.

Psychological Factors

Several years ago an expert in traffic control, Henry A. Barnes (1963), gave a report of the traffic engineer's role in accident prevention in which he made note of an occurrence that underscores the unknown human factors in urban traffic accidents. He indicated that the New York City Department of Traffic was ". . . in the process of launching a new safety education program utilizing the services of a practicing psychoanalyst as a special advisor." He mentioned that psychological factors as a cause of dangerous driving and walking behavior were to be probed and a public research and information campaign instituted. The findings of this research and the success of application of the findings are not known. Evaluation of the human-machine-environment interactions is most complex and difficult and sometimes not as thorough as the behavioral scientist might like.

Nature of Trauma

A team of researchers in Australia (Robertson, 1967) intensively investigated representative highway accidents in 1963 and 1964 to ascertain their nature. Particular attention was given to the immediate characteristics of the colliding objects and the trauma to the body. In this study, 408 collisions were thoroughly studied; 79 collisions involved 82 pedestrians—over 19 percent of the total. The collisions consisted of the following strikes to the pedestrians:

63 by 61 cars
7 by trucks and buses
7 by motorcycles
4 by cars with trailers
1 by a pedal cycle

The casualties could be classified into three groups: males under 20 years; males between 35 and 64, "many of whom were affected by alcohol"; and males and females under 65 years of age. The results were broken down into what might be called suburban and city accidents; in 34 suburban and 10 city casualties pedestrians were careless or drunk; in 24 suburban and 10 city casualties the pedestrian had taken all reasonable care.

One enlightening aspect of this study concerned the analysis of the accident elements, specifically, the injuries to the body. Broken lower limbs and pelvis, and damage to the abdomen and thorax were prominent; concussion was frequent.

The pedestrian was described as not "run over" by cars, but rather most often "run under." When he was struck by the vehicle, he was thrown into the air by the initial impact with the bumper and front of the car. Then the thorax and head struck the hood and windshield. If the vehicle speed was relatively slow, he then fell to the pavement. However, if the vehicle speed was high, he would rotate about his head and somersault onto the roof and from there fall to the pavement. The uncontrolled fall from this height and speed (for he would be traveling at the speed of the car) would produce many abrasions and other bodily injuries.

These occurrences are basically confirmed by the studies of Severy (1963). In particular, there is concurrence in the very damaging secondary impact due to gravity—the fall to the pavement. The impact forces acting on a hit pedestrian are quite large. For example, it is reported that the collision accelerations for the pedestrian, when struck by a vehicle moving at 30 mph, are of greater severity than for an unbelted passenger decelerating within a car in a head-on collision at 30 mph.

One could take the position that not much can be done about reducing pedestrian trauma of impact, but at least one author believes the modern motor car is unnecessarily lethal to the pedestrian (MacKay, 1965). He makes several points: there should be a reduction in sharp edges and points; it is better to stay with the vehicle to dissipate the impact injury; a broken leg is preferable to a ruptured kidney; and all impact surfaces should undergo plastic rather than elastic deformations in order to spread the forces of impact over as large an area as possible.

Interstate and Other Inconsideration

The minimum standards of the Design Standards for the Interstate System, as prepared by the American Association of State Highway Officials, states only, "a safety walk shall be provided in tunnels." It is not the purpose of this discussion to question the rightness of this scant consideration, but we must wonder if there could be incorporated in this extensive highway system a compatibility of vehicle and pedestrian and more extensive fail-safe features than that contained in the above quote. Certainly, in our society, justly proud of its freedom of movement, signs reading Pedestrians Prohibited cannot be construed as friendly.

One writer (Benepe, 1965) emphasizes this by saying: "In recent years, however, the automobile has taken away rights the pedestrian may never again enjoy." He illustrates his point by an incident reported by *The New York Times* in 1960, during Dr. Barbara Moore's 3200 mile walk across the United States:

"Dr. Moore got a special dispensation to cross the bridge which spans the Delaware River . . . but she was denied permission to take the New Jersey turnpike. . . . The Turnpike Commission said it was too dangerous. . . . Dr. Moore . . . has occasionally lost her temper over certain denials or lack of pedestrian facilities. . . ."

Benepe notes that "miles of right-of-way are purchased, and highways constructed at public expense deny access to individuals on foot, horse, or bicycle." He goes on to say: "Added to these developments are the many road widenings and sidewalk narrowings undertaken in recent years to increase traffic capacity; all of these measures have one goal: to accommodate more vehicles, both moving and stored, usually at the expense of the pedestrian."

Pedestrian Signals

Pedestrian signals are traffic signals erected for the exclusive purpose of directing pedestrian traffic at signalized locations. Generally the words "WALK" and "DONT WALK" will be spelled out and be either of the gas-filled tubing type or the incandescent type. The preferred color will be green or white for the "WALK" signal, and red or orange for the "DONT WALK." Neither signal should be used without the other. Size should be adequate for clear reading. There have been many variations, some with research goals, but generally not with good purpose. Some consideration, for example, has been given to other words or symbols, and there have been instances when the pedestrian considers the permissive signal to be so short that the word "RUN" would be appropriate.

The effectiveness of flashing "WALK" or "DONT WALK" signals on pedestrian behavior was determined through activity sampling of unsafe behavior. The unsafe acts were these:

1. Crossing at the intersection when the vehicular signal is green or red and the pedestrian signal is red.
2. Crossing away from the crosswalk, and coming from behind parked cars at any time.
3. Standing in the roadway when the pedestrian signal is red.

The behavior studied was at a street crossing before and after installation of the signals. It was found that the overall percentage of unsafe acts *before* the pedestrian signals were installed was 28.8 percent, while *after* installations, it was 29 percent. Such a difference was not statistically significant (Fleig and Duffy, 1967).

Besides the unsafe acts criterion for evaluating the effectiveness of signals, a search was made of accident records for the several intersections. The findings of this investigation are given in Table 5.

It was assumed, or seemed logical, that the only change at the intersection during the two-year study was the installation of the pedestrian traffic signal. Thus we see that the unsafe act criterion and the accident criterion agree in indicating the ineffectiveness of the pedestrian traffic signal.

The "WALK" light that is on when vehicles are permitted to turn a corner can be a hazard, because it may delude the pedestrian into thinking that he has freedom to move without vehicle interference. Furthermore, his attention is focused in large part on the light that has given him this information, and he may thus be relatively inattentive to traffic in his vicinity.

There are a number of signs, based largely on traffic engineering ex-

Table 5 Accidents One Year Before and One Year After Pedestrian Signal Installation at Several Intersections

Intersection	Before	After
1	7	4
2	2	4
3	1	0
4	2	1
5	3	1
6	2	4
7	3	0
8	1	3
9	1	1
10	3	3
11	2	4
	—	—
Total	27	25

After Fleig and Duffy, 1967.

perience, that help to regulate pedestrian behavior. Such a sign as "WALK ON LEFT FACING TRAFFIC" has the face validity that by so doing, the pedestrian will be able to monitor visually the oncoming car and then move out of the vehicle's way to avoid collision. A thoughtful and safety-conscious police department in Longview, Washington, placed a large sign adjacent to the pedestrian exit from the port facilities which gives this message in nine languages, in addition to English, to the many persons arriving on foreign ships.

Caution signs to warn of pedestrian presence are used extensively, especially in residential areas. They have received informal research attention from time to time, including changing the human figures from running to walking, and the use of various colors. Then, too, there have been fairly elaborate studies of ways to get cars to stop for pedestrians. These have included so-called "Zebra" markings with wide alternate white and black marks on the road surface the width of the crosswalk, and "Ped Xing" painted on the pavement. Also, there are traffic signs that warn of a nearby school or playground.

The use of the pedestrian-actuated signal would seem to have merit, but the public (again especially the very young and very old) may need more education in its use than just the usual small sign, "For Walk Signal Push Button."

The merit of standardization is implicit in the *Manual of Uniform Traffic Control Devices*, which has the support of many groups interested in traffic control.

Value of Facilities

The value of facilities such as playgrounds can be determined in various ways. One, of course, is participation in the recreation provided; another relates to the safety that results. An investigation (Bartholomew, 1967) was conducted in a large eastern city of the frequency and location of pedestrian street accidents in the vicinity of several playgrounds. *Before* and *after* data were obtained. The findings are shown in Table 6.

Table 6 Accidents Before and After Installation of Playground[a]

Recreation Facility	Before	After
Ames	103	74
Lee	22	6
Mander	42	24
Rose	1	1
Taney and Pine	3	5
Towey	10	11
Venice Island	7	5
	188	126

[a] Number of accidents in a two-year period within one quarter-mile radius.
After Bartholomew, 1967.

Here we see a clear-cut decrease in accidents in the zone of one-quarter mile radius from the facility. The table presents the decrease for the highly vulnerable age group of five to nine years, a group that made much use of these playgrounds.

As a specific facility for pedestrian use in the current urban setting, nothing deserves more attention than sidewalks. One planner (Conner, 1967) states that the minimum width for sidewalks for residential areas where there is low intensity of use is 15 feet, in order to provide 5 feet for clear walking, with an outer strip of 5 feet and an inner strip of 5 feet. The outer strip can contain such aesthetic features as thin-trunk trees (but even these can be dangerous if hit by a car), while the inner strip will be needed for building entries and so on. In the event that true consideration is to be given for the amenities such as plantings, then as much as 25 to 30 feet of sidewalk area will be needed. Furthermore, this is the same width as is needed for shopping frontage with reasonably intensive use where loading and parking are permitted, even where there is a minimum of amenities.

Conner challenges a long-standing precept when he suggests we must wonder at times about the practice of removing snow from roads and streets as a public service, but leaving the cleaning of sidewalks to the abutting property owners. When cleaning is not done, pedestrians often use the street in competition with cars that may, in addition, in such weather, have vision restricted.

Then, too, we see many otherwise expensive developments where sidewalks are lacking. Conner, in discussing the public responsibility aspects of facilities for pedestrians, states: "a reasonable premise appears to be that sidewalks are desirable in the interest of public safety and that they should be required, provided and maintained" (Conner, 1967).

There are other physical situations that seem careless and inconsiderate, especially of children, for example, permitting trees to grow so large that they obscure children at a place where they step into the path of passing automobiles. A similar state exists where traffic signal devices, poles, and mailboxes are located near the roadway.

In many suburban neighborhoods, there is a resistance to sidewalks because they tend to look "citified." In some instances, it has been possible to put the sidewalk on the road shoulders and disturb trees as little as possible. Thus, the appearance remains much the same, but the walkers are off the highway. In such instances, easements may be obtainable at no cost from property owners and thus the overall cost of a sidewalk adequate to meet the demand is minimal.

It is impossible to study the topic of safe pedestrian handling and not conclude that many and varied physical facilities must be provided. These range from the simplest—relatively smooth walking surface, through barricades, to bus stops with amenities, to encompass complete malls where the pedestrian is "king." Illustrative of the last but not in the commercial context are park-and-campus-like installations where vehicle movement is severely restricted. For some of these the claim will be they are too expensive. It is not the purpose of this discussion to evaluate cost-effectiveness, but when highways today are costing multi-millions per mile, then is a quarter-million dollar overpass too expensive?

The use of overpasses or underpasses is usually justified when there is either great hazard due to fast traffic or wide roadway or there is a large volume of pedestrians in the area. (See Figure 10.) The underpass will usually be cheaper to build but may be more difficult to maintain because of lighting needs and drainage problems. Some of the newer planned metropolitan areas, such as Reston, Virginia, use underpasses extensively, and they are judged to be beneficial. Overpasses must have high clearance in many cases to permit truck movement, and if in a remote area, they should be enclosed to prevent vandals tossing objects onto the roadway. Ramps leading to the overpass will usually be more acceptable than stairs. In the case of either underpasses or overpasses, it will

Figure 10. Modern pedestrian overpasses in a rural (park) and in an urban setting.

be necessary to provide a formidable barricade to prevent pedestrians from using the direct route across the roadway.

If at no other time, everyone will be a pedestrian at the transfer point between one transportation mode and another. This will happen at bus stops and airports. Such locations will have occasionally severe congestion and therefore warrant comprehensive planning and building of facilities. Figure 11 illustrates a design incorporating a "pedestrian bridge," which if escalators or elevators are provided from parking levels I and III, will minimize the conflicts between those on foot and moving vehicles. Planning for pedestrian use at the design stage will yield efficient movement of people in the terminal complex.

A director of public works described one city's efforts to *plan for the pedestrian* (Bird, 1969). He made some pithy comments in the process of giving a number of down-to-earth suggestions. He suggests that (*a*) the traffic-signal system be coordinated so as to favor the pedestrian, not the automobile; (*b*) mid-block crossing with signals be provided; (*c*) sidewalks be widened at intersections to discourage traffic and give more room for pedestrians; and (*d*) one-way traffic be instituted along with restricted turning.

He states: "The pedestrian is a humble man, who has been pushed around first by a man on horseback, then by a man in a carriage, and now by others in cars and trucks." But he notes realistically that the pedestrian is important because ". . . commercial districts cannot live without him."

He describes some of the building and rebuilding techniques that have been successful in Cincinnati, such as an arcaded area as part of the business building tastefully done in a fashion to appeal to the pedestrian-shopper.

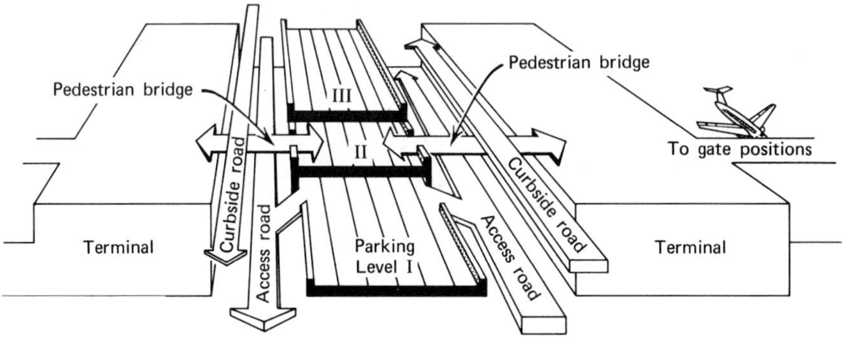

Figure 11. Design concept for airport parking in the terminal area. (From Haverty, 1968.)

This planner talks, too, about a second-level walkway. The simplicity of his statements and their logic bear repeating if one really cares about the pedestrian who is a potential customer in downtown shopping areas. He states succinctly the criteria of a good walkway from the user's standpoint:

"The walkway must be attractive, convenient, and of comfortable width. It should have escalators, at least in the up direction. Preferably it should be enclosed and it should be provided with ventilation and heating."

In the context of overall area planning such relative innovations as the arrangement of dwellings used in some areas, called cluster developments, would seem to have merit because it restricts in quantity and speed the movement of motor vehicles. An example of the cluster development layout is shown in Figure 12.

Street Capacity

The potential for improving the lot of the pedestrian by building separating facilities may yield benefits to the driving population. The task of driving will be easier and more pleasant minus the activity of watching for and avoiding pedestrians. The somewhat macabre joke is

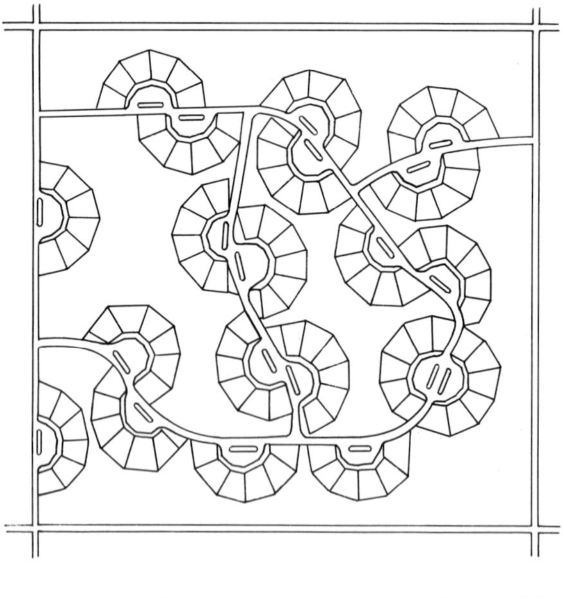

Figure 12. An example of cluster housing development layout. (From Institute of Traffic Engineers, 1965.)

told of the taxi driver who lamented the frequent pedestrian-cab conflict by saying, "You don't want to hit one of them or you'll spend all day down at the police station filling out forms." Not sharing the highway with pedestrians may lead to simpler problems in highway design for maximum capacity.

In an analytical study done by Vuchic (1967), he notes that "signalized intersections are usually critical points with respect to capacity of a street network." He goes on to say: "Excessive width of street approaches without median dividers may, however, not only decrease safety and convenience of pedestrians, but it may not achieve the desired increase of vehicular capacity on that particular approach." The essence of his analysis is that wide roadways necessitate long pedestrian crossing time so that the "go" period for the vehicles will be short. Thus, there is a width beyond which capacity decreases. His analysis shows that ". . . all two-way arteries with more than four driving lanes should have either median dividers or a special refuge island." The design of such refuge islands in turn should be designed with human behavior as a major consideration.

IMPORTANCE

Evidence of the importance placed on pedestrian safety by the Congress is presented in the following quotation from the legislative history:

> "No safety program will be adequate that does not include requirements with respect to pedestrian education beginning at the elementary school level, as well as signs and traffic signals specifically designed for pedestrian protection, construction of sidewalks as part of residential street constructions, continuing enforcement of pedestrian traffic laws, and any other program that can be devised to keep both drivers and pedestrians aware that all the fatalities are not inside the cars" (House of Representatives, 1966).

This endorsement of pedestrian safety programs has not been backed up by the magnitude of research and administrative strength that would seem warranted when we consider that about 10,000 on-foot Americans per year are dying as a consequence of collisions with motor vehicles.

Some action is being seen, though, in the realm of regulations. The National Highway Safety Bureau has promulgated a *Pedestrian Safety Standard*, which calls for states to include in their traffic records systems data with respect to numbers of pedestrian accidents, deaths, and injuries, and procedures for development of statistical analyses of these data. States are also being asked to develop plans that will provide protection for pedestrians through improvements in driver-pedestrian interaction, regulations governing driver and pedestrian rights and responsibilities, a system of environmental controls, and treatment for special problems in and around areas that generate unusually large pedestrian volumes.

REFERENCES

American Association of State Highway Officials, *A Policy on Design Standards,* June 1967.

American Automobile Association, *Manual on Pedestrian Safety,* 1964.

American Automobile Association, AAA Special Study of School Child Pedestrian Accidents, *Pedestrian Safety Report,* **1**, 1 (1968).

Baerwald, J. E., ed., *Traffic Engineering Handbook,* 3rd ed., Institute of Traffic Engineers, Washington, D.C., 1965.

Barnes, H. A., The Traffic Engineer's Role in Accident Prevention—The City Planner's Responsibility, *Liberty Mutual Council on the Automobile and Public Health,* November 22, 1963.

Barrett, G. V., Kobayashi, M., and Fox, B. H., Feasibility of Study Driver Reaction to Sudden Pedestrian Emergencies in an Automobile Simulator. *Human Factors,* **10**, 1 (1968).

Bartholomew, W. M., Pedestrian Accidents in Service Areas of Selected City Recreation Facilities, *Traffic Safety Research Review* (December 1967).

Benepe, B., Pedestrian in the City, *Traffic Quarterly,* **19**, 1 (1965).

Bird, A. D., How to Plan for the Pedestrian, *The American City* (July 1969).

Conner, S. H., The Public Works Official and Pedestrian Safety, *Public Works,* **98**, 12 (1968).

Eysenck, H., The Personality of Drivers and Pedestrians, *Accident Research,* Harper & Row, New York, 1964.

Fleig, P. H. and Duffy, J., A Study of Pedestrian Safety Behavior Using Acivity Sampling, *Traffic Safety Research Review,* (December 1967).

Haverty, E. H., Planning for Airport Parking, *Airport World* (December 1968).

Hazlett, R. D. and Allen, M. J., The Ability to See a Pedestrian at Night: The Effects of Clothing, Reflectorization and Driver Intoxication, *American Journal of Optometry and Archives of the American Academy of Optometry,* **45**, 4 (1968).

Institute of Traffic Engineers, *Recommended Practices for Subdivision Streets,* June 25, 1965.

Jacobs, G. D., *The Effect of Vehicle Lighting on Pedestrian Movement in Well-Lighted Streets,* RRL Report LR214, Road Research Laboratory, Crowthorne, England, 1968.

Jones, B. F., et al., Fatigue and Hours of Service of Interstate Truck Drivers. *Public Health Bulletin No. 265,* 1941.

MacKay, G. M., Automobile Design and Pedestrian Safety, *International Road Safety and Traffic Review,* Summer 1965.

Metropolitan Life Insurance Company, Pedestrian Mortality from Traffic Accidents, United States, 1958–66, *Statistical Bulletin,* August 1969.

National Joint Committee on Uniform Traffic Control Devices, *Manual on Uniform Traffic Control Devices for Streets and Highways,* U.S. Department of Commerce, Bureau of Public Roads, Washington, D.C., June 1961.

Outdoor Recreation Resources Review Commission, *Outdoor Recreation for America,* January 1962.

Petersen, S. G., *Walking Distances to Bus Stops in the Residential Areas of Washington, D.C.*, 1968, Dissertation for Master's Degree, Catholic University.

Robertson, J. S., McLean, A. J., and Ryan, G. A., *Traffic Accidents in Adelaide, South Australia, Summary 1963–64,* Australian Road Research Board Report No. 1, 1967.

Severy, D. M., Auto-Pedestrian Impact Experiments, *The Seventh Strapp Car Crash Conference,* 1963.

Sjostedt, L., *Behavior of Pedestrians at Pedestrian Crossings,* National Swedish Road Research Institute, Stockholm, Sweden, July 15, 1967.

U.S. Department of Transportation, *Pedestrian Safety, Highway Safety Program Manual* (May 1968), 14. (Draft)

U.S. Department of Transportation, *Alcohol and Highway Safety,* August 1968.

U.S. Department of Transportation, *Alcohol Problems and Transportation Safety: The Need for Coordinated Efforts* February 20, 1969.

U.S. House of Representatives, 89th Congress, 2nd Session, *Report No. 1700,* July 15, 1966.

Vuchic, V. R., Pedestrian Crossing Time in Determining Widths of Signalized Traffic Arterials. *Transportation Science,* **1**, 3 (1967).

Weiner, E. L., The Elderly Pedestrian: Response to an Enforcement Campaign, *Traffic Safety Research Review,* **12**, 4 (1968).

Yaksich, S., Pedestrians with Mileage: A Study of Elderly Pedestrian Accidents in St. Petersburg, Florida, *American Automobile Association,* March 1964.

XI

HUMAN FACTORS IN DRIVER TRAINING AND EDUCATION

Lawrence E. Schlesinger

Lawrence E. Schlesinger is Director of Research, National Children's Rehabilitation Center, Leesburg, Va. He is a psychologist who has been conducting research in driver improvement and education for the past nine years. Formerly director of the Driver Behavior Research Project at George Washington University, he is currently combining the careers of researcher, lecturer, writer, and consultant. As an associate of the National Training Laboratories Institute for Applied Behavioral Sciences, he is evaluating the effectiveness of action research teams of students, faculty, and administration in making changes on campus.

Dr. Schlesinger received his B.S., M.A., and Ph.D. degrees from Boston University. He has conducted research in group dynamics, communication, and organizational behavior at M.I.T., the Human Resources Research Organization of Alexandria, Virginia, the University of Michigan, and George Washington University. He has taught psychology at Boston University and Wayne State University and his latest teaching post was professor of psychology at the U.S. Naval Academy.

A consultant to several federal agencies, private foundations, and business, Dr. Schlesinger is also a lecturer and the author of *Is There a Teen Age Driver in Your House?*, *Safety Communications in Industry*, and numerous articles in professional journals.

What capabilities are needed to live in a motor age? The question of goals is especially relevant now as our nation is involved in a major effort to expand driver education programs throughout the country. In the 1967–1968 school year over 13,000 high schools provided driver education courses for about 2 million students, or about 65 percent of those eligible (Tarrants, 1970). In addition, more than 2000 commercial schools teach over 2 million young people and adults to drive each year (Teal, 1968). The total annual operating cost of the current high school driver education program is approximately $142 million and the annual operating cost of commercial and special purpose programs is estimated to be about $225 million. With increasing federal, state, and private incentives, the percentage of students is increasing rapidly so that the national investment in high school driver education may exceed $250 million a year in the first half of this decade. To enhance the value of this training effort the National Highway Safety Bureau, acting under congressional mandate and with federal funds, is supporting a series of studies designed to increase the effectiveness of driver education and training programs in their contribution to efficient, safe, and responsible driving.

By comparison, a recent survey of driver education in Great Britain (Sargent and Colborne, 1969) indicates that driver education courses are held in 11 percent of their schools involving at most 1.2 percent of the school population in the age group eligible. Some flavor of the character of these courses may be obtained by noting that almost half of the cars used in these courses were gifts of private individuals, many of which proved embarrassing to the recipients. They were too old to maintain and use and it would have been unkind to scrap them! Three Austin-Sevens of 1930 vintage were well preserved in one school with the aid of the youngsters and local scrap dealers!

By contrast, our nation is devoting substantial resources to programs in this field. These costs are miniscule, in comparison to other costs in transportation, but they do raise the question of what education is needed by the Motor People for the Motor Age—to use Black's (1966) terms for indicating the predominance of the automobile in our civilization. The question has been framed by Moynihan (1968) in a report to a federal advisory committee on the contribution of driver education to traffic safety:

"Unfortunately, the present state of knowledge as to the effectiveness of driver education provides no certainty, and much doubt, that the return of this enormous prospective effort will be commensurate with the investment. A broad and systematic inquiry is needed into the general question of how automobile driving is acquired, and how automobile drivers can be taught not only to operate automobiles, but to understand the major problems of highway safety."

Efforts to develop a research-based curriculum as recommended by this report may be seen as a retro-fit of the existing educational programs to the outcomes of research with all the problems of communication and resistance to change involved. The problems of modifying existing driver education-training programs in the light of subsequent research begin to emerge and can be viewed in the workshop summaries of a National Highway Safety Bureau symposium (1968–1969) where federally supported and other researchers held a joint session with driver educators and operators of commercial schools. As yet, the issues involved in translating research findings into learning experiences have not reached a critical stage, for the amount of research support for driver education is far less than 1 percent of expenditures for the educational programs.

The National Highway Safety Bureau, however, is currently sponsoring short- and long-term research programs on driver education, the keystone to which is a study of the driver task (Tarrants, 1970, p. 40). This federal effort to upgrade the quality of driver education through research on the critical task of efficient and safe performance by the driver has as its ultimate criterion the reduction of driver-responsible traffic accidents. Yet an even broader analysis of the tasks of man in relation to the motor vehicle, and the motor vehicle environment, indicates that safe driving performance is but one of many critical human tasks. The automobile itself is a personal and social space in which a variety of essential behaviors take place in addition to movement from one location to another. And the consequences of the man-motor vehicle unit to human life and the environment go beyond even the senseless slaughter of drivers and pedestrians. Viewed from the perspective of the continual pandemic crisis of traffic deaths, the need to focus on upgrading safe driving performance may seem to obliterate or at least overshadow any other educational requirement. However, the skills necessary to master the motor car and the impact of the motor car in order to preserve human life and achieve positive human benefits include, but are not circumscribed by, operator performance.

To understand the tasks of the driver in the motor vehicle, we should begin with a broader view of man, the motor vehicle and the relevant environments. Constraining the task of the human to that of vehicle operator may give greater feasibility to the technical job of understanding the capabilities required to operate a vehicle efficiently and safely, but may overlook a number of important interactions of operator roles with other personal and social roles played out in connection with the vehicle. In addition, this limited frame overlooks the tasks imposed on people as a consequence of the effects of the automobile on the human, social, and manufactured environments. Indeed, a glance at current textbooks in driver education reveals a formal travesty. These texts give a picture of young automobile drivers and their environment that is very distant from the obvious meaning and impact of the cars in their lives—an impact that cries out for explication, understanding, and change. The problem undertaken by the texts is how the automobile and the traffic-highway system works. The human problem is how to make it work better (Bishop, 1970, p. 2; Nader, 1966). The interests of young people and driver education intersect around the issue of learning to drive sufficiently well to pass through the ritual of getting a license, and perhaps fulfilling the requirements to be eligible for a reduced insurance rate. Other than that, the driver education teacher's job of translating these texts into live and humanly significant terms is formidable.

Driver education as reflected in high school textbooks is at variance with both subjective experience and public fact. The discrepancy between the conventional, formal view and that held privately is illustrated in a study of interviews about driving with subjects in both ordinary and hypnotized states (Black, 1966, Chap. 5). In the first interviews, the drivers tended to reflect the "official views" of automobile advertising and traffic safety communications. They indicated a concern with design of cars, desire for a better car, concern with the costs of driving, shoddy workmanship, and anxiety about road deaths and the need for greater safety in the habits of drivers and road design. Under hypnosis, these same drivers had no concern with safety and no anxieties about costs and accident probability. The car was seen as an object of wish-fulfillment, related to fantasies of movement, freedom from authority, expression of social and sexual desires, and aggressive risk-taking. While the study may be faulted in a number of ways, it points out that the way young people feel about cars and the kinds of concerns they have learned to express are quite different.

This difference between private attitudes toward automobiles as mobile rooms in the service of enjoyment and official attitudes toward automobiles as means of transportation is well known. Much of the efforts of educators to personalize driver education go in that direction. A more serious deficiency is the lack of awareness in driver education texts of the fact that the automobile has transformed the face of the environment—natural, man-made, and social—and thus presented us with a number of tasks critical to survival, health, and well-being. When the problems of vehicle impact become overwhelmingly noxious, as with automobile pollutants or highways that slash through the center of cities, young persons are quick to respond to the environmental challenge. Yet our awareness of the impact of the vehicle on the face of our society has not been collected, codified, and made available to students in driver education and related courses, as a basis for their attention, energies, and action. Both public and private events remain outside educational cognizance. The officially defined interest does not match private or public experience. Let us turn now to a brief review of the driver education movement as it currently exists.

CURRENT DRIVER EDUCATION

Driver education may be viewed as an effort to help young people learn to cope successfully with one significant element of our technological civilization, the motor vehicle and the traffic and highway system. The general domain is man and technology, the specific, man and motor car.

This perspective can provide learning experiences that may help the student to generalize to other aspects of his life in an industrial mechanized society. The central issue in our civilization is our ability to manage a machine-dominated society (Black, 1966, p. 22). In extreme terms, can we learn to humanize the machinery we have created or, in the words of architecture critic, Sigfried Giedion (1948) "will mechanization take command?"

This issue is reflected in a number of recent books (*The Machine in the Garden; Silent Spring; God's Own Junkyard*) and is close to the heart of the generation conflict, the conflict in the streets, the ghettos, and the colleges. Some young people, blacks, and students in the high schools and colleges are confronting a world dominated by machine values with rage and rejection. This thesis is obviously both too large and not relevant to a technical paper, but it indicates the motivation for the tone and content of this section.

Humanizing the automobile and the transportation system means using these objects as a means of achieving human values, quite specifically, practical usefulness, health, safety, and enjoyment. Obviously their current yield is a mixed bag. The Freudian notion of ambivalence fits most pungently. Yet 1970 marked the two millionth automobile fatality in this country.

The carnage started slowly. In 1809 there were probably not more than a dozen automobiles in New York City, but in September of that year H. H. Bliss was assisting a woman alighting from a trolley car when he was struck by one of the new "horseless carriages." Bliss died the following day, the first recorded victim of what was to become America's most lethal weapon.

By 1904 the nation's supply of automobiles was still scattered thinly around the country. In Kansas City, Missouri there were only two, but that turned out to be one too many—they collided at an intersection.

The carnage multiplied with the increased number of vehicles, and the safety education movement was initiated in the late 1920's and early 1930's as a countermeasure. Driver education became a separate curriculum offering in the high schools, accepted for its contribution to both safety and general education. In a span of 18 years, 90 percent of the high schools in the United States adopted driver education. The materials and methods were neither new nor sophisticated and consisted of classroom training and practice at the wheel. The classroom training included manuals of traffic laws, cautions for safety, and some descriptions of the way the vehicle operated. Practice at the wheel included driving in quiet areas, in traffic, dual-control cars, simulator training, and driving ranges.

The courses were adopted by the high schools as a result of community pressure, generated by parents' fears for the safety of their children. Automobiles were made available free of charge by the major manufacturers and their local dealers. Moreover, there was strong support by local governments, state highway departments, and insurance companies —even to the extent of reducing premiums to teenagers who had taken a driver education course.

Since accident records were the only quantitative, real-life, critical and measurable outcome of driver training that was of interest to curriculum decision-makers and school boards, a number of studies have been performed to compare the graduates of these courses with nongraduates. Initially this common-sense connection of driver education and accident-violation reduction seemed to be upheld by a substantial number of studies. A summary of a number of these studies by McFarland (1964) indicated that the accident rates of trained drivers were only half as high as those of untrained drivers, at least for the first few years of driving. These reports also showed that trained drivers had fewer subsequent traffic violations and that classroom instruction supplemented by behind-the-wheel training was more effective than classroom instruction alone.

Some 26 evaluation studies of driver education, which used as their performance criteria the official records of accidents and violations, were summarized by the Commission on Safety Education of the National Education Association (1961). The report also concluded that drivers who are graduates of a high school course in driver education have fewer accidents and violations than drivers who have undergone no formal high school driver education course.

The effect of driver education seemed most evident in the early stages of driving; as experience increased the performance of formally trained and untrained drivers seemed to equalize. Moreover, the more rigorously the two groups in the studies were matched for such factors as age, educational achievement, driving exposure, urban-rural residence and other factors, the smaller were the differences in accident and violation rates.

Differences were still evident and consistently demonstrated by the different studies. The authors of the NEA study felt that a difference between the driving records of trained and untrained drivers had been established, but that a causal relationship between the educational experience and subsequent performance had not been demonstrated.

The fact that differences in the driving records of trained and untrained drivers were reduced by controlling for student characteristics led Rainey, Conger, and Walsmith (1961) to examine differences in the personality makeup of students who voluntarily elected to take driver education and those who elected not to take it. The hypothesis that the association between driver education and reduced accidents and violations might be attributed in part to differences in personality between those electing and not electing to take the driver education course was supported by their study. Non-driver education students were significantly higher on general activity level, ascendant behavior, interest in social participation and masculine interests on the Guilford-Zimmerman Temperament Survey; they were less esthetically inclined on the Allport-Vernon-Lindzey Study of Values; they had fewer feelings of inadequacy, less concern about physical defects and nervous manifestations, as measured by the California Mental Health Analysis.

A study by Asher (1968) confirms the hypothesis of personality differences associated with selection of driver education. Using data from project TALENT (a representative national sample of high school seniors), Asher compared students who had and had not taken driver education, when it was available, on a wide variety of measures. Driver education students scored higher in knowledge of literature, music, social studies, mathematics, and biological sciences. They also scored higher in such measures of intelligence as abstract reasoning, reading comprehension, and mathematical ability. They took more foreign language courses and had plans for going on to college. They also differed in some nonschool activities; they started earning money at an earlier age and were likely to have fewer dates per week.

These preexisting personality characteristics may be associated with accidents and thus should be controlled in studies of driver education effectiveness. Another notable omission in the earlier studies is control for driving exposure. McGuire and Kersh (1970) and Conger, Miller, and Rainey (1966) report that accident- and violation-free subjects report significantly fewer miles driven than those who had at least one accident associated with a moving violation. Other studies have indicated that accident and violation rates may be influenced by age, sex, and socioeconomic status, indicating a need for control of these factors.

A more extensive study of over 6000 males and females in the age range

16–19 was conducted in California using driver records by Coppin, Ferdun, and Peck (1965). Controlling for sex, age, and exposure, these authors found that driver education did not produce fewer accidents, but fewer violations. However, as Coppin notes, the untrained group drove significantly more miles than the trained, and since both accidents and violations are related to exposure, the superior accident record of the trained group is rendered more uncertain and the failure to find a difference between the groups even more conclusive. The untrained group should have had higher accident and violation rates.

McGuire and Kersch (1969) matched 158 students for whom formal driver education was the main method of learning to drive with samples who had no formal instruction. These groups matched on biographical factors that had been found to be associated with accidents—age, sex, occupation, amount of local driving—and showed no difference in the number of driver-responsible accidents. The outcome of these studies is stated pithily by Tarrants (1970):

"Prior evaluation studies have not provided clear, consistent, objective evidence that allows an impartial person to conclude with confidence, one way or another, that one type of driver-education and training program, as currently taught, is more effective as a countermeasure than any other type of program. Clearly then there is an urgent and critical need to evaluate the accident countermeasure efficacy of driver education and training programs that contribute more substantially to accident control objectives."

The outcome of these evaluation studies is not at all surprising. Most high school programs follow, more or less, a "standard" of 30 hours in the classroom and 6 behind-the-wheel hours or their equivalent in simulators. My own observations of students who had completed these courses, and who had *no other* driver training, formal or informal, or driving experience, was that they were barely able to navigate the car on traffic-less suburban streets! Regardless then of statements of objectives or aspiration, most high school driver education courses are obviously aimed at the attainment of entry-level skills in the behind-the-wheel portions of the course.

The current government emphasis is on increasing the accident avoidance aspects of training. Certainly any measure that will help reduce the accident rate significantly is welcome. The question remains: Will an outright attempt to change driver skills help solve the problem or is the continued accident problem symptomatic of a deeper private and public issue? What assurance do we have that more skilled drivers will use their skills to avoid accidents, rather than slice the margin of safety more closely? At a more practical level, improved skills would seem to be of value only to those drivers who are already predisposed to drive safely. The bulk of the evidence we have on educational programs of every sort, from advertising, propaganda, political campaigns, psychotherapy, physical and social rehabilitation is that they convert no one. They are successful only in giving people a *nudge* in the direction they were already predisposed to move.

Despite this caveat, Blumenthal's (1968) hypothesis that the only educationally influenceable attribute that distinguishes drivers' accident records is *experience* underlines the importance of increasing behind-the-wheel experience for driving tasks known to be accident-generating. This recommendation is certainly fully consonant with a major study of the conditions influencing learning in a sample of the nation's schools. One of the three major variables that influenced student scores on achievement tests, according to the American Institute for Research's project TALENT, was the amount of time the student spent studying the subject. The other two in order of importance were the socioeconomic background of the student and the training of the teacher. Students who knew more to begin with scored higher, and the students whose teachers knew more also scored higher. These findings are readily applicable to driver education.

HUMAN TASKS IN THE MAN-MOTOR VEHICLE SYSTEM

Controlling the Transportation System

The tasks of the human in the system are twofold. First, he has to learn to operate the system as it exists, to drive the cars sold by the manufacturers. Second, unlike military or industrial systems in which the human is seen as an operator, the men in this system "own" the system. It is theirs to control. What does this "ownership" imply? To paraphrase a central tenet of the educational philosophy of John Dewey, the job of education is to socialize the student to play a role in the existing society, and to provide him with the skills that will enable him to reconstruct that society. Clearly role learning is only one-half of the job. The other is to enable the student to understand that part of the world he is studying, to see it as one of many possibilities, to make decisions about the alternatives that may be preferable, and to work with others to achieve desired changes. These tasks are vague and harder to specify objectively in terms of behavioral outcomes and measures of achievement. However, they are critical goals if the aim of education is to reconstruct the transportation system as well as teach young people to drive.

Certainly the educational domain of "driver education" does not cover such far-reaching topics as an understanding of the transportation system and its effects on our individual lives, communities, institutions, and society. Nor does it include a discussion of the effects of transportation on the natural environment, on population densities, cities, and the rest of the man-made environment. Minimally, however, driver education should be concerned with the role of the motor car in the transportation system, the effects of the dominant role of the motor car, and the alternatives possible. The deficiencies of current motor vehicle transportation need to be confronted by students. Dr. William Haddon, Jr., former director of the National Highway Safety Bureau, has suggested that driver education should be concerned with such topics as the hazards stemming from deficiencies of highway traffic and vehicular designs; knowledge of potential vehicular malfunctioning; support for higher standards of design; knowledge of the effects of alcohol and medical conditions on driver performance; the use of driver restraint systems; and techniques of handling emergencies and the post-crash phase of accidents (Haddon, 1968).

Vehicle Control—Analysis of the Driving Task

What kinds of educational experiences will help the new driver perform safely and efficiently? On what basis is driver training developed? Stated in human factors terms, the question of development of an educational-training effort has to be preceded logically by a number of other questions (Cogan, 1967). First, a human factors-systems analysis model of man, the motor car, and the environment in which they operate has to be developed. Second, the tasks of the man in this system have to be specified. Third, the knowledge and skills necessary to perform these tasks have to be defined. Fourth, the knowledge and skills that are the specific objectives of training must be delineated. Fifth, a training program and proficiency measures need to be developed to meet and measure these objectives. Sixth, the program has to be evaluated in terms of its effectiveness in meeting these learning goals. Finally, the contribution of the educational program is assessed in terms of its contribution to the operation of the system. Driver education has more or less intuitively followed this model, but the specific research efforts that are needed to support this educational program have not yet been accomplished.

The current pressure on driver education, stemming from the National Highway Safety Bureau's guidance, is on the task of safe performance of the driver. Recently four agencies were awarded contracts to develop evaluation procedures for driver education and training programs (Brody, 1968; Kennedy, 1968; Lybrand, 1968; and Teal, 1968) and their recommendations were reorganized by a fifth agency (Harman et al., 1969).

Symposia to distribute the results of these reports and related research to driver education specialists were sponsored by the National Highway Safety Bureau (1969). A related and excellent review and evaluation of major published research on human factors relevant to driver licensing and driver performance, also federally contracted, is reported as Volume 1 of a three-volume study (Miller et al., 1969).

The evaluation studies cited above led the National Highway Safety Bureau to contract with the Human Resources Research Organization for a systematic analysis of the driving task and the driving behaviors required for efficient, safe, and responsible performance (McKnight, 1969). This study is said to be the key to a set of further studies that are dependent upon it (Tarrants, 1970) and is scheduled for completion in 1972. However, several difficulties stand in the way of successful performance of a task analysis of driving. The need to base driver training objectives on a description of the behaviors required to perform safely is implied by the training development paradigm outlined above and has often been asserted (McKnight, 1969). However, as we shall see below, task analysis procedures may not be sufficiently powerful to yield a behavioral description of a dynamic control task like driving.

Task analysis procedures have been used: to identify information required by a human operator to perform his task; to identify tasks that are difficult to perform; to identify tasks critical to safe or effective performance; and to quantify the load placed on operator activities. If task analysis is to be used to satisfy any of the above objectives, certain conditions must be met: a representation of that task must be constructed in such a way that task elements can be ordered to produce the desired man-made outcomes. This ordered arrangement may be a checklist, block diagram, sequence to a fixed set of rules. Thus, task analysis, as a method, represents one type of system model. All models have a certain set of limiting conditions (or assumptions) under which they operate. The following is a list of conditions, based on a review of task analysis procedures, which must be met if task analysis is to be applied to a man/system interface.

Operational Definition. All operator functions must be compatible with an exhaustive set of mutually exclusive operations selected for use in task analysis elements. These elements, usually taken from an operator model such as those presented by Schlesinger (1967), Lybrand (1968), and Miller (1969) may include overt and/or covert activities depending on the nature of this model.

Finite Response Set. The number of responses available to an operator must be finite. For each meaningful response to a given situation, a separate analysis must be made, thus the number of subtask analyses is dependent on the "complexity" of the task.

Environment Specificity. The description of the operator's environment and any changes in it over time must be defined sufficiently to allow the enumeration of all conditions that might be expected to influence operator performance.

Ordering. Tasks must be capable of being ordered by some logical or physical relationship. If there is no structured sequence, task analysis must be performed on each allowable sequence.

Operation Closure. All operator functions represented in the task analysis must have a well-defined beginning and end point.

This set of limiting factors has discouraged the use of task analysis in other than the most structured situations. Usually, as in the case of weapon systems, task analysis is applied to those operator activities in which the operator's task is to respond to a well-defined set of system conditions by employing an overt set of responses, such as switch setting or information transmittal. In most cases all important situational variations can be specified, and all responses structured in a temporal and spatial sequence.

When dynamic tasks, such as docking a spacecraft, landing an aircraft, or surfacing a submarine, are the job of the operator, mathematical models are used for estimating the impact of the operator on system effectiveness, and whole-task simulation as well as on-the-job training are used to instruct the operator in the correct performance of his task. The complex nature of psychomotor functions has prohibited the use of "paper and pencil" analysis of control tasks. The only partitioning of these tasks has been in the specification of task "phase," for example, take-off, in-flight, or landing of an aircraft. This type of partitioning has served to emphasize the more difficult activities; however, it has not changed the basic modes of training, simulation, and on-the-job training. The same type of partitioning of tasks and subsequent devotion of training emphasis could be obtained in driver education through the use of simulator and in-car experiences to teach the driving skills required for safe and efficient vehicle control in accident-provoking situations.

In summary, the driving task does not meet the conditions necessary for the application of task analysis methodologies. The first and most obvious inadequacy is that there is no driver model sufficiently well defined to allow the development of an exhaustive and mutually exclusive set of driver activities. The current state-of-the-art is a rudimentary information flow procedure. It is not developed enough to allow the derivation of measurable behaviors directly influenced by variations in the efficiency with which the activity is performed. This statement is not meant to imply that there is always a complete operator model whenever task analysis can be correctly applied. Often the task is sufficiently structured to allow the analyst to assume a simple machine analogy (e.g., digital or analog computers, or a communications network) as a model.

The second factor limiting the application of task analysis to driving is that many of the identified operations have no well-defined beginning or end point. The operation of "search" as contained in Schlesinger's (1967) model, must be on-going throughout the entire time a vehicle is in transit. This means that the majority of factors important in vehicle control cannot be adequately described by the task analysis model.

In any given situation, there may be many correct responses open to the driver. Not only is this response set numerous, but it varies with the environmental and vehicle factors present in each individual condition. This fact, while not prohibiting task analysis, does greatly increase the number of analyses that must be performed to assure valid results. In addition the number of environments in which the operator may find himself is virtually limitless. The perceptual and cognitive rules by which he summarizes these different situations are not known; therefore, any meaningful task analysis must be iterated over a large sample of possible environments.

Thus, a well-defined task analysis of driving does not seem feasible at this time. An alternative procedure, and in fact the one that seems to be the basis of the current "task analysis" of driving (McKnight, 1969), is a systematic search of the literature for data on driving behavior and the variables that influence it, and the organization of these data according to a formal scheme that yields trainable driver tasks. This procedure is empirical, logical, and systematic, and is capable of ordering the information available on both driving behavior and the conditions that influence it in order to derive training objectives.

This procedure is not a formal model, in the sense of a set of interrelated variables that include the driver, the vehicle, and the environment. Attempts to date at more formal analysis of driving have been either severely limited or over-general. Many analyses have been specifically concerned with but one facet of driving, such as car-following or passing. Other models that have attempted to deal with the driving task in its entirety have been singularly empty of content useful to the driver educator.

Let us examine one such model of the driver tasks as a means of ordering the objectives of a training program, the methods used to attain these objectives, and evaluation procedures.

Toward a Model of Driving

What is the nature of the skills or human functions that are required to perform the critical tasks of driving? The notion that we teach "defensive driving" or the "strategy and tactics" of driving has to be supplemented by inculcation of specific procedures. Procedures are generally considered to be such routines as passing, turning, stopping, and other specific maneuvers. Can some procedures be identified which are used in all of those maneuvers and in most driving situations? Or does the driver need to learn a set of different procedures for different driving situations? Probably both: the cues used and the responses may vary, but the underlying driver functions may be common. A parsimonious hypothesis is that there is a common model of driver behavior underlying such diverse behaviors as parallel parking and making a U-turn at very low speeds; moving the vehicle at moderate to high speeds on roads containing other vehicles, people, and objects—including such maneuvers as passing, changing lanes, and turning; and responding to such unpredictable events as skids, spinouts, hydroplaning, or blowouts. The development of such a model is obviously a long-range project of some magnitude. The following section indicates the reasons for believing such a model is possible and the direction development might take. Similar models have been postulated by Forbes (1960), Cumming (1964), Lybrand (1968), Bishop (1970), and Miller (1969).

GUIDANCE AND CONTROL

There are two classes of behavior required of the driver (Michaels, 1961; Ross, 1961): (1) guidance, the cybernetic task of obtaining and processing information from the environment; (2) control, the task of translating guidance data into decisions and psychomotor control of the vehicle (see Figure 1).

These guidance and control functions enable the driver-vehicle unit to move forward at a rate and direction partly self-paced and partly determined by the environment, and to maintain separation from other vehicles and objects. Generally, our description of the driving task

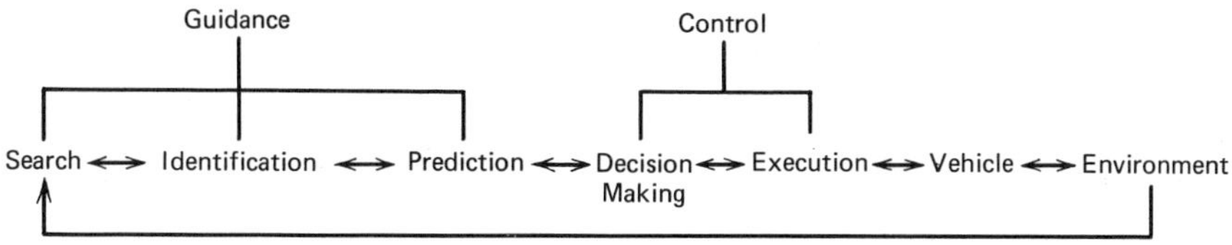

Figure 1. Elementary driver function model.

utilizes a servo analogy in which the function of the driver is described as the maintenance of speed, direction, and separation by overcoming perturbations arising from himself, his vehicle, and the environment. Taken together, the guidance and control functions enable the operator to maintain a desired state with respect to these parameters.

Guidance: Search, Identification, and Prediction

The guidance task, or perceptual task as it is sometimes called, can be broken down into three subtasks: search, identification, and prediction. The procedures of performing these subtasks tell the driver where and when to look, what to look for, and what to make of it. The subtasks answer the questions: Is anything going on that should influence my driving? What is it? What can be expected to happen? Search consists of the observational behaviors used by the driver to note the presence or absence of critical characteristics of the driving environment. Identification requires the classification of these observations according to their information content. Prediction involves the estimation of future states of the environment and the vehicular system from presently available information. Efficient and accurate performance of these guidance procedures provides the driver with the ability to rapidly characterize the current driving situation, predict the accident potential of developing situations, and plan the steps that will carry him along his route safely and efficiently.

Control: Decision-Making and Execution

Accurate prediction enables the driver to formulate alternative actions, select the most satisfactory, and execute the required maneuver. The control task, then, can be broken down into two subtasks: decision-making and execution. Decision-making procedures are concerned with the question of what to do, and execution obviously with the driver's responses to the vehicle. In approaching a signal, for example, the driver must decide whether to stop, where to stop, and how hard to press the brake. Then he must carry out the appropriate control actions. Decision-making involves the cognitive selection of response alternatives based on information gained from performance of the information-processing subtasks. Execution involves the driver's input to the vehicle and feedback from the vehicle to the driver, a psychomotor cybernetic task that operates within the larger servo mechanism outlined in Figure 1.

Summary: Guidance and Control

As changes occur in the driving environment, the driver matches these changes by manipulating his vehicle to maintain the desired speed, direction, and separation. The stimuli that govern the driver's behavior are deviations from the desired states and, as the stimulus picture changes, the driver controls the vehicle to compensate for these changes. In this task of matching output to input in a continuous flow of action, the driver is confronted with a number of sources of change. The road that he is tracking might change direction and incline, requiring him to turn the steering wheel and change the amount of pressure on the accelerator. The driver must compensate for changes in the road topography and surface, signs and signals, intersections, other vehicles and pedestrians, physical objects, and the driver's own vehicle. The task of anticipating these changes involves three stages of human functioning: searching, identifying, and predicting. These stages are sequentially linked and each is a necessary but not sufficient condition for efficient performance of the next stage. The task of changing the direction or acceleration of the vehicle to compensate for these environmental changes involves decision-making and execution of the response. Training in driving then means learning systematic procedures for conducting each of these subtasks under "normal" driving conditions and conditions known to generate accidents.

Sequential Relationship between Response Stages

We assume that these responses are sequentially related so that the output for any one class is the input for the subsequent class. For example, the output for the search response is some probability of signal detection, which then becomes the input for the identification response. Identified stimulus situations become the input to the estimation stage, and these estimations provide the input for decision-making. The selection of an alternative becomes the input for the vehicular control responses, and this output becomes part of the subsequent stimulus input.

In sum, our description of the driving task utilizes a servo analogy. For a more detailed cybernetic model in which individual control of the vehicle is related to traffic control and environmental control, the reader is referred to Howland's excellent appended report to Kennedy's (1968) study of driver education.

Simultaneous Cycling and Attention to Subtasks

We also assume that the operator is performing a number of these response classes "simultaneously." He is controlling the vehicle while searching the environment, for example. Or within the same time frame he may be required to make a number of related estimates, as in deciding whether to pass through an uncontrolled intersection. Many drivers have observed that they perform the tasks of vehicular control on "automatic pilot" when the guidance tasks are insufficiently attention arousing. The problem of allocation of attention among these subtasks is probably solved by focusing attention on the task with greatest situational demand. Let us turn now to a more detailed examination of training for these tasks, the training methods used, and methods of evaluating the acquisition of these skills.

OBJECTIVES OF DRIVER TRAINING, TRAINING METHODS, EVALUATION TECHNIQUES

Search

Smith (1956) has reported that accident-free drivers could be distinguished from accident-producing drivers by their methods of observing the driving scene. The accident-free drivers, according to Smith, had developed systematic observational routines, while the poorer drivers gave more time to vehicular control and nondriving stimuli such as scenery, events inside the vehicle, and personal thoughts.

Search may be defined as the observational procedures used to note the presence or absence of critical objects or differences in the driving scene. The search subtasks may be further subdivided into at least three components: (a) focus of attention; (b) search rate; (c) search pattern. "Focus of attention" refers to where and what the driver looks at as he confronts an ever-changing environment. This focus may need to change with speed, visibility, road topography, traffic volume, and density. A recent analysis of the tasks of driving (Allen, Lunenfeld, and Alexander, 1971) suggests that the subtasks fall in a hierarchical scale with steering and speed control at the lowest level; responses to road and traffic situations at an intermediate level; and planning and preparing the trip and finding and following the route at the highest level. When load shedding is required, these authors suggest, subtasks higher in the hierarchy are shed by focusing attention at the level demanded by the situation. "Search rate" is concerned with how frequently the driver searches his environment. The problem here is one of time sampling; what portion of his time should the driver spend in looking at the various elements of his environment such as the current location of his vehicle; the road ahead, behind, and to the side; the instruments in the vehicle? The third component, "search pattern," is concerned with how efficiently the driver samples his environment. For example, in passing a vehicle on a two-lane highway, should the driver use a consistent search procedure pattern, such as looking ahead for oncoming cars, to his left side for cars that may be immediately passing him, and to the rear to be certain that he has room to return to his previous position in the event of emergency? The formulation and evaluation of efficient communicable search procedures is an obvious research need (Rockwell and Ernst, 1967).

Training in Search Procedures

Differences in sensory capacity, such as visual and auditory acuity, for the normal range of drivers have not been successfully related to driving performance in the studies summarized by Goldstein (1961), but findings relating dynamic visual acuity to driving records indicate some positive relationships (Burg, 1968). The critical factor seems to be the ability of the driver to use his capacities in a systematic way. Under the pressures of time, the driver must develop an efficient observational procedure that enables him to sense changes in a sequential search routine, as taught in the Smith system (Smith and Cummings, 1956; Worner, 1961). Thus, the observing behavior is carried out under a set of instructions in which the individual continues to "tell himself where to look" (Gagne, 1962). Some kind of scanning and search routine is evidently a requirement for efficient driving, and the kind of search routine to employ may not be intuitively obvious. Studies are needed to explore the advantages of different scanning and search routines for varying driving conditions (night versus day, for example).

Criterion Tests

No studies of training in observational procedures have been reported. An evaluation of the Smith system (Payne and Barmack, 1963) was not concerned with the observational procedures developed and provided no evidence for efficacy of this training method. A study by Waldram (1960), which recorded eye movements of observers (with a Mackworth camera) while they were viewing a film of streets taken from a vehicle at night, suggests that this technique may be used to identify the observational procedures used by experienced drivers, as well as to evaluate the observing procedures of newly trained drivers. For example, Waldram suggests that "the experienced driver reads the scene ahead of him rather as the experienced reader reads print, taking in features at a glance. . . . A great part of his information is received parafoveally, and he is content to let it remain so, provided that the object concerned is not of special interest. . . ." Driver eye movements seem to be stimulated by unpredictable or unrecognizable objects, or objects that call for special action. As the driver approaches a traffic knot, for example, his eyes move rapidly from one vehicle to another as he appraises the patterns of motion. Advances in the techniques of recording eye movements, by camera and by electroretinography, may make this evaluation procedure ultimately available for classroom use (Rockwell, Overby, and Mourant, 1968).

Identification

Identification refers to the classification of the environmental stimuli into recognizable and meaningful categories based on information stored in memory. These responses may be viewed as the application of decision rules to detected changes. As with search, there are classification responses and classification results. The environmental stimuli may be tentatively categorized into five different groups: (1) stimuli seen as a threat or obstacle to safe driving; (2) stimuli seen as nonthreatening; (3) informational stimuli; (4) misidentified stimuli; and (5) stimuli that are not seen.

(1) Threatening stimuli may be further divided into: (a) stationary obstacles, such as stalled vehicles or construction barriers; (b) moving obstacles—other vehicles, bicycles, or pedestrians; or (c) barriers to sight—night, headlight glare, crests of hills, blind corners, and so on. (2) Nonthreatening stimuli cover all the various stimuli that the driver attends to but that do not have an immediate effect on his driving behavior. (3) Informational stimuli may be subdivided into three more or less distinct subcategories: (a) control information provided by the roadway—lane markings, speed signs; (b) route information provided by the roadway; and (c) incidental information—gas and motel signs. (4) Misidentification may be subdivided into: (a) stimuli that cannot be properly identified because of insufficient cues, such as signs that are illegible because of insufficient illumination; and (b) stimuli that are not identified because of an inadequate or faulty memory. The latter category is more appropriately called misperception. A number of accidents have been attributed to this factor alone. The reasons for misperception are many and varied and not completely understood. The last category, (5) stimuli not seen, is a catchall to cover a variety of situations in which relevant stimuli are not seen for diverse reasons, for example, drunkenness, inadequate illumination, lack of attention, blind spots of the vehicle, or blind corners.

Research support for the importance of identification skills is provided by several sources. Gagne (1962) has reported that training in identification of the visual input cues has had marked effects on the performance of tracking tasks, such as gunnery and aircraft maneuvering. Spicer's (1962) study of accident and violation-producing drivers finds that better performing drivers can more successfully identify the salient features of a driving scene presented in a slide taken from the driver's seat.

Training in Identification

Recognition of critical cues in driving requires a capacity to detect and classify environmental changes that may require compensatory action. The role of training in identification is to provide the trainee with a set of instructions telling him "what to look for" and provide practice in these procedures. Although a great deal of information may be gleaned from existing driver manuals and training programs about driving cues that signify danger, no systematic routines to identify the significant cues in the environment and the vehicle have been evaluated.

The use of simulation to train drivers in identification of hazard cues is illustrated by the training filmstrip, "Perception of Driving Hazards," developed for Shell Oil Company by the Center for Safety Education, New York University. By practice in sharpening recognition skills, drivers may increase their proficiency in identifying cues to potentially dangerous situations. The subjects view a frame for 5 seconds and discuss the hazards they perceived; after a discussion, the frame is shown again and the instructor reviews the hazards he perceives.

Criterion Tests

In a series of studies that attempted to differentiate accident-free and negligent drivers, Spicer (1962) has demonstrated the validity of a measure of identification skill in differentiating between these two groups. Spicer showed subjects driving scenes filmed from the front seat and asked observers to check off from a list of items those that were actually present in the driving scene. This test did not require subjects to note potential hazards, simply important elements present. According to these findings, those subjects who had a better capacity to read the driving scene and identify the salient features were less likely to have been involved in accidents. The procedure of training drivers in recognition and testing them using filmed scenes can obviously be used readily in a school situation, and allows the possibility of practicing on a wide variety of driving environments.

PREDICTION

Prediction refers to the translation of stimulus information into possible future outcomes on the basis of "rules" stored in the memory. These rules include: (a) explicit rules of the road; (b) "rules" having to do with human behavior in general; and (c) "rules" of vehicular dynamics derived from driving experience. These rules form the basis of most predictions the driver must make concerning the control of his own vehicle and his interaction with other drivers or traffic events.

Five tentative categories of estimations can be identified as important:

(1) speed, (2) distance, (3) miss distance, (4) direction, and (5) other driver behavior. Although speed and distance estimation may be treated as independent categories, they are highly interrelated in many complex situations.

(1) Two basic questions arise concerning how a driver estimates the speed of other vehicles—the cues the driver uses to estimate the speed of another vehicle and the accuracy of estimation. Accuracy of speed estimation is important when the estimator is stationary as, for example, when waiting at an intersection to make a left-hand turn across an oncoming lane of traffic, and when the driver is moving and must estimate the speed of an oncoming car in order to determine whether it is safe to pass or not.

(2) The same questions of cue identification and accuracy of estimations also apply to distance estimation. The high degree of interrelationship between speed and distance is indicated by such findings as: following distance is highly correlated with speed; and lateral displacement during passing increases as a function of speed.

(3) Miss distance is a variant of distance estimation, and covers a number of areas usually not considered in distance estimation. It may be considered an index of the amount of error the driver will tolerate in a given situation. For example, how much lateral displacement would a driver make in order to pass a given obstacle such as a construction barricade or truck parked along the side of the road? Miss distance is also concerned with such problems as the acceptance of minimum lateral separation in tunnels or other bottlenecks.

(4) Direction is concerned with the cues that permit a driver to estimate when, where, and what change in course another vehicle will take. The information may range from the presence of blinking turn signals to the observation that the car behind intends to pass by its continual maneuvers to check for the presence or absence of oncoming traffic.

(5) The prediction of other drivers' behavior involves the general rules of human behavior that apply to the driving situation and how and when to predict situations in which human behavior may break down and become unpredictable. That is, what are the cues that drivers use to determine whether the behavior system of other drivers may become unpredictable?

Estimates of speed, distance, and miss distance are all involved in a key driver variable, the maintenance of a separation between his vehicle and other vehicles and objects. Following the model of Gordon and Mast (1968) we can see that for any control maneuver, separation can be measured by two variables: A is the gap time or distance involved in the separation; B is the gap time or distance required by the driver-car combination to perform the maneuver. In car-following, for example, A

is the distance or time gap between the lead car and the following car and *B* is the time or distance required by the following driver to stop his vehicle before colliding with the lead vehicle. In overtaking and passing, the driver must carry out the maneuver in the time or space available. In a study of overtaking and passing by Gordon and Mast, *A* is the gap time or distance separating the overtaken and opposing vehicles; *B* is the time or distance required by the driver-car combination to perform the overtaking-passing maneuver. It may readily be seen that these two variables also apply to such maneuvers as merging, passing an intersection, and to other driver tasks as well. When the driver makes a U-turn, the width of the road is related to the turning radius of the car. In pulling into a parking space in a lot, the space available is *A*, and the width of the car plus room to open the doors is *B*.

To maintain separation, *A* obviously has to be greater than *B*. As the ratio approaches unity, separation goes to zero and an accident occurs. In an early paper, Gibson and Crooks (1938) suggest that the ratio of *A* to *B* averaged over a series of driver control maneuvers measures the margin of safety. The driver may accept a narrow margin of safety by his own driving decisions or by entering a busy freeway.

Generally the ratio of these two variables provides the task input to the driver. This ratio can be increased or decreased in magnitude by manipulation of conditions such as the width and curvature of the road, the placement of fixed objects, the following distance imposed, gaps between vehicles in merging and passing, and so on. The ratio can also be characterized by its variance, or rate of change over time. The driver's task is to maintain separation in an adaptive control system sense. As the input to the driver changes, his task is to compensate for or match these changes by his control responses in order to maintain an input state in which the ratio is greater than unity.

More specifically the driver has to locate and identify separation situations that may be critical and must then estimate the two parameters involved. These estimates result in two additional quantities, *A*, the driver's estimate of the gap available, and *B*, the driver's estimate of time or distance required to perform the maneuver (Gordon and Mast, 1968). Ability to estimate time or distance gaps and the time or distance required for vehicular performance may be important learned aspects of driving skills. Gordon and Mast, in their study of overtaking and passing, found that drivers made better predictions of overtaking performance in their own cars than in an unfamiliar experimental vehicle. These authors suggest that the driver's ability to estimate braking, U-turns, parking, and car-following requirements may furnish a useful measure of his skill and effectiveness.

Following the estimation of these two parameters, the driver's decision involves a comparison of *A* and *B*. If the outcome is favorable with the gap available judged to be longer than the time or distance required with adequate safety margin, the driver will accept the gap. If not, he will reject it. In car-following the driver faced with an unacceptable separation will attempt to slow down. In making binary decisions such as merging or overtaking and passing, the driver will decide either to perform or not perform the maneuver.

Training in Prediction

No training methods deal in detail with procedures for accurate and rapid estimations. A few demonstrations designed to upset the complacency of the student with respect to his capacity to estimate have been used repeatedly. A well-known demonstration deals with the discrepancy between actual and estimated stopping distance.

There are, however, some examples of training in some of the more overall strategic problems of prediction. A number of training programs provide practice in interpreting the behavior of the other driver. One section of a driver improvement program designed by Fletcher (1962) provides systematic training in predicting the moves other drivers might make that will endanger him. The driver learns to associate potential dangers with the current spatial relations of the two vehicles, by learning to anticipate the kinds of change that may predictably occur.

Training in the perceptual functions—observation, identification, and interpretation—may benefit by the technique of "commentary driving." The methods used by the London Metropolitan Police School and the Institute for Advanced Motorists, as described by Carmichael and Hugunin (1956), demand that the driver comment on the hazards perceived, the possible hazards impending, and his plans to avoid them. Commentary driving might be used successfully with a simulated driving scene or, indeed, in verbal description of a scene to a trainee. Carmichael and Hugunin (1956) have reported that commentary driving increases the sensitivity of drivers to the requirement for observational routines, cue identification, and interpretation of the problems presented by the driving task. Drivers become aware of distraction, the cues they are missing, and problems they had not thought of solving. The role of self-instruction, verbal plans and strategies in the acquisition of motor skills has been pointed out by psychologists Miller, Galanter, and Pribram (1960). As these authors indicate, behavior that is originally under the control of verbal instructions becomes automatized and the mediating verbal instructions fall out. It may be necessary for the experienced driver to restore the primacy of verbal control by using commentary driving to correct his habitual performance.

Criterion Tests

Direct studies of how people normally behave in traffic situations are few as compared to accident studies, and only a handful of research studies have been performed on the accuracy of predictive judgments. Barch (1968) examined the effects of speed adaptation on estimates of distances and velocities with negative results. However, he used very short trips and may not have achieved adaptation. Suhr, Lauer, and Allgaier (1958) compared the judgments of speed on a highway and on an auto trainer and found similar estimation errors in both situations, suggesting that simulation techniques might be used to measure estimation. Olson, Wachsler, and Bauer (1961) found that subjects tend to underestimate the relative speed differential between their car and the one in front of it. Wright and Sleight (1962) found that drivers are unable to estimate distances in car length when one car is following another and consequently unable to apply the rule with any degree of precision of allowing one car length for every 10 miles of speed. Furthermore, they found that drivers who were taught to apply this rule using special judgment aids felt uncomfortably close at the distances required in car lengths for higher speeds. Hakkinen (1960) found that estimation of velocity was a more sensitive measure of changes in driving skill due to alcohol than practical tests of driving or a discrimination reaction time test. Bjorkman (1963) used a film technique to present the driving information and found two kinds of errors, overestimation of distances and underestimation of velocities. Since these errors combine to the greatest possible disadvantage, Hakkinen suggested that considerable training is necessary to overcome them. From these studies it is quite clear that the importance of accurate prediction is just beginning to be established in research studies. The development of methods for training drivers in making accurate predictions and evaluating their proficiency in these skills needs to be studied further.

DECISION-MAKING

Decision refers to the cognitive formulation of a course of action with intent to execute it. Following the driver's appraisal of the driving scene he must select some course of action. Cumming (1964) has suggested that there is an upper limit to the rate at which the driver can make decisions. Obviously the decisions that a driver must make are many and varied, ranging from minor automatic to highly complex decisions relating to potential accident situations. Examples of decisions made by the driver are determination of route, lane, speed, and following distance. Some decisions are dichotomous—passing, merging, stopping—and some continuous—speed, direction.

Training in Decision-Making

Undoubtedly, ingenious driver instructors have devised systematic procedures for training in decision-making and mock-ups of driving situations with movable vehicles may be very helpful. Commercially available training simulators contain decision problems in the filmed driving scenes. In a training program for aircraft operators, the Air Force has used decision-making problems of gradually increasing complexity until the pilots were handling problems more complex than those usually encountered. This increase in complexity was intended to increase the efficiency of performance of the more normal piloting tasks.

A series of filmstrips providing training in "passing" produced by the Ford Motor Company follows this procedure of moving from simple to more complex problems. Introductory nondynamic problems can be introduced to the learner with static mock-ups. More complex decision problems with a time dimension can be presented with simulators using films or a more flexible input device.

Criterion Tests

Methods for measuring the quality and speed of decision-making are not presently available, but may be possible with sufficient attention and funds. A paper and pencil test of driver decisions has recently been produced by Fine, Malfetti, and Shoben (1964) based on a collection of critical incidents of driver behavior gathered from professionals. The test requires a multiple-choice selection of the appropriate response to a number of driving problems. Decision-making problems can also be represented via film and simulator.

Several indirect measures of the quality of driver decision-making can be inferred from research studies. If we assume that drivers who are uncertain, or who do not know how to respond to a problem, will reflect that uncertainty and confusion in their behavior, then we may infer the quality of decision-making from the degree of tension in their performance. Michaels (1960) has demonstrated that the magnitude of tension, as measured by the galvanic skin response, is related to the complexity of the task faced by the driver. His study indicated that a road generates tension in drivers inversely with the predicability of the interferences and directly with the complexity of the traffic situation with which drivers must deal. In addition, the magnitude of tension is directly related to the rate at which decisions are forced on the driver by the traffic. The utilization of this tension response for measuring driver proficiency has not yet been examined. Logically, the complexity of the task and predictability of the interference are both functions of the objective situation and driver capability. By keeping the objective features constant, this might provide a measure of driver capability.

Another indirect measure of driver tension has been suggested by Greenshields (1961; 1963) and Platt (1963). These authors have suggested that a measure of frequency of steering wheel reversals, when the measure is so fine that it does not reflect turning of the tire, but the coupling of the driver to the wheel by very small movements, may reveal driver characteristics. A steering wheel reversal rate that is higher than the driver's base rate may reflect fatigue. The use of this measure to reflect these driver states has not yet been experimentally confirmed, but suggested in some very stimulating pilot studies.

Summary: Decision-Making

One subtask of driving has been described as decision-making, the formulation of alternatives and the selection of a response from among those alternatives. Decision problems are generated by uncertainty, unpredictability, or complexity of events in the environment. They may also be generated by conflict among alternative choices. Each choice involves knowledge of the alternative behaviors possible and anticipation of the consequences of the respective alternatives.

Systematic expositions of problem situations in driving calling for decisions have not been performed. This exposition should include an analysis of the driving situations that produce problems, the criteria for acceptable solutions, the principal factors that need to be coped with, the principal response alternatives available to the driver, methods for increasing the amount of information available, and errors the driver should guard against. Methods for evaluating driver decision-making are currently under development. They include road tests, paper and pencil tests calling for the selection of the right solution, and indirect measures such as tension, steering wheel movements, and response delay.

EXECUTION

Execution or performance as used here refers to the basic control actions the driver makes: steering wheel manipulation, brake and accelerator application, and their influence on the vehicle. Two different sets of skills, hierarchically ordered, are involved, the ability to control the vehicle well within operating limits, and near and beyond the limits of performance of the man-machine unit. The second is characteristic of racing driving and emergency situations.

The skills necessary to control a vehicle well within the limits seem to be acquired fairly readily. Ellingstad (1970) has recently identified three separate dimensions of this subtask in a factor analytic study: steering control, speed control, and a tracking error dimension independent of both steering and speed control. Steering and speed control have been shown to be positively correlated for experienced drivers and negatively correlated for highly inexperienced drivers, even on the simple task of driving on a traffic-free track (Safren, Cohen, and Schlesinger, 1970).

The skills required to control a vehicle at or near limits of capability of the driver-vehicle combination have not yet been systematically analyzed. Except for racing and test driving the necessity for vehicular control under extreme conditions occurs with low probability but high seriousness. However, inability to control the vehicle as the limits are approached may contribute to accident generation.

Training in Execution

A number of research studies comparing different methods of training drivers in the handling of the vehicular controls have been reported. These studies typically are concerned with comparing range, on-the-road, and simulator training. Unfortunately, none of these studies has dealt with the *content* of the training, the major focus has been on *method.* Training in speed and direction control and tracking is primarily teaching a motor skill. Learning a motor skill requires the stimulation provided by kinesthetic feedback from the muscles—"getting the feel of the car." Practice in a car on a variety of roads is essential for learning this skill. Simulator practice is of little value unless the simulator reproduces the "feel" of the vehicle.

Once these basic skills are acquired, the simulator can be valuable in learning to control the car so as to maintain separation, or avoid collisions with other objects, cars, or people. A much wider range of situations can be presented for practice than would be possible by using the automobile alone.

A major gap in education for accident avoidance is training in responding to unpredictable events by recognizing the cues that presage these events and taking appropriate actions (*Journal of American Insurance,* 1969). The driver needs to learn skills specific to such problems as driving on snow and ice (*Traffic Safety,* 1968); maintaining directional control after going over a bump; straightening the vehicle after beginning to skid, slide, spinout, hydroplane or unexpectedly run off the road (Cardno, 1969; *Traffic Safety,* 1964). "Skid pans," large circular pads where drivers can learn how to control skidding cars on wet surfaces, are currently in use (*Motor*, 1968). Drivers also need to learn countermeasures to handle blowouts, evasive maneuvers, and related problems of general vehicle control.

Criterion Tests

A variety of techniques have been used in attempts to measure driver performance (Allgaier and Yaksich, 1959; Lauer, Suhr, and Allgaier, 1958; Uhlaner, 1956): paper and pencil tests, psychomotor apparatus, simulators, and on-the-road tests. Two performance measures have been suggested which describe the motion of the vehicle and reflect the speed, force, and precision with which the driver uses the controls. These are *speed changes over time* and *direction changes over time*. Changes in direction reflect the driver's ability to accurately track the roadway keeping the lateral displacement of his vehicle at a minimum (Domey and Paterson, 1962; DeFerarri, 1961). Variability of acceleration reflects the smoothness of a driver's speed changes over time. This measure indicates a driver's skill in maintaining a safe following distance, anticipating the actions of other drivers or traffic events, and making accurate decisions in advance as he drives through traffic. On a driving range without other vehicles or obstacles present, it would reflect more simply his ability to move the car smoothly. Of course, the measures of direction and acceleration could be combined into a single vectorial measure. Variance in acceleration, termed acceleration noise, is defined as the root mean square value of the acceleration with respect to time, the variability recorded in the speed-time graph. Clearly, the variability will depend on the nature of the road, the traffic conditions, and the driver's skill, among other things. If factors such as road conditions and traffic were to be controlled or randomized experimentally, then acceleration noise should be useful as a measure of driving skill. The smoothness of a driver's speed-time plot or direction change-time plot will reflect the nature of the roadway and traffic conditions. But, in addition, these plots will reflect skill in processing and organizing the information from the driving scene. There is currently a lively interest in research on measurement of driver performance and a number of instrumented vehicles, varying considerably in the sophistication of their gadgetry, are being employed in this research (Snider and Rockwell, 1963; Michon and Koutsaal, 1969; Greenshields and Platt, 1964; Platt, 1969). Some of the less complex measurement devices are being examined for their contribution to driver training and driver evaluation.

Greenshields (1961; 1963) has been interested in identifying differences in groups varying in driving experience and accident records. He has used an instrument called the Drivometer which records: number of steering wheel reversals, number of accelerator depressions, number of brake applications, frequency of speed changes (an approximation of acceleration variability), total time, and delay time. He reports that drivers with different degrees of experience and accident records have different patterns of driving, as indicated by these measures. He also reports that drivers of different skill levels (as measured by their driving histories) varied in the total number of control responses made.

Summary: Execution

One objective of training is precise and smooth control of the vehicle: speed and direction control and maintenance of separation, at conditions within and close to the extremes of vehicular control, and under conditions of low to high saturation of the highway with moving traffic, fixed objects, and pedestrians. Training strategies for the accomplishment of this task have not been examined as carefully as the value of varying methods and durations of training. Technology in measurement of driver actions and vehicular output indicates considerable advance in our capability to measure this aspect of driver performance directly by using relatively simple apparatus such as the Greenshields Drivometer or a tachometer.

SUMMARY: THE DRIVING TASK

This chapter has attempted to specify the major behavioral skills required in driving based on an analysis of the driver's task (Miller, 1962). On the basis of a formulation of the major driving task and a review of the skills required to perform this task, an attempt is made to make a preliminary map of the driver training course, its objectives, methods, and criterion tests. The map is admittedly sketchy, and several observations become clear in reviewing it. First, there is a gap between what we currently know about the behavioral skills to be attained in driving and what we need to know to produce skilled drivers. Second, the content and methods of driver training need considerable reconstruction if we are to optimize the small amount of time allotted to driver training. Third, the criterion tests currently available fall far short of the driver educator's need. This map, then, is an invitation to the reader to revise or fill in the sketchy portions and to take part in the research expeditions aimed at identifying the gaps in the driver education process.

If this description of a driving model seems sketchy, our understanding of the processes of planned change in transportation referred to earlier in this chapter and how they can be communicated to new members of society is at a bare beginning. A theoretical underpinning to the enterprise at the societal level is provided by Etzioni (1968), and the work of human relations practitioners in the field of planned change is summarized in a book of readings (Bennis et al., 1961).

Finally, this chapter has attempted to provide some markers in two distinct paths, in the direction of improving safe driving by indicating the skills that need training in driving, and by emphasizing the importance of introducing into our educational systems some more basic understanding of how sociotechnical systems, like the one associated with the automobile, work and more than that, how to make them work.

REFERENCES

Allen, T. M., Lunenfeld, H., and Alexander, G. J., Driver Information, Paper presented at the Highway Research Board, Washington, D.C., 1970.

Allgaier, E. and Yaksich, S., Effectiveness of a Driving Simulator, 1956–1958, American Automobile Association, Traffic Engineering and Safety Division, Washington, D.C., 1959.

Asher, J. W., Do Driver Training Courses Produce Better Drivers? An Alternative Hypothesis, *Traffic Safety Research Review,* **12**, 1 (1968, 2–6.

Barch, A. M., Judgments of Speed on the Open Highway, *Journal on Applied Psychology,* **42** (1958), 362–366.

Bennis, W. G., Benne, K. D., and Chin, R., *The Planning of Change,* Holt, Rinehart and Winston, New York, 1961.

Bishop, Richard, *A Resource Curriculum in Driver and Traffic Safety Education,* Automotive Safety Foundation, Washington, D.C., 1970.

Bjorkman, M., An Exploratory Study of Predictive Judgments in a Traffic Situation, University of Stockholm, Sweden, 1963.

Black, Stephen, *Man and Motor Cars,* Norton, New York, 1966.

Blumenthal, Murray, What Can We Expect from Driver Education? Appendix F in *Driver Education and Training Project for NHSB,* El Segundo, Cal., 1968.

Boorstin, Daniel J., preface to John B. Rae, *The American Automobile,* University of Chicago Press, Chicago, Ill., 1965.

Brody, Leon, Driver Education and Training—Plans for Evaluating the Effectiveness of Programs, New York University Center for Safety, N.Y., 1968.

Burg, A., Vision Test Scores and Driving Record: Additional Findings, Final Report, Institute of Transportation and Traffic Engineering, University of California, Los Angeles, Cal., December 1968, p. 139.

Cardno, H. Sideways for Safety, *Motor,* September 1969, 33–36.

Carmichael, G. V. and Hugunin, E., Experiment in Commentary Driving, *Traffic Digest and Review,* **4** (1956), 14–16.

Center for Safety Education, *Driver Education and Traffic Safety,* Prentice Hall, Englewood Cliffs, N.J., 1967.

Chandler, R. E., Herman, R., and Montroll, E. W., Traffic Dynamics: Studies in Car Following, *Operative Research,* **6** (1958), 165–184.

Cogan, Eugene A., The Evaluation of Systems-Analytic Training Programs, Human Resources Research Organization, Alexandria, Va., 1967.

Conger, John J., Research in Driver Education, in *Proceedings of National Driver*

Education and Training Symposia, Institute for Educational Development, El Segundo, Cal., 1969, 107–126.

Conger, J. J., Miller, W. C., and Rainey, R. V., Effects of Driver Education: The Role of Motivation, Intelligence, Social Class, and Exposure, *Traffic Safety Research Review,* **10**, 3 (1966), 67–71.

Coppin, R. S., Ferdun, G. S., and Peck, R. C., The Teen-aged Driver, California Department of Motor Vehicles, Report No. 21, February 1965a.

Cumming, R. W., The Analysis of Skills in Traffic, *Australian Road Research,* Victoria, Australia, 1964.

DeFerrari, A., Design Experimentation With a Device for the Detection of Driver Alertness During Actual Road Tests, unpublished doctoral dissertation, Massachusetts Institute of Technology, 1961.

Domey, R. G. and Duggar, B., The Orthopedically Impaired Person: V. Measurement of Capacity to Operate Commercial Vehicles, Harvard School of Public Health, Boston, Mass., 1962.

Domey, R. G. and Paterson, D., Development of a Vehicle Simulator for Evaluating Driver Performance, Harvard School of Public Health, Boston, Mass., 1962.

Driessen, Gerald, The Fallacy of the "Untrained Driver," *Traffic Safety,* **6**, 3 (March 1969).

Ellingstad, V. S., A Factor Analytic Approach to the Driving Task, *Behavioral Research in Highway Safety,* **1**, 2 (1970), 115–126.

Etzioni, Amitai, *The Active Society,* The Free Press, New York, 1968.

Fine, J. L., Malfetti, J. L., and Shoben, E. J., Development of the Columbia Driver Judgment Test, Safety Research Education Project, Teachers College, Columbia University, 1964.

Fletcher, H., Driver Improvement Schools: A Guide for their Operation, American Automobile Association, Washington, D.C., 1962.

Forbes, T. W., Human Factors in Highway Safety, *Traffic Safety Research Review,* **4**, 1 (1960), 8–11.

Gagne, R. M., Human Functions in Systems, in Gagne, R. M., ed., *Psychological Principles In System Development,* Holt, Rinehart and Winston, New York, 1962.

Gagne, Robert M., Modern Learning Principles and Driver Education, in *Proceedings of National Driver Education and Training Symposia,* Institute for Educational Development, El Segundo, Cal., 1969.

Garner, W. R., *Uncertainty and Structure as Psychological Concepts,* Wiley, New York, 1962.

Gibson, J. J. and Crooks, L. E., A Theoretical Field-Analysis of Automobile Driving, *American Journal of Psychology,* **2**, 3 (1938).

Giedion, S., *Mechanization Takes Command,* Oxford University Press, New York, 1948.

Goldstein, L. G., Research on Human Variables in Safe Motor Vehicle Operation: A Correlational Summary of Predictor Variables and Criterion Measures. Driver Behavior Research Project, George Washington University, Washington, D.C., June 1961.

Gordon, Donald A. and Mast, Truman M., A Study of Driver's Decisions in Overtaking and Passing, *Highway Research Record,* 1968, 42–50.

Greenshields, B. D., Investigating Highway Traffic Events in Relation To Driver Actions, *Traffic Quarterly,* **15** (1961), 665–676.

Greenshields, B., Driving Behavior and Related Problems, *Highway Research Board Bulletin,* **25** (1963).

Greenshields, B. D. and Platt, F. N., Objective Measurements of Driver Behavior, SAE Automotive Engineering Congress, Detroit, Mich., 1964.

Haddon, W., Jr., Haddon on Highway Safety, *Analogy,* Winter 1968.

Hakkinen, S., The Effect of Alcohol on the Driving Skill, *Alkoholipolitikka,* **25** (1960), 8–18 (in Finnish and Swedish).

Hakkinen, S., Estimation of Distance and Velocity in Traffic Situations, Rept. No. 3, Institute of Occupational Health, Helsinki, Finland, 1963.

Harman, Harry et al., Evaluation of Driver Education and Training Programs, National Academy of Sciences, Highway Research Board, Washington, D.C., 1969.

Herbert, M. J., Analysis of a Complex Skill: Vehicle Driving, *Human Factors,* August 1963, 363–372.

Holmes, H. H. and Whitworth, R. A., How To Lay Out a Winter Driving Snow Course, *Traffic Safety,* **68**, 2 (February 1968).

Hulbert, S. F., Driver's GSR's in Traffic, *Perception and Motivational Skills,* **7** (1957), 305–315.

Jones, T. R. and Potts, R. B., The Measurement of Acceleration Noise: A Traffic Parameter, *Operation Research,* 1962, 745–763.

Journal of American Insurance, Crisis Conditioning—New Approach to Driver Training, *Journal of American Insurance,* **45**, 4 (Sept.–Oct. 1969).

Kennedy, John., Driver Education and Training Project for the National Highway Safety Bureau, Institute for Educational Development, El Segundo, Cal., 1968.

Lauer, A. R., Suhr, V. W., and Allgaier, E., Development of a Criterion for Driving Performance, *Traffic Safety Research Review,* **2**, 1 (1958), 24–29.

Lybrand, William, A Study on Evaluation of Driver Education, American University, Washington, D.C., July 1968.

McFarland, R. A., Health and Safety in Transportation, in W. Haddon, E. A. Suchman, and D. Klein, *Accident Research: Methods and Approaches,* Harper and Row, New York, 1964.

McGuire, F. L. and Kersh, R. C., An Evaluation of Driver Education. *Publications in Education,* **19** (1969), University of California.

McKnight, James., Detailed Plan for Development of Driver Education Objectives: A Driving Task Analysis, Human Resources Research Organization, Alexandria, Va., 1969.

Michaels, R. M., Tension Responses of Drivers Generated on Urban Streets, *Highway Research Board Bulletin,* 271, 1960.

Michaels, R. M., Human Factors in Highway Safety, *Traffic Quarterly,* **15**, 4 (1961), 586–599.

Michon, J. A. and Koutsaal, G. A., An Instrumented Car for the Study of Driver Behavior, *American Psychologist,* **24**, 3 (March 1969).

Miller, G. A., Galanti, E., and Pribram, K. H., *Plans and the Structure of Behavior,* Holt-Dryden, New York, 1960.

Miller, Louis, et al., Driver Licensing and Performance, *Research Review and Recommendations,* **1** (1969), Spindletop Research, Lexington, Ky.

Miller, R. B., Analysis and Specification of Behavior for Training, in Glaser, R., ed., *Training Research and Education,* University of Pittsburgh Press, Pittsburgh, Pa., 1962.

Motor, Let's Go Skidding, November 1968, 41–42, London.

Moynihan, Daniel P. et al., Report of the Secretary's Advisory Committee on Traffic Safety, U.S. Department of Health, Education and Welfare, Washington, D.C., February 1968, 147 pages.

Nader, Ralph, *Unsafe at Any Speed,* Simon and Schuster, New York, 1966.

National Education Association, Committee on Safety Education, Summary of Results of Studies Evaluating Driver Education, 1961, 17 pp.

National Highway Safety Bureau, *Proceedings: National Driver Education and Training Symposia,* Washington, D.C., 1968–1969.

Olson, P. L., Wachsler, R. A., and Bauer, J. J., Driver Judgment of Relative Car Velocities, *Journal Applied Psychology,* **45** (1961), 161–164.

Payne, D. E. and Barmack, J. E., An Experimental Field Test of the Smith-Cummings-Sherman Driver Training System, *Traffic Safety Research Review,* **7**, 1 (1963), 15–22.

Platt, F., A New Method of Measuring the Effect of Continued Driving Performance, *Highway Research Record,* 25 (1963).

Platt, F. N., The Highway Systems Research Catalog, *Proceedings: National Driver Education and Training Symposia,* Washington, D.C., 1969.

Rainey, R. V., Conger, J. J., and Walsmith, C. R., Personality Characteristics As a Selective Factor in Driver Education, *Highway Research Board Bulletin,* **285** (1961), 23–28.

Rockwell, T. H. and Ernst, R., Research on Visual Requirements in Night Activity, Final Progress Report, Ohio State University, Engineering Experiment Station, Columbus, Ohio, April 1967, p. 220.

Rockwell, T. H., Overby, C., and Mourant, R. R., Drivers Eye Movements: An Appartus and Calibration, *Highway Research Record,* 1968, pp. 29–41.

Ross, H. L., Schematic Analysis of the Driving Situation, *Traffic Safety and Research Review,* **4**, 3 (1960), 4–7.

Safren, M., Cohen, S., and Schlesinger, L., The Drivometer as a Measure of Driving Skill, *Journal of Safety Research,* **2**, 1 (March 1970), 30–35.

Sargent, K. J. and Colborne, Helen V., Pre-driver and Driver Training in Secondary Schools, Road Research Laboratory, LR 263, Crow Thorne, Berkshire, 1969.

Schlesinger, Lawrence E., Objectives, Methods and Criteria on Tests in Driver Training, *Traffic Safety Research Review,* March 1967, 18–24.

Schlesinger, J. E. and Safren, M. A., Perceptual Analysis of the Driving Task, Paper read at the 43rd Annual Meeting of the Highway Research Board, Washington, D.C., January 1964.

Shell Oil Co., Perception of Driving Hazards. Part I (Filmstrip), Center for Safety Education, Shell Traffic Safety Center, New York University, New York.

Smith, H. L. and Cummings, J. J., Let's Teach Drivers How To See, *Traffic Digest and Review,* 1956, 7–13.

Snider, J. M. and Rockwell, T. H., The Development of an Instrumentation System to Measure True Driving Performance. *Traffic Safety Research Review,* **7**, 3 (September 1963).

Spicer, R., Human Factors in Traffic Accidents, Hawaii Department of Health, Progress Rept, 1962 (unpublished).

Tarrants, William E., Current Research in Driver Education, Special Report 107, Highway Safety, Highway Research Board, Washington, D.C., 1970, pp. 34–40.

Teal, Gilbert, Driver Education and Training, Dunlap and Associates, Darien, Conn., 1968.

Traffic Safety, Teach Skidding 'Know-How' at Liberty School, **4**, 11 (November 1964).

Uhlaner, J. W., Tests for Selecting Drivers, Papers read at Eastern Psychological Association, 1956.

Waldram, J. M., Vision and Eye Movements of Motor Drivers, *The New Scientist,* 8 (1960), p. 10.

Worner, C. K., I Didn't See Him, *Indiana Bell News,* **1** (1961), 34–36.

Wright, S. and Sleight, R. B., Influence of Mental Set and Distance Judgments Aids on Following Distance, *Highway Research Board Bulletin,* 330 (1962).

XII
EFFECTS OF DRIVER FATIGUE

Slade Hulbert

EXTENT OF PROBLEM

Falling asleep at the wheel and running off the roadway is merely the unfortunate endpoint which makes it obvious that many more motorists are on the highway in a state of drowsiness but they do not run off the roadway far enough to incapacitate their vehicle. Others, who are less fortunate than either of these groups, have collisions with other vehicles. These sleepy drivers may never be recorded as having been drowsy or actually falling asleep. For these reasons, the true magnitude of the problem is not known; however, the data indicate that from 35 to 50 percent of highway fatalities are directly attributable to fatigue or drowsiness (Kearney, 1966; Forbes, 1958). This may be only the visible tip of a gigantic iceberg constituting a national driving problem about which very little is known.

TYPES OF FATIGUE

As early as 1920 researchers recognized difficulties in defining the term fatigue (Muscio, 1920). Therefore, researchers have had to rely on a descriptive definition of just what each person means by the term. Two major categories are "task-induced" fatigue and fatigue due to other (nondriving) factors such as sleep deprivation. Both of these are undoubtedly playing a part in traffic accident causation (Crawford, 1961). Sleep deprivation is by far the most widely studied of the two and the more easily generalized from nondriving studies.

SLEEP DEPRIVATION EFFECTS

Sleep loss in most studies produces some decrement in performance skills such as hand steadiness, motor coordination, and reaction time. However, there is a remarkable ability to perform well on skill tests of short duration even after two or more days without sleep (Warren and Clark, 1937). This phenomenon is strongly related to motivational factors. Driving, however, is a continuous task and has been shown to reveal clear-cut lapses in attention (drowsiness) associated with loss of sleep. McFarland and Mosely (1954) tested one driver who had been kept awake for 24 hours; 4 hours of "driving" in a training simulator showed a fall-off in efficiency and "the subject's insight into his own condition lapsed." Hulbert (1963) tested 11 male drivers (firemen) after 24 hours without sleep and found marked effects of drowsiness during a 45- to 60-minute drive in the UCLA Driving Simulation Laboratory over a two-lane mountain road. The following behaviors were noted during the drive as several of the drivers clearly were observed falling asleep at the wheel:

1. In controlling vehicle speed, the alert subject usually accelerated and decelerated sharply. The tired subject had long, slow speed changes, and when he became drowsy the speed changed very slowly or not at all.
2. In steering the vehicle, the alert subject usually made many small corrections and had a correspondingly high steering reversal count. The fatigued subject did not steer as much, and when the subject dozed his steering ceased.
3. In reacting to traffic events, the alert subject usually exhibited a change in galvanic skin response (GSR). The fatigued subject's GSR record showed less reaction, and when the subject dozed the GSR gradually lessened.
4. In breathing, the alert subject usually had a change in respiration pattern at events. The tired subject did not react, and when the subject became drowsy his breathing became very regular and shallow.
5. The fatigued driver performed many body movements and actions as rubbing his face or head, stretching, smoking, closing eyes, and so on. The alert driver was relatively inactive.

Forbes et al. (1958) observed 24- to 36-hour sleep-deprived drivers on the actual highway as they drove a dual-controlled car. During a 5-hour drive, response frequency was tabulated for weaving, drifting, unnecessary speed changes, eye blinks, eye closures, glances at dashboard indicators, checking outside mirror, checking inside mirror, calling potential hazards and estimated distances (car lengths) between the test vehicle and the car ahead when pulling out to pass, estimated by one observer. (In one set of runs, two observers made the same estimates for a check of reliability.)

Other events recorded were observance of speed zones, restlessness and position-changes indicating fatigue, any critical incidents of special importance, reports on judgment of fatigue every half hour, and voluntary, unsolicited comments of the driver whenever given. They found a statistically significant difference between driving efficiency for sleep-deprived and normal runs. In the extreme deprivation runs, four out of five subjects actually dozed at the wheel and the fifth very nearly did so.

TASK-INDUCED FATIGUE

Many studies involve both loss of sleep and long hours of driving, which is called task-induced fatigue. Safford and Rockwell (1967) had drivers perform continuous 24-hour periods of driving and found that as the hours on the road increased, they could no longer do a satisfactory job of *simultaneous* speed and path following. They monitor either speed (maintain constant speed) or steering and perform reasonably well but they could not do both tasks at once. This same lack of ability to simultaneously track and maintain speed was found by Hakkinen in tests of rally drivers after several hours of competition driving, which may account for the behavior of Safford and Rockwell's seven drivers who were required to drive the 24 hours with stops only for refueling. Results showed changes in velocity means, velocity variances, steering wheel reversals, and gas pedal reversals with passage of time. However, trends for the same variable occurred in either direction and they stated, ". . . an increase or decrease in the value of one of the dependent variables cannot be taken as an indication of fatigue without knowing the specific characteristics of the subject driver that produced the increase or decrease." This is exactly the type of result we would expect if the tired drivers were alternating between speed monitoring (gas pedal reversals and velocity variation) and path following (steering reversals). Platt (1964) and Greenshields (1963) had noted similar differences in tired drivers with regard to steering reversals that had a marked tendency to change (faster or slower) as compared with the individual's nonfatigued rate.

Nine hours of driving off-road vehicles was found by Herbert and Jaynes (1964) to be associated with poorer scores on driving tests where a precise path had to be followed and also in backing and parking in close quarters. It is quite interesting to note that as these drivers neared the end of their "work shift" of 9 hours, there was some improvement over their previous scores, which had been progressively worsening in tests conducted after zero to 7 hours of driving.

Brown, Simmonds, and Tickner (1967), however, after measuring drivers for up to 12 hours of nearly continuous driving, concluded that performance was not adversely affected with respect to vehicle movement and vehicle control changes. Performance varied on two different types of subsidiary tasks. The motor task was affected more than the perceptual vigilance task. Depending on the sensitivity of the vehicle control scores and the relative importance placed (by the driver) on the subsidiary task, such results could well be obtained and not necessarily be in conflict with previous research.

Because continuous driving periods in excess of 12 hours begin to include sleep deprivation along with task-induced fatigue effects, it is not possible at this time to clearly describe the effects that may be solely induced by the driving task. One other contaminating factor is the natural tendency of some motorists to become drowsy while driving. If this factor is not taken into account, it could greatly bias the results.

DROWSINESS AND TRIP PLANNING

A recent study by Hulbert et al. (1970) approached this question of individual differences in fatigue effects on driving judgment. This work was influenced by the work of Yoss at the Mayo Clinic (1969) concerning "normal amounts" of drowsiness. Yoss suggests that some degree of narcolepsy* is quite likely to be present in many motorists and undoubtedly is markedly present in some drivers. The UCLA study selected 11 drivers who had been classified as having poor trip-planning habits and who admitted to having trouble staying awake on driving trips, and compared their performance against a group of 9 drivers who had been classified as having good trip habits and who said they never had any problem staying awake at the wheel. Both groups were compared against an unselected sample of drivers. It is interesting to note that nearly half of 126 drivers interviewed admitted to one or more instances of sleeping or dozing during extended periods of driving.

The classification into poor versus good trip habits was done in a separate study (Mellinger, 1970) where over 700 motorists were questioned about their long trips. The "poor" group is characterized by lack of advance planning and a tendency to overextend themselves and thus become fatigued. The "good" group is at the other extreme and tends to drive fewer hours between well-planned stopping places. The tendency

* A clinical condition characterized by a tendency to fall asleep easily and repeatedly despite adequate nocturnal sleep.

to have trouble staying awake was distributed equally between the two groups. The third group was unselected in respect to either trip habits or drowsiness.

The three groups of drivers did not differ markedly on the computer-generated scores for the total trip. Nor were there significant differences in the scores computed for the subportions of the trip (called "events"). There were marked differences in the proportion of times drivers in the three groups failed to safely respond to nine "Traffic Collision Situations" in the filmed drive. Sixty-seven percent of the times that the drowsy group met these situations, they failed; while the alert group failed only 45 percent of these events and the control group failed 58 percent of the time. The difference, 67 versus 45 percent, is significant between the .05 and .01 levels of statistical confidence. Neither the 67 versus 58 percent nor the 45 versus 58 percent is significant at the .05 level.

As mentioned above, the UCLA study found almost one-half of the drivers questioned freely admitted to having trouble staying awake while driving. This is surely an unfortunate state of affairs considering the relatively poor performance of such a group and the high incidence of "ran off the road" single-car accidents that are caused by falling asleep at the wheel.

Certainly this study should add significant weight to the argument for a driver license screening examination and a countermeasure program of education and perhaps the medical prescription of appropriate stimulant drugs.

COUNTERMEASURES

With regard to countermeasures, Harris (1967) in his thesis presented the review reprinted below.

"Drivers have been faced with the problem of drowsiness for a long time and apparently no 'solution' has been found. Some methods for the alleviation of drowsiness that have been suggested are: singing, chewing a pack of gum, taking off the right shoe, and sitting on something hard. It is a simple and tempting matter to suggest solutions for a common problem such as drowsiness and the suggested solution may serve for some people thus providing evidence for them (and for others) that it has merit. It is very difficult, however, to collect reliable evidence to substantiate the general value of some method. There may, in fact, be no reliable method for most people. Nevertheless, the problem is sufficiently serious in its consequences in the driving situation to call for continued research.

Mechanical Devices

"In recent years, inventors have attempted to develop devices to assist the driver with this problem. *Traffic Safety* (1959) reported:

". . . Auto gadgeteers are coming up with anti-nod buzzers and bells for weary drivers. No substitute for sleep, they at least help drivers remain alert until they reach a coffee stop or motel. Two of the newest gimicks in the motorists' non-dozy future:

"1. Electronic Transistor Safety Alarm. Made of lightweight plastic (2 oz.) it curls neatly around the driver's ear, buzzes a safety signal when his head nods.

"2. Button Steering Wheel Alarm. When plugged into car radio, driver can't release button without triggering alarm.

"The first of these devices, the electronic transistor safety alarm, makes the assumption that the driver nods as soon as he loses alertness. From the study of drowsiness, the individual has lost much alertness before he first nods. Hence, the driver may have lost control of the vehicle or be off the road before the device is activated.

"The second device is even less feasible in that it requires somewhat unnatural pressures with the fingers or thumb on the button. In addition, the device would have to be deactivated when the hands were moved in a turning maneuver, because of its position on the steering wheel.

"Williams (1966) developed a device called the ALERTMASTER. It consists of a pedal, similar to the accelerator pedal, which is positioned on the floor to the left of the clutch pedal for use with the left foot. It is small and self-contained with its own horn alarm and battery. Designed for intermittent use, the device is activated only when the driver finds himself becoming drowsy or fatigued. It is activated by depressing the pedal all the way to the floor or until it clicks. When activated, the horn will sound unless the pedal is depressed. As long as light foot pressure is exerted, the horn remains silent. According to the inventor, when drowsiness begins, the left foot of the driver naturally relaxes and the horn sounds. Renewed pressure of the foot again silences the horn.

"Frederik (1966) conceived a device called the Alert-O-Matic to prevent highway accidents due to driver's sleepiness or fatigue. It weighs 3 pounds and can be wired into the electrical system of any car by a mechanic. In simple terms, it produces a sequence of three alerting signals of increasing severity. First, a light flashes on. If the driver is alerted by the light, he turns it off by tapping lightly on the horn button, which is wired into the Alert-O-Matic circuit. If he fails to notice the light for a period of 5 seconds, the Alert-O-Matic sets off the car horn. This should arouse the driver. If it does not for a period of 3 seconds, the device turns the ignition off and on rapidly for a duration of 5 seconds. Should the driver continue to doze, the device shuts off the ignition completely. The driver can cut off the cycle at any time by depressing the horn button. The first signal (the light) reappears every 60 seconds.

"No information regarding the testing of this device was found in the literature. Cudworth (1966) stated: 'We made only rough field tests on the device since it became apparent that some sort of variable timing was necessary . . . .'

"It seems probable that such a device would be readily adapted to by any driver in a relatively short time because of the monotonous sequence of stimuli, that is, the signal light appears every 60 seconds of driving. In fact, Oswald (1962) reported that some subjects exhibited a 'sleeping' pattern, which was interrupted periodically by the subject's response to the periodic stimuli to which he was subjected. In other words, subjects awoke only to execute the necessary response and then lapsed almost immediately into sleep. It seems that a driver could do likewise when exposed to this device.

"Delco Radio (1961) developed a highway-to-car communications system. This system blankets a reception area 50 to 100 feet wide across the highway and up to at least 2000 feet along the highway. Two transmitters are located in a waterproof enclosure along the road. One of these sends out a continuous signal in a loop extending about 50 feet along the road upstream from the transmitter. This length is called the trigger zone. Extending downstream is a loop radiating voice information that may extend any reasonable distance. A loop of 500 feet required about 6 seconds to pass at 65 miles per hour and allows a 3-second message to be repeated twice before a car is out of range.

"The receiver in the car would be inoperative until the car entered the trigger zone. When the trigger transmitter is picked up, the receiver is sensitized for listening to the voice signal. As long as the voice is picked up, the receiver is turned on and held on, but after the car passes beyond the range of the voice loops, the receiver reverts to its insensitive condition and no further operation will occur until the car again passes through a triggering zone. On a permanent installation, the car radio might also be switched off by the voice signal. The Highway Communication System could operate signal lights or buzzers in a car or transmit voice signals to alert the drowsy driver who failed to respond to signals initiated by the roadside system.

"Of the inventions discussed above, some may have possibility but others are useful only in that having been described they can be rather quickly set aside to clear the air for further work. The more professional research on drowsiness has turned to the study of a variety of non-mechanical stimuli. In subsequent paragraphs, research is reviewed according to the type of stimuli activity or situation used to relieve drowsiness.

Amphetamine Drugs

"Because of the serious accidents that have been caused by drivers who have driven for very long hours and are under the influence of drugs, drugs are usually not recommended to reduce drowsiness. Typical of this attitude is that of Schwenk (1960), who states: 'Keep yourself mentally alert with proper ventilation. If you are sleepy, pull off to one side of the road for a nap. NEVER rely on stimulating drugs to keep you awake.' This is a rather sweeping judgment because it seems that some drugs might have some entirely beneficial effects. At least this possibility should not be ruled out from further research.

"Rodger (1956) made the comment: 'The monotony of driving apparently for some people will produce fatigue of the central nervous system even when they have had adequate sleep.' Being concerned with this problem, he searched the literature for studies on the effects of drugs and concluded by recommending that drugs be used to relieve drowsiness. However, it must be said that Rodger published this in *GP*, which is a journal for the medical profession. He was recommending that doctors prescribe drugs in the driving situation, and that they closely supervise their patients' use of these drugs.

"McFarland et al. (1955), in summarizing the experiments on drugs to relieve drowsiness, said that Benzedrine and Dexedrine (an isomer of amphetamine) in 5- to 10-mg doses reduced the need for sleep without impairing either psychomotor or psychological efficiency. However, improvement was noted only in those cases where the individual's alertness was already impaired. They also commented that subjects exhibited a wide variety of reactions to these drugs and some of these responses were counter to those desired. Also, after a time, the individual becomes adapted to the drug used. It seems, for this discussion, that drugs of this kind should only be recommended for use under a doctor's scrutiny.

Caffeine

"Rodger (1956) comments that caffeine is a cerebral stimulant. He says that the stops to get it and the later stops to get rid of it help to break driving fatigue. But, some people get little effect from it.

" Kleitman (1963) observed that the following conclusions had been made by experimenters: (a) the amount of caffeine contained in 1 or 2 cups of coffee decreased reaction time slightly, (b) caffeine improved performance in tests requiring muscular strength and speed of movement, and had no adverse affect on steadiness. He then commented 'Whatever its mode of promoting wakefulness, caffeine, because of its availability and safety, is an excellent antihypnotic agent.'

"McFarland et al. (1955) summarized the usefulness of drinks containing caffeine:

"Drinking coffee is commonly held to be the method by which the long-haul driver wards off drowsiness and fatigue. In the laboratory caffeine has been shown to result in slightly faster reaction times, while producing a decrement in hand steadiness. The slight increase in tremor of the hands would not appear to be detrimental to driving skill. When the driver has no physical condition which makes the use of caffeine inadvisable, tea and coffee in ordinary amounts can result in improved alertness, postponing drowsiness."

It is to be noted that Kleitman and McFarland disagree on caffeine's affect on steadiness; however, they are in agreement as to its effectiveness in relieving drowsiness.

Rest and Refreshment

"Lauer and Suhr (1958) made a study of the effect of rest pauses and refreshment on driving efficiency. They used the controlled experimental approach with matched groups to determine the nature of their performance in a simulated driving situation continuing for a 3-hour period and for a 6-hour period. Groups were matched as nearly as possible to sex, age, and driving experience. There were 56 drivers: 38 male and 18 female. Ages ranged from 18 to 66 years, with a median age of 24 years for male and 25 years for female. The criterion used for minimum driving experience was three years or 10,000 miles. The actual median of the sample was eight years driving experience.

"The first group was called the no-pause group and they drove for 3 and 6 consecutive hours on the two phases of the test. The second group, the pause group, was served tea just before the test and again during the 15-minute halt after 1½ hours of driving, during the first phase of 3 hours, and again during the second phase of 6 hours.

"A device called the Drivometer was used for the simulation of the driving situation. It is so constructed that the subject sits in a stationary mock-up car using full-size automobile controls to drive a miniature car around a traveling roadway. The Drivometer is located in a special booth so that the driving environment can be controlled.

"Lauer and Suhr's conclusions were: 'It would seem that the refreshment pause not only increased the effectiveness of steering per half hour of simulated driving, but also tends to delay the onset and reduce the extent of decrement in performance.' In addition, higher concentration and great zest were noted for the refreshment pause group.

"There is little doubt that rest and refreshment can relieve drowsiness. However, many individuals find themselves in a drowsy condition when they are 10 to 15 minutes away from the nearest rest stop or otherwise unable to stop and rest. It is this situation for which a solution is sought.

Ingestion of Food

"Hulbert (1963) studied the effect of the ingestion of a nutritive substance on the performance of a simulated driving task. Two groups were tested, using the subjects as their own control. Group I (extreme fatigue, ingestion of a large quantity of a nutritive substance) consisted of 11 volunteers from the Los Angeles Fire Department and 1 volunteer from the University of California. Each subject was given three tests: the first under normal, nonfatigued conditions; the second and third with the following stipulations: 24 hours without sleep, 12 hours without food, and 4 hours without coffee, tea, or beverages. Half ate a nutritive substance on the second test and the other half ate it on the third test. Those not receiving the nutritive substance received a nonnutritive food stuff, a placebo. Presumably, subjects could not distinguish between the nutritive and nonnutritive substances.

"Group II (moderate fatigue, less quantity of the nutritive substance) consisted of 22 college students. Each subject was given two tests, both with only 3 to 5 hours of sleep the previous night. On one test, half the subjects ingested a larger quantity of the nutritive substance and the other half ingested a lesser quantity of it. The subjects were reversed on the second test.

"The nutritional value of the substance swallowed was known only to a third party who packaged the substances and scheduled which package was to be eaten by which subject on which replication. The driving test was conducted in a driving simulator (see Chapter 3).

"The test drive consisted of a 45- to 65-minute trip (depending on the actual speed at which the subject 'drove' the car) over a continuous two-lane mountain road. During the trip only four vehicles overtook the simulator vehicle, no vehicles were overtaken, and 54 vehicles were encountered as opposing traffic.

"The results of the experiment were: for Group I when the nutritive substance was ingested, the subjects had less difficulty remaining alert. For Group II (who had more sleep and less of the nutritive substance than Group I) there was no such clear-cut difference in ability to remain alert for those having nourishment. Hulbert's conclusion was that the initial research should be carried further *before* it would be safe to recommend the ingestion of this particular nutritive substance as a means of effecting fatigue while driving."

ROADSIDE RESTS

Case et al. (1969) studied the utilization and safety benefit of roadside rests at several locations in California by analyzing accident records, interviewing motorists, and photographing motorists in and near these roadside rests.

This recent report, "Evaluation Study—Safety Aspects of Roadside Rest Program," suggests that task-induced driving fatigue may take the form:

$$E_F = bx$$

where E_F is the fatigue contribution to the accident rate at point x, which is the distance from the point at which the average motorist last paused for rest, and b is the slope that best represents the relationship.

Assuming a linear relationship between distance traveled and the fatigue effect, it was possible to estimate the slope (b) to be .01. Using the estimated value of .01 which quantifies the zone-of-influence effect, it was possible for the first time to numerically express this effect in the form of the following equation:

$$E_F = .01x$$

The study went on to produce a strategy for computing the *average* fatigue effect for a portion of a highway. The relationship takes the form:

$$\bar{E}_F = .01x/2 = .005x$$

where $\bar{E}_F$ is the average fatigue effect for the portion of the highway from 0 to x. A nomograph was prepared to help make this computation for any particular roadway where trip lengths are known or can be estimated.

This work was performed using several sets of accident and travel data from only one highway location and involved fitting straight lines to each of the several sets of data and making the assumption that "basic skill" and "traffic density" effects account for no more than 20 percent of the accident rate. The authors themselves state:

"It must be emphasized that this estimate of the fatigue effect is based on meager, highly selected data and that the fitted lines are not a statistically determined, 'least square' fit to the data (in fact, better fits are likely—if equal slopes for eastbound and westbound data are not a condition). Moreover, assuming a linear function is an oversimplification—over a greater distance the fatigue effect must become exponential. Perhaps, as Haber, Brenner, and Hulbert (1954) suggest, the fatigue contribution to accident rate should be a function of hours on the road rather than distance traveled to take account of the fact that motorists drive at different speeds. In fact, some kinds of driving—whether measured by miles or hours—may be more tiring than other kinds, for example, in urban congestion or on mountain roads as contrasted with straight and level, freely moving traffic."

RECOMMENDATIONS FOR LOCATING REST AREAS

The cost/benefit analysis did not provide a straightforward answer to the question of whether *all* proposed rest areas are justified on the grounds of their safety benefits. However, the following recommended procedure was developed for creating an effective network of rest opportunities, using the insights that emerged from this study.

Rest stops are not equivalent in their effect. The questionnaire data and accident data analysis provide ample evidence that different rest stops are utilized at different rates and for somewhat different purposes.

A rest stop is a part of a configuration of rest opportunities in a context of travel patterns among cultural features along a particular route. Adding a rest stop, or rest stops, is a matter of modifying that configuration to reduce the average distance traveled between rests by attempting to change prevailing patterns of driving and resting. The question is how to do this and, especially, how to do it most economically so that a safety intervention of establishing rest stops competes with the benefit-to-cost ratios of other kinds of highway improvements.

The following suggested procedure (Case, Hulbert, and Mellinger, 1969) derives not so much from hard empirical evidence as from clues that emerged from the analysis combined in a reasonable rationale:

"Step 1. *Selecting a length of highway for study* 200 miles or more long, on which a significant fraction of trips are greater than 200 miles in length.

Step 2. *Prepare an overall summary* of accident history, traffic flow and nature of the accidents.

Step 3. *Prepare accident rate profiles by year by direction.* These profiles should be studied in conjunction with detailed plan views and vertical evaluations of the roadway in order to try to hypothesize the major influences on accident rate at each five-mile segment.

Step 4. *Survey of motorists' driving patterns* to estimate typical trip lengths and estimate stopping patterns.

Step 5. *Survey of the route.* Rest opportunities of all kinds, not just roadside rests, must be taken into account to determine the average distance between stops.

Step 6. *Summarize existing situation.* Prepare a composite configuration for the route as it exists (or for anticipated major changes) showing trip lengths, terminal points, rest stops and their use. Estimate the average distance traveled between rests, and check these estimates against the profiles to see whether they arc rcasonablc.

Step 7. *Design an improved configuration.* Consider different interventions to achieve a more desirable driving and stopping pattern.

Step 8. *Estimate benefit to cost ratios.* Estimate the reduction in accident rate using the 'b' values of .01 and .005 and check the estimates against the route profiles for their reasonableness."

SUMMARY AND CONCLUSIONS

Despite the fact that accident records as normally generated do not keep separate tallies of "falling asleep" accidents, there are a few studies that show we are having "asleep at the wheel" accidents on our highways at an alarming rate (Kearney, 1966; Forbes et al., 1958). It is possible that drowsiness is involved in many more accidents than the 20 to 30 percent that are so classified in these accident records. Some drivers can and do drive for prolonged periods without mishap or obvious drowsiness; nevertheless research studies (Forbes et al., 1958; Crawford, 1961; McFarland and Mosley, 1954; Hulbert, 1963; Safford and Rockwell, 1967; Herbert and Jaynes, 1963) indicate that their performance level is bound to be reduced as the trip progresses. Loss of sleep, itself, also tends to reduce human performance at sustained or continuous tasks (Brown, Tickner, and Simmonds, 1966; Mellinger, 1970).

Thus, both sleep loss and the nature of the driving task are shown to be potential contributors to falling asleep at the wheel accidents. One study (Case et al., 1969) found fully 50 percent of a sample of motorists complained of having difficulty staying awake while driving on trips. Yoss's work at the Mayo Clinic (1969) indicates there may be a way to determine objectively which drivers are more susceptible to drowsiness.

Many techniques and devices have been described to help keep drivers alert. A critical review (Harris, 1967) of these is presented which indicates that there is no easy solution to the problem. Roadside rests have been created to help the tired motorist. Roadside rests have been officially designated as part of the federal highway system, and several state highway systems also include them. Motorists do make good use of these and there is undoubtedly some safety benefit; however, it is difficult to measure due to the nature of available accident records and highway use records. A recent California study of roadside rest effectiveness (Case et al., 1969) includes a formula and eight-step plan for deciding where to place these rest facilities based on a derived relationship between time-on-road and accident rate.

REFERENCES

Brown, I. D., Tickner, A. H., and Simmonds, D. C., Effects of Prolonged Driving Upon Driving Skill and Performance of a Subsidiary Task, *Industrial Medicine In Surgery,* September 1966, 760–765.

Case, H. W., Hulbert, S. F., Mellinger, R. L., and Patterson, O. E., Evaluation Study—Safety Aspects of Roadside Rest Program, Report No. 69-69, University of California, Los Angeles, 1969, 94 pp.

Crawford, A., Fatigue and Driving, *Ergonomics,* 4 (1961), 143–154.

Cudworth, A. L., Personal communication with the author, Liberty Mutual Insurance Company, Hopkinton Research Center, Hopkinton, Mass., 1966.

Delco Radio, *Highway Communicator,* General Motors Corporation, Kokomo, Indiana, 1961.

Forbes, T. W., et al., Sleep Deprivation Effects on Components of Driving Behavior, *Highway Research Abstract,* 28, 1 (1958), 21–26.

Frederik, W. S., Alert-O-Matic, Liberty Mutual Research Center, Hopkinton, Mass., 1966.

Greenshields, B. D., Changes in Driver Performance with Time in Driving, University of Michigan, Ann Arbor, 1963.

Haber, H., Brenner, R., and Hulbert, S., Psychology of Trip Geography, *Highway Research Board Bulletin,* 9 (1954), 1–21.

Hakkinen, S., personal communication, Assistant Director of Psychology Department, Institute of Occupational Health, Helsinki, Finland.

Harris, W. V., The Effect of Ammonia and Ammonium Carbonate in the Reduction of Drowsiness in the Human Operator, Masters Thesis, Department of Systems Engineering, University of Arizona, 1967, 118 pp.

Herbert, M. J. and Jaynes, W. E., Performance Decrement in Vehicle Driving, U.S. Army Medical Research Laboratory, Fort Knox, Kentucky, Report No. 597, November 1963.

Hulbert, S. F., Blood Sugar Level and Fatigue Effects on a Simulated Driving Task, Engineering Report 63-53, University of California, Los Angeles, October 1963, 24 pp.

Hulbert, S. F. and Mellinger, R. L., Effects of Fatigue on Skills Related to Driving, Engineering Report 7060, University of California, Los Angeles, January 1970, 51 pp.

Kearney, P. W., *Highway Homicide,* Cromwell, New York, 1966.
Kleitman, N., *Sleep and Wakefullness,* University of Chicago Press, Chicago, Ill., 1963.
Lauer, A. R. and Suhr, V. W., The Effects of Rest Pauses and Refreshment on Driving Efficiency, *Traffic Safety Research Review,* March 1958, 4–9.
McFarland, R. A., Moor, R. C., and Warren, A. B., Human Variables in Motor Vehicle Accidents: A Review of the Literature, Harvard School of Public Health, Boston, Mass., 1955, 203 pp.
McFarland, R. A. and Mosley, A. L., Human Factors in Highway Transportation Safety, Harvard School of Public Health, Boston, Mass., 1954, 295 pp.
Mellinger, R. L., Long Trip Driving Habits of California Drivers: General Findings, Engineering Report 70-89, University of California, Los Angeles, April 1970, 118 pp.
Muscio, B., *Lectures on Industrial Psychology,* Routledge, London; E. P. Dutton, New York, 1920.
Oswald, I., *Sleeping and Waking,* Elsevier Press, New York, 1962.
Platt, F. N., A New Method of Measuring the Effects of Continued Driving Performance, *Human Factors,* **6** (1964), 351–358.
Rodger, J. R., The Sleepy Driver as a Preventive Medicine Problem, *GP,* **14**, 2 (1956), 90–94.
Safford, R. and Rockwell, T. H., Performance Decrement in 24 Hour Driving, *High-Way Research Record,* 163 (1967), 68–79.
Schwenk, L., Ten Tips for Night Driving Safety, Blueprint for Health, 1960.
Traffic Safety, 127 (March 1959), 12.
Warren, N. and Clark, B., Blocking in Mental and Motor Tasks During a 65 Hour Vigil, *Journal of Experimental Psychology,* **2** (1937), 97–105.
Williams, H. B., personal communication with the author, Alertmaster Company, Houston, Texas, 1966.
Yoss, R., A Test to Measure Ability to Maintain Alertness and Its Application in Driving, *Mayo Clinic Proceedings,* **44**, 11 (1969), 769–783.

XIII

EFFECTS OF ALCOHOL AND DRUGS ON DRIVING BEHAVIORS

Matthew Buttiglieri, Anthony J. Brunse, M.D., and Harry W. Case

Matthew W. Buttiglieri is Chief of the Psychology Service at the Sepulveda V.A. Hospital in California. He was born in Boston, Massachusetts. During World War II he was a navigator in the Eighth Army Air Force. Later at Northeastern University (Boston), he received his B.A. in psychology and then his Ph.D. in clinical psychology at Washington University (St. Louis). He spent the next two years working on the Neurology Service at the Jefferson Barracks (St. Louis) V.A. Hospital where he was impressed with the damage to the human body from automobile collisions.

For the next four years he was a counseling psychologist on the staff of the Brockton (Massachusetts) V.A. Hospital combining that with two years of school consultation out of the Judge Stone Clinic. The next jump was all the way to the West Coast in 1960.

An interest in developing a system analysis approach to study and improve the critical path traveled by the mental patient from community to hospital and back to the community, and transportation problems of the released mental patient led to his current interest in the effects of illness and medication on driving. He has been studying this subject with colleagues from the V.A. and from the UCLA Institute of Transportation and Traffic Engineering. Other professional interests include behavior modification and semiautomated assessment techniques.

Anthony J. Brunse, M.D. is Associate Chief of Staff for Research of the Sepulveda V.A. Hospital in California. After receiving his A.B. at Columbia University, he studied medicine at the University of Chicago, receiving his M.D. from Rush Medical College there in 1942. After military duty as a battalion surgeon in Pacific combat areas and in the Surgeon General's office, he served a psychiatric residency at Walter Reed General Hospital and St. Elizabeth's Hospital, the federal psychiatric hospital in the District of Columbia.

Training and studies followed at the Washington School of Psychiatry, the Washington-Baltimore Psychoanalytic Institute, and the Psychodrama Institute, concurrent with duties as resident and then staff psychiatrist at St. Elizabeth's and as psychotherapist at the Arlington County Mental Hygiene Clinic, Virginia. He served as director of group psychotherapy and psychodrama and chief of a psychiatric service at St. Elizabeth's Hospital.

In 1952 Dr. Brunse joined the V.A. in Los Angeles where, as chief of a psychiatric unit, he supervised residents in training and developed social psychiatric programs. In 1962 he joined the Sepulveda V.A. Hospital as chief of psychiatry and also served as chief of the psychiatry research program.

He was chairman of the Research and Education Committee for several years until 1969, when he became Associate Chief of Staff for Research at Sepulveda. He is Assistant Clinical Professor of Psychiatry at the University of California, Los Angeles, School of Medicine, and a member of the American Psychiatric Association, American Association for the Advancement of Science, World Federation for Mental Health, American Society for Psychodrama and Group Psychotherapy, the Southern California Psychiatric Society, and the New York Academy of Science.

Harry W. Case is professor of engineering and psychology and associate director of the Institute of Transportation and Traffic Engineering, University of California, Los Angeles. He obtained his Ph.D. in psychology from the University of California, Los Angeles.

Dr. Case has been professor of psychology and engineering at UCLA since 1946 and is active in both departments. He has been associated with the Institute since it was founded in 1947, and has directed activities at the Los Angeles branch of the Institute since 1963. His numerous research activities have resulted in many publications on psychological aspects of safety. He is on the Research Review Committee of the American Society of Safety Engineers and has served on numerous advisory committees in safety research.

Dr. Case is a member of the American Psychological Association; the American Society of Safety Engineers, Review Board; the American Society of Engineering Education; and other professional associations in traffic and safety areas. He has served on committees of the Highway Research Board of the National Academy of Sciences, National Research Council. Dr. Case was the 1967 recipient of the Paul Gray Hoffman Award for Distinguished Professional Services in Highway Safety.

Society today is a drug-taking society. This inescapable fact is reflected in the amount of drug/alcohol production, drug/alcohol advertising, and drug/alcohol usage.

A nationwide survey done in 1957 (Anderson, 1957) indicated that the purchase of drugs and medicines outside of the hospital amounted to $1.5 billion or accounted for 15 percent of the total amount spent for personal health services. In that same year, the American Institute of Public Opinion found that 7 percent of the surveyed population admitted to using tranquilizers. A decade later, a survey conducted by the Social Research Group of George Washington University (Perry, 1968) indicated that 26 percent of the surveyed population admitted to using tranquilizers. This represents almost four times the usage rate of the earlier survey.

Self-medication practices have increased considerably (California Medical Association, 1967) resulting partly from the increased sophistication that people have about the substances available for purchase over the counter. The mass media suggest treatments for illnesses and conditions which previously have been restricted to medical doctors. This experimentation with drugs by adults is thought to contribute chiefly to the widespread experimentation by youth. This can soon reach the point where it will be the unusual student in high school who has not partaken of a variety of stimulant, depressant, and/or hallucinogenic drugs. The enormous variety of substances eaten, drunk, smoked, chewed, or otherwise used for nonnutritional reasons is truly astonishing.

Probably more is known about the effect of alcohol on man than about the effect of any other drug. Alcohol ingestion has a history that goes back to prehistoric man. However, as with the weather, much has been written about it but little has been done about it until recently. There is still much to be learned about the interactions between alcohol and drugs and among the drug classes. This is an extraordinarily difficult area to research because of the wide variability that exists with respect to the individual reaction to alcohol and/or drugs. As is the case with the more physical aspects of our environment, technology in the production of substances that affect the human body has simultaneously enriched and complicated our lives. The synthesized chemical products available today are as different from their naturally occurring counterparts as is the spaceship from the ox cart.

The oldest, most widespread, and still by far commonest of the substances ingested by man for nonnutritional reasons is alcohol. Alcohol usage dates back as far as we have recorded history. It is considered likely that the Mesopotamians originally cultivated grain for the purpose of making beer. They also had wine made from dates and from sesame seeds. Drunkenness seems to have been common in ancient Egypt where the people drank both wine and beer. Biblical mention of wine and drinking is also frequent. The discovery of how to distill strong drink from the weaker wines and beers is relatively modern and another example of the advantages and disadvantages to society of advancing technology.

The use of alcoholic beverages is so ubiquitous that exceptions are rare indeed. The aborigines of Australia had no fermented drink nor did the North American Indians until their contact with Europeans. Alcoholic drinks were largely unknown in many areas of the Pacific. Today the Pacific islanders make toddy from the sap of coconut palms while the drinking propensity of the North American Indian has been reiterated *ad nauseam* in Western movies. It is surprising that the North American Indian learned of the virtues of fermentation from the European rather than from the geographically closer tribes of tropical America where the fermentation process was well developed.

Through the ages the use and abuse of alcohol has been a major controversial subject (National Institute of Mental Health, 1968). The basic natural ingredients for the production of alcohol were present, according to experts, at least 200 million years ago. Where these ingredients occur simultaneously, it is almost impossible for alcohol not to be produced. With the appearance of man and with the development of the earliest civilizations the consumption of alcohol began. Throughout the history of alcoholic beverages, the ingestion of alcohol has been and still is associated with nutrition, medicine, and religious rituals.

Since it has caloric content, alcohol has been thought of as a food. However, alcohol contains no vitamins and like some other foods can be harmful when used to excess. With respect to medical usage, alcohol was at one time among the most widely prescribed drugs. Even today it is still thought of as a useful medical agent and is prescribed for diabetics, arthritics, cardiac cases, and for geriatric patients. In spite of the increased variety and number of tranquilizers now on the market, alcohol, which was the first tranquilizer known to man, remains the most widely used of all tranquilizers.

Goodman and Gilman (1955) describe a variety of medical uses for alcohol. It has been used in such medicinal mixtures as cough medicines and geriatric tonics. It is used to reduce fever. It is used in liniments, astringents, and as a skin disinfectant. The Russian literature and American Western movies document the use of alcohol as an anesthetic and as an analgesic. There have been reports of alcohol used to quiet patients, to increase appetite, to promote sleep, and to treat a variety of vascular and coronary arterial diseases. It has been used to treat the opium addict, the terminally ill patient, the alcoholic with acute delirium tremens, and the asthmatic.

The actual number of alcoholics in the United States is unknown. A good deal depends upon the definition of alcoholism that is used and in the method of acquiring data, as well as the willingness of the subject population to admit to alcohol usage or to apply for treatment. The excessive use of alcohol has been associated not only with traffic accidents but also with a $2 billion cost annually to industry, 45 percent of all arrests made nationally, increases in the rates of brain damage, divorce, and delinquency.

The effects of alcohol on the human body are much more complex than was first assumed. Although the effects of alcohol have been demonstrated on the liver, on the kidneys, in the gastrointestinal tract, and on the endocrine system, the most important and the most serious effects of alcohol are those attributed to its action on the brain. This action has been directly related to the alcohol concentration in the blood. Although there is a good deal of variation among individuals, for most people a blood alcohol level (BAL) up to 0.05 percent induces some sedation or tranquility; 0.05 to 0.15 percent may produce lack of coordination and produces behavioral changes which seem to suggest stimulation of the brain such as talkativeness, aggressiveness, and hyperactivity but which actually result from the depression of brain centers that normally inhibit such behavior. At about 0.15 to 0.20 percent intoxication is obvious and in some individuals incoordination, confusion, and disorientation are present. At 0.30 or 0.40 percent unconsciousness, stupor, anesthesia, or coma may occur. Levels of 0.50 percent or more result in death. The latest theories suggest that alcohol has its primary action on the reticular formation, which has been described as the master switchboard or activating system of the brain. At the present time, there is conflicting evidence with respect to the effect of very low BALs on skilled performance. At levels above 0.03 or 0.04 percent, performance in a variety of activities worsens. It is interesting to note that as a person's performance is impaired by higher BALs, his judgment frequently worsens and he believes that he is performing more adequately. This points out the urgent need for accurate feedback of impaired performance.

ALCOHOL USAGE

A review of the scientific literature on the effects of alcohol alone and in combination with other drugs was published by Hine and Turkel (1966). In 1950 an estimated 40 million males, equal to 26 percent of the total population, consumed 181 million gallons of alcohol, 80 percent of the total consumption. This male population was divided into three population groups consisting of 3.3 million alcoholics, 7.3 million moderate drinkers, and 28.6 million occasional drinkers. Daily these groups consumed, respectively, 8 ounces, 3.5 ounces, and 0.5 ounces of alcohol.

It was estimated in 1955 that there were some 80 million adults in the United States who drank beverages that contain alcohol (Greenberg, 1955). A Gallup Poll conducted in May 1960 reported that alcohol was consumed daily by 62 percent of the American population. In 1958 a New York survey showed that 71 percent of householders had served alcoholic beverages during the month preceding the inquiry.

Drinking of alcohol is related to age and reaches a peak in the age group between 35 and 40. The drinking is not done randomly throughout the day or week. Peak-drinking centers around evening hours and weekend-drinking far exceeds that done during the working day. More recent statistics on alcohol usage are contained in a traffic safety monograph published in 1969 by the National Safety Council (Anderson and Lhotka, 1969). Approximately 90 to 95 million persons in the United States drink alcoholic beverages at least occasionally. It has been estimated that 80 percent of men and 67 percent of women over the age of 21 drink. Impairment of function has been directly associated with the percentage of alcohol in the blood stream. BAL is found to be related to the amount of alcohol ingested, the body weight, the amount and kind of food in the stomach at the time of drinking, the length of time since the last drink, and the length of time since drinking began.

Although relatively little is known about the effects of combining alcohol and drugs, there have been several studies that indicate that there is a combination effect that may be much more dangerous to health and to highway safety than the effect of either alcohol or drugs alone. Social scientists who have made studies of traffic safety are aware of the enormous complexities involved in these studies. Crucial variables in accident research must include not only the impairment of performance capabilities, but the preimpairment level of capability. For instance, a person who is very skillful at driving could have his capabilities impaired to a much larger extent without appreciable increase in accident risk than could the inexperienced or poor driver.

The interaction between alcohol and highway safety has now been definitely established. At the turn of the century within only a few years of the first fatal motor vehicle accident in the United States, the scientific literature was already referring to alcohol in driving as a serious social and health problem (*The Quarterly Journal of Inebriety,* 1904). In 19 of 25 fatal accidents, investigation disclosed that the drivers had ingested alcohol within an hour of the accident. It was predicted at that time that accidents would increase dramatically and that only total abstainers would be permitted to drive.

It soon became apparent that the motor vehicle codes that were being enforced did not provide sufficient safeguards to control the drinking driver. By 1924 one-fourth to one-third of the automobile accidents were at least partly chargeable to the drinking driver by knowledgeable investigators. However, accident data were so imprecise that more accurate assessments of the driving-drinking problem could not be made.

More precise methods to determine BAL concentrations were conducted in the 1930's in the United States and in Sweden. The findings of BALs in drivers involved in crashes has been remarkably consistent, to the point where alcohol is now felt to be the largest single factor leading to fatal crashes. The BALs of drivers who were in serious or fatal crashes has been found to differ greatly from those of drivers not involved in crashes (Holcomb, 1938, Lucas et al., 1955; McCarroll and Haddon, 1962; Borkenstein et al., 1964). In many of these studies carefully chosen sampling criteria were selected in advance to properly match crash-involved and noninvolved drivers. Despite the widely divergent times, locations, and methods employed, the findings were astonishingly consistent. These findings indicate that alcohol is not used to any measurable extent by the overwhelming majority of drivers on the road even at the times and the places of fatal and other crashes. Only 1 to 4 percent of non-accident involved drinking drivers have been found with BALs at or above 0.10 percent by weight, a level which would definitely classify them as drinking drivers in at least 11 of the states that have developed chemical test laws. Other research findings indicate that from 48 to 57 percent of drivers fatally injured in one-car collisions had BALs in excess of 0.10 percent by weight (Borkenstein et al., 1964; Nielson, 1965; Davis and Fisk, 1964; New Jersey Department of Law and Public Safety, 1964; Haddon and Bradess, 1959). Putting these findings together results in the observation that 1 to 4 percent of drivers on the highways have BALs at or above 0.10 percent by weight, the level present in approximately half of the fatally injured drivers involved in single-vehicle crashes.

With respect to multiple-vehicle crashes, these high BALs have also been found in approximately 45 percent of drivers fatally injured in crashes that involved more than one vehicle (Nielson, 1965, 1967). It is especially interesting to note that of drivers killed in collisions with trains or whose vehicles went into canals, 60 to 80 percent of those who had been drinking had BALs in the very high range, that is, 0.10 percent by weight and higher. The BALs of drivers believed to have been killed as a result of the action of others have been found to be more similar to those of non-involved drivers than to those of drivers responsible for fatal crashes. In these crashes the surviving other driver with high BAL has been found to be at fault, while almost 80 percent of the innocent drivers have blood that is completely free of alcohol. Barmack and Payne (1961) have noted that the drinking driver rammed into other drivers four times more frequently than he was rammed.

Combining data on fatal crashes of all descriptions reveals that almost half of the drivers were found to have high BALs (Nielson, 1965, 1967; Davis and Fisk, 1964; New Jersey Department of Law and Public Safety, 1964; Freimuth, Watts, and Fisher, 1958). As mentioned previously these high BALs are rarely present among non-accident involved drivers. It has also been noted that drivers with BALs readily reached by heavy social drinking, 0.05 to 0.09 percent by weight, are more often involved in fatal crashes than would be expected in proportion to their presence in the driving population.

Although extremely high BALs have been frequently found among drivers fatally injured in crashes, there has been less documentation with respect to BALs of drivers nonfatally but nonetheless seriously injured. Studies done in Illinois and in Michigan (Holcomb, 1938; Borkenstein et al., 1964) indicate that extremely high BALs are present in about 25 percent of these serious crashes. The percentage would undoubtedly be higher if the data were screened to exclude drivers not responsible for the crash. With respect to run-of-the-mill crashes, alcohol is assumed on the basis of limited evidence to contribute to at least 6 percent of the crashes. Since the number of the run-of-the-mill crashes is so much greater than the serious or fatal crashes, it is estimated by the National Safety Council that alcohol plays a role in at least 800,000 of the 14 million run-of-the-mill crashes annually, as well as contributing to approximately half of the 55 million fatal highway injuries (National Safety Council, 1969).

The higher the BAL of a driver the greater is the likelihood that he will be involved in a crash as compared to drivers who have not been drinking (Borkenstein, 1964). It has been estimated to be six to seven times as great for the driver with a BAL at 0.10 percent. The likelihood of crash is estimated to be 25 times as great at 0.15 percent BAL. These BALs, though they may seem high to the casual observer, are very frequently exceeded by accident-involved drinking drivers.

The evidence makes it clear that crash probability is increased at a BAL of 0.05 percent and that these probabilities become progressively higher at the higher BALs at a geometrically accelerating rate. In the relatively low BALs, further research is needed to clarify the difference of opinion between experts as to the crash probabilities.

According to the Committee on Alcohol and Drugs of the National Safety Council (1960), driving abilities of some individuals are definitely impaired at a BAL of 0.05 percent. At a 0.10 percent BAL, all individuals are definitely impaired with respect to driving ability. The common misconception that low concentration of alcohol improves performance has not been sufficiently documented. The committee concluded that evidence is lacking that any level of alcohol in the blood improves performance. Their considered judgment was that crash probabilities for the higher BALs are underestimated and that the extent to which alcohol is involved in run-of-the-mill accidents is also underestimated.

An indication of the excessive BALs of drunken drivers is provided in studies by Shupe and Pfau (1966), Waller (1967), and Hyman (1967). They have found that the drunken driver commonly has a BAL substantially in excess of the 0.10 percent by weight that is considered the standard in many states. BALs of 0.15 percent are common and substantially over half of the samples studied had BALs in excess of 0.20 percent by weight. As mentioned previously, a BAL in this higher range is a rarity when one considers all drivers. The conclusion to be drawn from these data is that the drunken driver who was arrested is a different person altogether from the ordinary social drinker. He is very likely to have a BAL so high as to be in a separate class altogether from other drivers with or without a measurable BAL who are not involved in crashes. The persistent problem-drinker tends to be the one who finally gets caught rather than the social drinker who merely happens to be picked up fortuitously (Selzer et al., 1967; Selzer and Weiss, 1966; Brenner, 1967).

Accidents that involved drinking drivers tend to be much more severe and occur at substantially higher speeds as a function of the BAL of the crash-involved driver. In other words, the higher the BAL concentration of the driver, the greater is the probability that the accident occurred at a high speed and that it was consequently a more serious or even fatal crash.

It has been well known for years that individual response to drugs varies considerably. With alcohol the same situation obtains. Even at the same BAL, there is a differential response in individuals. It has also been known that acquired tolerance develops with the habitual use of alcohol. This phenomenon causes the user to ingest a larger amount than was previously necessary in order to produce the same reaction.

The effect of alcohol on the individual is dependent upon the concentration of alcohol in the nervous system, which is closely correlated to the concentration of alcohol in the blood. The rate of the removal of alcohol from the body varies considerably but is relatively constant for any individual. The average rate is 100 milligrams per kilogram per hour, which means that a man who weighs approximately 155 pounds eliminates each hour roughly the amount of alcohol that is present in a small whiskey (Lewis and Sarlanis, 1969). Since the elimination rate is for all practical purposes constant for an individual, it takes that individual a longer period of time to eliminate higher concentrations of alcohol.

A number of studies have been done of fatally injured automobile drivers in a variety of geographical locations. Postmortems on these drivers were done in order to find whether or not alcohol was present. In a California study (Nielson, 1965) 52 percent of the fatally injured drivers had a BAL in excess of 0.05 percent, 36 percent of the drivers a BAL of 0.15 percent or more. Consistent with these findings is a Baltimore study (Freimuth, Watts, and Fisher, 1958) in which it was found that 58 percent of the fatally injured drivers had a BAL of 0.05 percent, 37 percent of the total had a BAL of 0.15 percent or more. Further confirmation is in a New Jersey study (1964) where 53 percent of the fatally injured drivers had a BAL of 0.05 percent and 28 percent of this total group had a BAL of 0.15 percent or more. In yet another study done in Westchester County (Hadden and Bradess, 1959) 69 percent of the fatally injured drivers were found to have a BAL of 0.05 percent and an astonishing 49 percent of the fatally injured drivers were found with a BAL of 0.15 percent or more. These studies, all of which were done in the United States, determined that from 55 to 70 percent of fatally injured drivers were found in postmortem examination to have alcohol in the body. A study done in Australia (Birrell, 1965) indicates that postmortem examination of fatally injured drivers revealed that 83 percent of the drivers had alcohol detected in the body.

A study by McCarroll and Haddon (1962) used non-accident involved drivers as a control group. Also controlled was the site of the fatal accidents, the hour and day of the week, and the direction of travel. His study indicates that only 29 percent of the fatally injured drivers had a BAL below 0.02 percent while more than 77 percent of the controls had that BAL. While 50 percent of the fatal victims had a BAL of 0.25 percent or more, none of the control drivers had that level of alcohol in his system. This study, which was done in New York City, indicated the very strong association of alcohol with single-vehicle fatal accidents, most of which occurred at night, which also coincides with the most frequent drinking time.

The relationship of alcohol to accidents not necessarily resulting in the death of the driver has been studied in Evanston, Illinois (Holcomb, 1938), in Toronto (Lucas et al., 1955), and in Grand Rapids, Michigan (Borkenstein et al., 1964). In the Illinois study 94 percent of the non-accident controls had BALs below 0.05 percent, as contrasted to 67 percent of the injured drivers. While 14 percent of the injured drivers had a BAL of 0.15 percent or more, less than 1 percent of the non-accident controls had that BAL. The Toronto study matched accident site and time of day. Ninety-one percent of the controls had a BAL of 0.05 percent or less, but only 78 percent of the accident-involved drivers had a BAL of 0.05 percent or less. At a BAL of 0.15 percent or more, there were 1 percent of the controls and 11 percent of the accident-involved drivers. The largest sample of accident-involved drivers consists of 5984 drivers in the Michigan study. The control group consisted of 7590 non-accident involved drivers. Both of these samples had high percentages of drivers with a BAL of less than 0.05 percent. The figures are 97 percent for the control group and 90 percent for the accident-involved group. At the much higher concentration of 0.15 percent or more were 3.2 percent of the accident-involved drivers but only 0.18 percent of the controls. The crucial findings from these studies is not that alcohol is detected in non-accident involved drivers but that BALs, often at the very high level, are detected much more frequently among accident-involved drivers than among non-accident involved drivers.

Waller (1966a, 1966b, 1966c, 1967; Waller and Turkel, 1966), one of the most prolific writers in this field, has concluded that there is considerable evidence to support the notion that it is the consistently heavy drinker who drives rather than the light social drinker who drives who contributes substantially to alcohol-involved accidents. He warns against the danger of placing the responsibility of such accidents exclusively on alcoholics just as in the past this responsibility was placed on the social drinker (Waller, 1965).

The studies that have been done indicate that the association of high BAL with accidents lessens with decreasing accident severity. While severe and even fatal accidents are strongly related to high BAL, the rate for accidents of all kinds may not be significantly higher for the alcoholic than it is for the general population.

In a study of alcoholics, drinking, and traffic accidents, Schmidt and Smart (1959) concluded that it is the effect of the alcohol per se and not the characteristics or the personality dynamics of the alcoholic that contributes largely to the high accident rate. Additional studies highlighting the role of the chronic problem drinker as a traffic hazard have been reported by Goldberg (1955) and Popham (1956).

The consensus of many investigators in the field is that driving impairment occurs above 0.05 percent BAL (Loomis and West, 1958; Bjerver and Goldberg, 1950). Postmortem studies of fatally injured drivers who have some alcohol but less than 0.05 percent indicates that this occurs in only 2 to 6 percent of all fatally injured drivers. Therefore, practically all of the fatally injured drivers with alcohol in their systems found by postmortem examination have a BAL of 0.05 percent or more. The majority of these fatally injured drivers had been drinking heavily and their impairment was such as to be caused by the consumption of 10 ounces or more of liquor in a period of an hour. There is evidence to indicate that errors of judgment are more frequent at a given BAL when the level of alcohol is ascending rather than when it is descending (Lewis and Sarlanis, 1969).

CONTROL OF DRIVER

Attempted control of driving after drinking varies widely (Monroe, 1947; Braunstein, Weinberg, and Dal Cortivo, 1968). Laws prohibiting driving while under the influence of alcohol are much more stringent in other countries than they are in the United States. While the Uniform Vehicle Code defines driving under the influence of alcohol and sets up standards to determine BAL by chemical tests of breath, blood, or urine, the enforcement of penalties has little consistency or effect. While the code provides that habitual drunkards should not be issued a driver's license, this particular provision is not strictly enforced. The penalties for driving after drinking can be severe; for example, a fine between $100 and $1000 or imprisonment from 10 days to one year. Most states do not enforce these provisions of the vehicle code. In Sweden, a country which has very strict drinking and driving laws, a blood alcohol level of 0.05 percent in a driver can call for rather stringent measures. These drivers would be convicted of second-degree intoxication while driving and would be almost certain to be fined. In any case, the driving license would be suspended and would be reactivated not sooner than one year later and then only upon a reexamination. Of those convicted of first-degree drunk driving (0.15 percent BAL or greater), almost three-fourths are given jail sentences of a month or more. These drunk drivers would also have their licenses suspended for at least one year to be restored only after satisfactory reexamination. The United States lags far behind other countries in penalizing the drunken driver. While adequate laws have been established and while enforcement of the laws by the police occurs, penalization of the violator is so inconsistent that potential violators do not associate violation with penalty. To illustrate this, a California study of 1147 drivers who accidentally killed someone while driving under the influence of alcohol indicated that only 24 percent of those drivers were convicted of felony drunk-driving and only 4 percent were sent to jail or prison. Chicago police reports indicate a 57 percent conviction rate on charges of driving while intoxicated although they do not give data on penalties. That strict enforcement can significantly reduce accident rate has been demonstrated in Detroit and in New England. Nevertheless, controls, though logical and widely used, have not proven to be very successful. Furthermore, there is little reason to believe that the controls will become more successful unless there is a profound change in attitude toward drinking and driving.

Perhaps the most practical countermeasure for the present is to concentrate on making roads and automobiles safer and to provide more effective medical response to accidents. One of the most intriguing approaches to this is one by Voas (1969), who suggests that we have reached the state-of-the-art where we can now build automobiles that drunks and other impaired people cannot drive. Pointing out that no automobile will operate for the driver who is so impaired that he cannot place the key in the ignition, he suggests that more sophisticated devices are within the realm of possibility which could measure the condition of the driver and refuse to start unless the driver passes some previously determined test. Voas suggests that an alcohol safety-ignition interlock system can and should be seriously considered and evaluated. It should have the capability of (1) sensing blood alcohol level, (2) sensing the deterioration of the driver's performance, (3) sensing the identity of the driver thereby keeping the previously identified problem drinker from driving, and (4) sensing the time of day thereby preventing driving at night when the danger of accidents is greater. It is only a small step from such a system to a system that would continuously monitor the driver with respect to the deterioration of necessary driving skills such as loss of concentration, coordination, or attention due to fatigue, drowsiness, or drug ingestion. Tests have been developed to measure the ability to divide attention between two messages being presented simultaneously one to each ear. Such a test developed by Moskowitz at UCLA (Moskowitz and DePry, 1968) has been found to be very sensitive to even relatively small amounts of alcohol. Tests such as this may be found to be fully as useful for continuous monitoring of the driver's performance and could activate warning systems or actually cause the vehicle to come to a safe stop.

DRUG USAGE

It is difficult to predict in what terms historians of the future will refer to our present era. It is conceivable that one designation might well be the Age of Pills. Ironically, when harassed parents point with critical concern to the use of various "drugs" by their youngsters, a not uncommon response is to have pointed out the overstocked medicine cabinet whose contents eloquently attest to the important part that a number of medications play in the daily diet of the typical adult (Anderson, 1957; Parry, 1968; California Medical Association, 1967). While there is no doubt of the vast and significant role of alcohol and alcoholic beverages in producing such levels of toxicity as to adversely affect driving behavior as well as a multiplicity of other aspects of living, it is becoming recognized increasingly that intoxication is a frequent, though often unplanned, consequence of taking various medications and other pharmacological preparations. In moving from the subject of alcohol to that of drugs, it might be mentioned that a frequently overlooked factor is the synergistic effect of alcohol and many other drugs upon each other, in which one potentiates the effect of the other, so that what might be a relatively safe amount of either alone, when combined in an unplanned way could result in adverse effects on driving as well as other behavior (Forney and Hughes, 1967; Zirkle, King, and McAtee, 1959; Zirkle et al., 1960). It is characteristic of drugs, as distinguished from alcohol, that most of those with adverse effects produce these effects in relatively small doses. Furthermore, most adverse effects are not easily or conveniently detected in the living subject and many of them are slowly metabolized resulting in long-term effects of relatively small doses.

Although clear knowledge of the effect of alcohol on driving is still far from adequate, careful and objective studies of the effects of various drugs on driving behavior and skills are indeed most meager. Consequently, our discussion of drugs indicates target effects and side effects that affect those aspects of behavior which are most likely, in turn, to affect driving performance. Primary and secondary effects of various drugs and medications which may adversely affect driving may interfere with various levels and categories of functioning. For example, drugs causing constriction or dilatation of the pupil and affecting the ability of the lens to focus, could produce a serious visual handicap, even where this is only secondary to the primary, desired effect of the medication. At the other end of the spectrum, motor functioning may be hampered to the detriment of driving ability by such drug effects as weakness, spasticity, gross tremors, or even convulsions. Some drugs can seriously affect attention, distractability, concentration, alertness, and apathy while others may produce perceptual distortion in such dimensions as spatial orientation, physical dimensions, time duration, and the like. It is apparent that such effects would be a serious handicap to exercising adequate judgment not only in critical highway situations, but even in the normal tasks of driving.

In the following section we describe central nervous system drugs and others which have either already demonstrable or highly probable potential for adversely affecting driving.

SEDATIVES AND HYPNOTICS

Many diverse drugs of widely varying chemical structure have in common a depressant effect on the central nervous system, to the degree where they are useful as sedatives or hypnotics. They are commonly used for mild anxiety and tension, as well as for insomnia, in addition to their use in the hospital or clinic. Among the hoariest of these drugs is the group of bromides, although they have been replaced currently largely by less toxic and more effective drugs. However, they are still found lurking in various nostrums and proprietary remedies. They are important mainly because of the occasional case of intoxication which may, among other symptoms, produce mental disturbances such as impaired thinking or memory, drowsiness, dizziness, and even delirium or hallucinations (Goodman and Gilman, 1955).

Chloral hydrate has been a popular hypnotic achieving notoriety as an ingredient of the so-called "knock-out drops," but its use has to a large extent been supplanted by the barbiturates. Its habitual use may result in addiction and, possibly, withdrawal symptoms. Paraldehyde is a rapidly acting hypnotic whose use is largely confined to patients under close medical supervision. When used in the treatment of alcoholism, it may lead to addiction resembling alcoholism itself.

Glutethimide (Doriden) was first introduced as a substitute for barbiturates. It is a typical depressant whose main use should be as an alternative to the barbiturates. Dependence, addiction, and abstinence phenomena have been reported (Zivin and Shalowitz, 1962). Another frequently prescribed hypnotic is methytrylon (Noludar). It too may produce habituation, tolerance, and addiction. Withdrawal symptoms may include insomnia, confusion, and hallucinations.

BARBITURATES

The prototype and most commonly used sedative drugs are the barbiturates. First introduced shortly after the turn of the century, the number of these preparations has multiplied although the most commonly used ones are relatively few. In the younger drug-oriented population the barbiturates are not used simply for their sedative effect, but for a pleasurable sensation (Blum, 1964). The barbiturates are also used by this group to counteract the effect of excessive use of central nervous system stimulants, in which connection they are known as "downers." The soporific effect of the barbiturates may vary all the way from slight drowsiness to deep coma and even death. This is a function of the particular barbiturate used, the dosage, the tolerance of the individual, the presence of other drugs in the body, and the surrounding circumstances under which they are used. While the barbiturates can depress many tissues of the body, the concentration required to produce the CNS depressant action is too small to produce these other effects, although in acute intoxication with barbiturates there is danger of cardiovascular complications (Goodman and Gilman, 1955, p. 107).

The very short-acting barbiturates, such as hexobarbital (Eripal), methohexital (Brevital), thiopental (Pentathal), are used primarily for intravenous anesthesia. The most commonly used barbiturates are the short to intermediate acting. Short-acting barbiturates have become especially popular among drug abusers. The so-called "goof balls," most in use for this purpose and in general medical use as well, are amobarbital (Amytol), pentobarbital (Nembutal), secobarbital (Seconal), known in the vernacular, respectively, as "green hornets," "yellow jackets," and "red devils." Typical of the long-acting barbiturates are aprobarbital (Alurate) and phenobarbital (Luminal). The latter is widely used in medicine as a sedative and as an anti-convulsant. The side effects of the barbiturates may include photosensitivity, dizziness, excitement, euphoria, and restlessness. Their primary effect may be augmented by many other drugs including tranquilizers, antihistamines, narcotics, and certain antidepressants.

ANALGESICS AND PAIN REDUCERS

Particular mention should be made of certain analgesics or pain reducers which are also narcotic, that is, producing sleep, and which are also addicting in the sense that they produce physical and often psychological dependence. Opium, produced from the juice of the opium poppy, used since prehistoric times, and its derivatives such as paregoric, laudanum, and ipecac have fallen into relatively little use. Of its pharmacologically active ingredients (morphine, codeine, and papaverine), morphine has the greatest potential hazard in highway safety. It produces drowsiness, changes in mood, and mental clouding.

Recently acquired and complex learned responses appear to be the first affected. Drowsiness to deep sleep may occur, as well as difficulty in mentation, reduced visual acuity, and lethargy. An overdosage will result in stupor or coma (Reynolds and Randall, 1957). Along with morphine a number of its derivatives, such as heroin, dilaudid, metopon, hycodan, percodan, and levodromoran can produce nausea, vomiting, slowed respiration and vasomotor depression, and general depression. All of these can have a significant effect in reducing psychomotor skill. Methadone is a synthetic drug whose actions are very similar to those of morphine and can cause sedation. Meperidine (Demerol) is a synthetic analgesic similar in action to morphine and, together with other closely related drugs, can produce sedation, euphoria, and respiratory depression. One of the common characteristics of the narcotic and analgesics mentioned here are withdrawal symptoms. These are compounded of physical, psychological, and sociological factors; but it is important here to consider the marked physical distress: nausea, vomiting, sneezing, lacrimation, weakness, and depression, as well as the high degree of restlessness.

PSYCHOTHERAPEUTIC DRUGS

During the past 15 years an enormous armamentarium of drugs has become available to the physician in the treatment of psychological disorders. These have been classified in various ways but tend to fall into three overlapping areas: the "major" tranquilizers or antipsychotic drugs, the so-called "minor" tranquilizers or anti-anxiety drugs, and antidepressants. Among the antipsychotic drugs, the phenothiazine derivatives are most commonly utilized in psychosis (Brodie, Sulser, and Costa, 1961). The prototype of this group is chlorpromazine (Thorazine); and although the relative effectiveness of the other phenothiazines in the treatment of mental illness cannot be precisely assessed, there are differences in the production of side effects, some of which may have significance on the highway. Concurrent with the ameliorization of psychotic symptoms with the use of chlorpromazine is a tendency to marked sedative effect, although this frequently disappears after the early phase of treatment. Similar sedative effects are found with triflupromazine (Vesprin). Of considerable concern with this group of drugs are some of the toxic reactions and side effects, such as jaundice, blood disorders, skin reactions, and abnormal pigmentation (Hollister, 1964). However, among the more serious reactions to the phenothiazines are bizarre motor effects due to involvement of the extrapyramidal system. One syndrome may consist of motor retardation, depression, tremor, rigidity, and other symptoms of Parkinsonism; another group, dystonia and dyskinesia including wry neck, facial grimacing, abnormal eye movements, and other involuntary muscle movements; while in the third group akathisia is evidenced by motor restlessness, inability to sit still, and a strong urge to move about (Ayd, 1961). Fortunately, these symptoms can be controlled with anticholinergic drugs. These extra-pyramidal effects seem to be highest with triflupromazine (Permatil, Prolixin), perphenazine (Trilafon), prochlorperazine (Compazine), and trifluoperazine (Stelazine), and least in thioridazine (Mellaril).

Reserpine and Rauwolfia alkaloids were among the first antipsychotic drugs introduced in Western medicine, although the utilization of the Rauwolfia root in Hindu medicine can be traced back to ancient writings. The use of reserpine in psychiatry has been displaced by phenothiazines. It should be noted that in large doses it produces extra-pyramidal symptoms somewhat like those of the phenothiazines. More recently antipsychotic drugs which are nonphenothiazine have been introduced; among these are the butyrophenones such as haloperidol and triperidol. The advantage of these drugs is not in any markedly superior antipsychotic effect but rather as an alternative to the phenothiazines in patients who are sensitive or allergic to them. An interesting question is raised in the use of all of these drugs. To what extent does the psychosis per se affect driving ability? To what extent does the tranquilizing agent increase a patient's driving skills? To what extent do the side effects of the drug impair driving ability?

One of the first and most popular specific drugs for the treatment of anxiety is meprobamate (Miltown, Equanil). This is used in many conditions involving anxiety, whatever the cause, and is prescribed as a sedative in the daytime and a hypnotic in treating insomnia. Because it tends to increase ability to concentrate and to decrease distractibility, it may well be of value in enhancing driving skill in some persons. However, there are instances of drowsiness which should be counteracted by central stimulants (Rossi, 1964).

The series of benzodiazapine compounds is continuing to grow. The two best known derivatives are chlordiazepoxide (Librium) and diazepam (Valium). They both have mild sedative effects and are used mainly in treatment of anxiety. There is, in addition, a muscle relaxant effect, especially with Valium. There is considerable interest at present in their use for the treatment of alcoholism, especially in withdrawal symptoms and acute intoxication. Persons taking these medications must be concerned over possible drowsiness, fainting, dizziness. There may be some special hazard in their effect on driving; but, as with so many of the drugs, this question requires further investigation (Miller, 1962).

ANTIDEPRESSANTS

Episodes of sadness, grief, and mourning appear to be the lot of all men. However, these emotions may become exaggerated to such a degree of depression as to result in intense distress and incapacity. Depression may be reactive or exogenous when it is in response to external circumstances but its nature and degree will vary widely depending on personality variables as well as the nature of the external circumstances. Another group of depressions seems to be related primarily to internal rather than external events. This may be cyclic in nature and in many instances psychotic in degree. Because of the heterogeneity of the factors underlying the depressions, there is a wide range of treatments including social, psychological, and physical measures. Electroconvulsive treatment remains an important and useful measure for certain types of depression. For well over a decade, a variety of stimulant drugs such as the amphetamines, ritalin, and others have been used with little success in the treatment of depression. The first breakthrough in the chemotherapy of depression came with the introduction of the monoamine oxidase (MAO) inhibitors. Those which still survive clinically are isocarboxazid (Marplan), nialamide (Niamid), phenelzine sulfate (Nardil), and the more popular tranylcypromine (Parnate). These MAO inhibitors elevate the mood of depressed patients. The often equivocal results and the marked danger of toxicity have led to their relative disuse. It is important to consider here the effects of excessive stimulation which may result in tremors, agitation, and confusion on the one hand and dizziness, fatigue, and blurred vision on the other. The tricyclic dibenzazepine derivatives related structurally to the phenothiazines are imipramine (Tofranil), amitriptyline (Elavil), desmethylimipramine (Desipramine), and related compounds. They are currently used quite widely in the treatment of depression. One must be on the lookout for over excitement, euphoria, insomnia, blurred vision, dizziness, and possibly weakness and fatigue (Overall et al., 1962, 1964). Efforts are being made to fit specific agents to specific types of depression (Hollister and Overall, 1965; Overall, 1962). A word should be said about the use of lithium in the treatment of depression, especially in cyclic endogenous depression. Mainly in the form of lithium carbonate, this drug is being currently studied widely after having attained some clinical popularity in Europe. Because of the slight margin between the presumed therapeutically effective dose and a toxic dose, a person receiving this drug must be watched very closely. Nausea, ataxia, and confusion are among the symptoms of lithium toxicity which could present a serious highway hazard (Coats, Trautner, and Gershon, 1957).

CENTRAL NERVOUS SYSTEM STIMULANTS

The most popular central nervous system stimulant is caffeine, which is usually taken in the form of beverages such as coffee, tea, cocoa, maté, and cola-flavored "soft drinks." Caffeine is a powerful stimulant and is the principal ingredient of many proprietary preparations sold to combat drowsiness. On the whole, therefore, it probably makes a contribution to highway safety to the degree that it combats drowsiness in the driver. The amounts contained in four or more cups of coffee may however produce insomnia, restlessness, and excitement although lesser amounts may do the same with individuals who are hypersensitive to the drug (Foltz, Ivy, and Barborka, 1942).

Amphetamine and related compounds have become one of the most popular groups of self-administered drugs today. Amphetamine and dextroamphetamine (Benzedrine, Dexedrine) are potent central nervous system stimulants, the effect depending on the dose, the personality, and the current mental state. Usual effects are alertness, wakefulness, elevated mood, improvement in simple tasks, performance, and decreased sense of fatigue. These have been used illicitly for increasing the performance of athletes and race horses, but whatever gain is achieved is only temporary and must be repaid out of the total economy of the organism. Prolonged use or large doses are followed very often by depression and fatigue. Methamphetamine (Desoxyn, Methedrine, etc.) has become increasingly popular because it has the pronounced stimulant effect on the central nervous system with less corresponding peripheral effects than amphetamine, which is often used as a nasal decongestant although this use is on the wane. Amphetamine, methamphetamine, and similar compounds have been widely used as appetite suppressants and represent a serious health hazard. If used at all, they should be under strict medical supervision (Goodman and Gilman, 1955, p. 500). These drugs are becoming an integral part of the drug culture of today's younger generation where they are, among other terms, referred to as "uppers" (Blumer, 1967). Because of the widespread use, both acute and chronic intoxication is seen frequently. The effects commonly include restlessness, dizziness, tremor, hyperactive reflexes, overtalkativeness, irritability, and sleeplessness. Anxiety, confusion, panic, and even hallucinations may occur since psychotic reaction often of a paranoid type can develop with the large doses currently in use among individuals habituated to the drug (Leake, 1958).

ANTIHISTAMINES

There is a large group of drugs which share, in varying degrees, the ability to antagonize or neutralize the pharmacological action of histamine in the body. They diminish the symptoms of various allergic reactions including anaphylaxis (Bickerman and Barach, 1964). Because of their action they are found in many of the proprietary drugs sold over the counter for the treatment of some of the symptoms of the common cold and of various allergic reactions. In some instances, the antihistaminic effects of these drugs become much less important than other effects. Among these effects may be central nervous system stimulation or central nervous system depression. Somnolence is a very important effect and becomes the important indication for several of the antihistamines, one of these groups being the chief ingredient of a number of hypnotics sold over the counter. Another widespread use is in prevention or suppression of motion sickness. The most common side effect is drowsiness and sedation, useful before bedtime, but capable of causing lack of coordination, dullness, and psychomotor retardation, all of which can contribute to accidents (Wood, Kennedy, and Graybiel, 1965). The following are a few of the antihistamines out of the many currently being marketed. Only the proprietary name is given: Benadryl, Dramamine, Pyribenzamine, Anahist, Chlor-trimeton, Marezine, Phenergan.

THE HALLUCINOGENS

It is difficult to find the proper term for a group of drugs which are psychotomimetic, that is, producing conditions resembling a psychosis, or psychedelic. The psychedelic drugs produce altered states of consciousness and state of mind covering the gamut of excitement, despair, power, release, calm, euphoria, detachment, new insights, new world views, new views about one's relationship with others, feeling of closeness to others or withdrawal, increased artistic or philosophical concern, and new experiences of the order of the mystical-religious, or a sense of unity with the universe, resembling those produced by yogi and other meditative disciplines. Toxic psychoses have been produced by a very large number of substances including most of the central nervous system-acting drugs, but these psychoses tend to be associated with organic symptoms, including delirium, disorientation, and clouded consciousness which are not usual with the hallucinogens. Although there are in use some exotic substances of this category such as that found in the seeds of some species of the American Tropical Morning Glory, psilocybin from the Mexican magic mushroom and others, these are of relatively minor importance compared to the more commonly used D-lysergic acid diethylamide (LSD) and mescaline, the active component of peyote obtained from cactus. Marihuana is another hallucinogen which, however, is classified legally as a narcotic (Cole and Katz, 1964). We are in a rather peculiar position today of living in a society where the use of these drugs has become extremely widespread particularly in the youthful age groups, but where objective knowledge is meager and where research is severely limited by legal restrictions.

Mescaline

Mescaline is of interest mainly because of its unusual psychological effects and visual hallucinations which consist of bright colors and designs, occasionally hallucinations of figures and persons, or hallucinations of a sexual content. Normally the sensorium is normal and insight is not impaired.

LSD

This potent drug has significant effects primarily upon the central nervous system. The symptoms and the dosages producing them vary widely, appearing to be a function of habituation, personality, setting, current state of mind, and combination with other drugs. It would appear that an individual suffering a drug-induced psychosis would have seriously impaired driving ability.

Cannabis

Cannabis is a very ancient drug obtained from the common hemp. In the Middle East and North Africa, the resinous extract is called "hashish." In India the materials obtained from different parts of the plant are called "bhang" and "ganja." In the United States the term marihuana is used for any part of the plant which is used to produce psychic change (Mayor's Committee on Marijuana, 1944). The physiological effects are minimal in terms of effect on driving, although the subjective effect may vary from a dreamy reverie to various changes in perception, including that for time and space, to the extreme of vivid hallucinations. The response is very much determined by the personality of the user and the immediate situation; but there may be marked alterations of mood varying from extreme well-being and joyousness to hilarity and occasionally depression. A recent study (Crancer et al., 1969) would indicate that a "normal social marihuana high" in experienced marihuana smokers in a simulated driving performance resulted in more speedometer errors, but under alcoholic intoxication there were more accelerator, brake, signal, speedometer and total errors.

OTHER DRUGS

There is a wide range of drugs used in the treatment of various ailments, which produce side effects that may adversely affect driving. Dizziness, drowsiness, blurred vision, confusion, psychomotor retardation, and incoordination may all result from such drugs. Even commonly used drugs such as aspirin may, in excessive quantity or in a hypersensitive person, cause serious undesirable symptoms. Particular attention should be paid to the potentially serious consequences of combinations of drugs that potentiate the effect of other drugs. Among the most common and most serious combinations are those of sedatives and hypnotics with alcohol (Hine and Turkel, 1966). In too many instances, it is impossible to predict the results of these combinations in the given individual. Any person receiving potent drugs or combinations of the sort just described should refrain from driving until it has been determined to what degree he will be affected, particularly in those functions relevant to driving.

CARBON MONOXIDE

There is a vast array of substances used for industrial, commercial, and household use that are toxic when imbibed, inhaled, or ingested and may cause various degrees of incoordination, clouded consciousness, and confusion such as to lead to a serious highway hazard. In some instances, these substances such as ether, carbon tetrachloride, benzene, gasoline, or glue solvents, are deliberately taken and produce a pleasant exhilaration or an euphoria, excitement, ataxia, blurred speech, double vision, even drowsiness, stupor, and unconsciousness. Damage to the viscera and brain are possible. Such behavior covers a wide range of personality types from experimenting juveniles to experienced truck drivers and is a matter of concern both to the legal authorities and the medical profession. It is impractical to cover the entire remaining field of toxicology here, but we will make special mention about one common environmental substance that has been a source of interest concerning its possible effect on driving. Carbon monoxide is a tasteless, colorless, odorless gas that produces no detectable sensation. It is present in some types of illuminating gas and in the exhaust from automobiles. Other common sources are furnaces, stoves, and cigarettes. The adverse effects of carbon monoxide (CO) result from the fact that it combines with the hemoglobin in the red blood corpuscles to form carboxyhemoglobin, which is not capable of transporting oxygen and which also tends to impede the transfer of oxygen from normal hemoglobin. The symptoms that result from this type of poisoning are those due to a low oxygen content in the tissues. It is possible to suffer only weakness and dizziness before unconsciousness but a variety of symptoms have been observed (Saures and Davenport, 1930). At the lower concentration of carboxyhemoglobin there may be headache, dizziness, weakness, nausea; as the concentration goes up there may be fainting, collapse, increase in pulse and respiration; and at the higher concentrations (from 60 to 80 percent of blood saturation) there may be coma, depression of heart action and respiration, and possibly death. Studies specific to the effect of carbon monoxide concentration have rarely been made, though studies have been made of hospitalized victims of automobile accidents which have not shown a significant level of blood saturation and a California study concluded that carbon monoxide was not associated with the fatal accidents investigated (Penn, 1965). In a study of driving performance with increases of carboxyhemoglobin up to 20 percent, there was a tendency to "smooth" velocity at the higher levels, that is, to drive faster on corners and slower on straightways as well as less precision in maintaining 200-feet separation distance and decrease in estimation of time (Ray, unpublished). There remains a need for further studies of the carbon monoxide factor in highway safety.

CONCLUSION

We live in a complex society where drugs such as alcohol and caffeine are accepted social beverages and patent drugs prescribed by physicians for the treatment of illness are used illegally by large segments of society for nonmedicinal purposes. There is an ever-increasing need for more scientific knowledge of the nature and effects of these substances on the behavior, performance, and fate of their users in lieu of the morass of ignorance and misinformation upon which are predicated most of the imperatives, moral and legal codes, and actions of the community and the larger society.

REFERENCES

Anderson, D. L. and Lhotka, D. C., On the Level, *Traffic Safety Monograph No. 1,* National Safety Council, Chicago, Ill., 1969.

Anderson, O. W., Family Costs for Drugs and Medicines, *Journal of the American Pharmaceutical Association,* **18** (March 1957), 148–149.

Ayd, F. J., A Survey of Drug-Induced Extrapyramidal Reactions, *Journal of the American Medical Association,* **175** (1961), 1054–1060.

Barmack, J. E. and Payne, D. E., Injury Producing Private Motor Vehicle Accidents among Airmen: Psychological Models of Accident-Generating Processes, *Journal of Psychology,* **52** (1961), 3–24.

Bickerman, H. A. and Barach, A. L., Antiallergic Drugs, in Modell, W., ed., *Drugs of Choice,* C. V. Mosbey & Co., St. Louis, Mo., (1964), 514–547.

Birrell, J. H. W., Blood Alcohol Levels in Drunk Drivers, Drunk and Disorderly Subjects and Moderate Social Drinkers, *Medical Journal of Australia,* December 1965, 949–953.

Bjerver, K. and Goldberg, L., Effect of Alcohol Ingestion on Driving Ability, *Quarterly Journal of Studies on Alcohol,* **2** (1950), 1–30.

Blum, R. H., *Utopiates: the Use and Users of LSD-25,* Atherton Press, New York, 1964.

Blumer, H., *The World of Youthful Drug Use,* ADD Center Project Final Report School of Criminology, U.C., Berkeley, 1967.

Borkenstein, R. F., Crowther, R. F., Shumate, R. P., Ziel, W. B., and Zylman, R., *The Role of the Drinking Driver in Traffic Accidents,* Indiana University Police Institute, Indianapolis, Ind., February 1964.

Braunstein, P. W., Weinberg, S. B., and Dal Cortivo, L., The Drunk and Drugged Driver versus the Law, *Journal of Trauma,* **8** (1968), 83–90.

Brenner, B., Alcoholism and Fatal Accidents, *Quarterly Journal of Studies on Alcohol,* **28** (1967), 517–528.

Brodie, B. B., Sulser, F., and Costa, E., Psychotherapeutic Drugs, *Annual Review of Medicine,* **12** (1961), 349–368.

California Medical Association, Self-Medication Practices, *California Medicine,* **107**, 5 (November 1967), 452–454.

Coats, D. A., Trautner, E. M., and Gershon, S., The Treatment of Lithium Poisoning, *Australian Annals of Medicine,* **6** (1957), 11–15.

Cole, J. O. and Katz, M. M., The Psychotomimetic Drugs, *Journal of the American Medical Association,* **187** (1964).

Crancer, A., Dille, J., Delay, J., Wallace, J., and Haykin, M., Comparison of the Effects of Marihuana and Alcohol on Simulated Driving Performance, *Science,* **164** (1969), 851–854.

Davis, J. H. and Fisk, A. J., The Dade County, Florida Study on Carbon Monoxide, Alcohol and Drugs in Fatal Single Vehicle Automobile Accidents, Dade County, Florida Coroner's Office, *Proceedings of National Association of Coroners,* 1964–66, 197–204.

Foltz, E., Ivy, A. C., and Barborka, C. J., Use of Double Work Periods in Study of Fatigue and Influence of Caffeine on Recovery, *American Journal of Physiology,* **136** (1942), 79–86.

Forney, R. B. and Hughes, F. W., Alcohol and Drugs, *Traffic Safety,* **65** (1967), 23.

Fox, B. and Fox, J., eds., *Alcohol and Traffic Safety,* Public Health Service publication No. 1043, U.S. Public Health Service, Washington, D.C., 1963.

Freimuth, H. C., Watts, S. R., and Fisher, R. S., Alcohol and Highway Fatalities, *Journal of Forensic Science,* 3 (1958), 65–71.

Goldberg, L., Drunken Drivers in Sweden, *Alcohol and Road Traffic,* Proceedings of 2nd International Conference, Toronto, Canada, 1955.

Goodman, L. and Gilman, A., *The Pharmacological Basis of Therapeutics,* 2nd ed., Macmillan, New York, 1955, 109.

Greenberg, L. A., The Definition of an Intoxicating Beverage, *Quarterly Journal of Studies of Alcohol,* **16** (1955), 316–325.

Haddon, W. and Bradess, V. A., Alcohol in the Single Vehicle Fatal Accident—Experience of Westchester County, New York, *Journal of the American Medical Association*, **14** (1959), 127–133.

Hine, C. H. and Turkel, H. W., Research of the Scientific Literature and Reports on the Effects on Man of Alcohol Alone and in Combination with Other Drugs, *Technical Report 63-22*. Arctic Aeromedical Laboratory, Fort Wainright, Alaska, July 1966.

Holcomb, R. L., Alcohol in Relation to Traffic Accidents, *Journal of the American Medical Association*, **111** (1938), 1076–1085.

Hollister, L. E., Adverse Reactions to Phenothiazines, *Journal of the American Medical Association*, **189** (1964), 311–313.

Hollister, L. E. and Overall, J. E., Reflections on the Specificity of Action of Antidepressants, *Psychosomatics*, **6** (1965), 361–365.

Hyman, M., The Social Characteristics of Persons Apprehended for Driving While Intoxicated, Presented at the 95th Annual Meeting, American Public Health Association, Miami Beach, Florida, October 26, 1967.

Leake, C. D., *Amphetamines: Their Actions and Uses*, C. C. Thomas, Springfield, Ill., 1958.

Lewis, E. M. and Sarlanis, K., The Effects of Alcohol on Decision Making with Respect to Traffic Signals, *Injury Control Research Laboratory Report 08-4*, Public Health Service, Washington, D.C., 1969.

Loomis, T. A. and West, T. C., The Influence of Alcohol on Automobile Driving Ability, *Quarterly Journal of Studies on Alcohol*, **19** (1958), 30–46.

Lucas, G. H., Kalow, W., McColl, J. D., Griffith, B. A., Smith, H. W., Quantitative Studies of the Relationship between Alcohol Levels and Motor Vehicle Accidents, *Proceedings of the 2nd International Conference on Alcohol and Road Traffic*, Toronto, 1955, 139–142.

Mayor's Committee on Marijuana, Report, Cattel Press, Lancaster, Pa., 1944.

McCarroll, J. R. and Haddon, W., A Controlled Study of Fatal Automobile Accidents in New York City, *Journal of Chronic Diseases*, **15** (1962), 811–826.

Miller, J. G., Objective Measurements of the Effects of Drugs on Driver Behavior, *Journal of the American Medical Association*, **179** (1962), 940–943.

Monroe, D. G., The Drinking Driver, *Quarterly Journal of Studies on Alcohol*, **8** (1947), 385–405.

Moskowitz, H. and DePry, D., Differential Effect on Auditory Vigilance and Divided-Attention Tasks. *Quarterly Journal of Studies on Alcohol*, **29**, 1 (1968), 54–63.

National Institute of Mental Health, Alcohol and Alcoholism, *Public Health Service Publication No. 1640*, Washington, D.C., 1968.

National Safety Council, Committee on Alcohol and Drugs, National Safety Council, *Minutes of the Meeting October 20, 1960*, Chicago, Ill.

National Safety Council, Statistics Division National Safety Council, *Accident Facts*, National Safety Council, Chicago, Ill., 1969.

New Jersey Alcohol Determination Program in Fatal Traffic Accident Cases—*Report of Findings Three Year Study 1961–1963*, New Jersey Department of Law and Public Safety, Division of Motor Vehicles, Traffic Safety Series, Trenton, N.J., 1964.

Nielson, R. A., *Alcohol Involvement in Fatal Motor Vehicle Accidents*, California Traffic Safety Foundation, San Francisco, Cal., September 1965.

Nielson, R. A., *A Survey of Post-Mortem Blood-Alcohols from 41 California Counties in 1966*, California Traffic Safety Foundation, San Francisco, Cal., April 1967.

Overall, J. E., Dimensions of Manifest Depression, *Journal of Psychiatric Research,* **1** (1962), 239–245.

Overall, J. E., Hollister, L. E., Meyer, F., Kimbell, I., and Shelton, J., Imipramine and Thioridazine in Depressed and Schizophrenic Patients: Are There Specific Antidepressant Drugs?, *Journal of the American Medical Association,* **189** (1964), 605–608.

Overall, J. E., Hollister, L. E., Pokorny, A. D., Casey, J. F., and Katz, G., Drug Therapy in Depressions, Controlled Evaluation of Imipramine, Isocarboxazide, Dextroamphetamine-amobarbital and Placebo, *Clinical and Pharmacological Therapy,* **3** (1962), 16–22.

Parry, H. J., Use of Psychotropic Drugs by U.S. Adults, *Public Health Reports,* **83,** 10 (October 1968), 799–810.

Penn, H. S., *The Role of Carbon Monoxide, Alcohol and Drugs in Fatal Single Car Accidents,* California Highway Patrol, November 1965.

Popham, R. E., Alcoholism and Traffic Accidents, *Quarterly Journal of Studies on Alcohol,* **17** (1956), 225–232.

The Quarterly Journal of Inebriety, editorial, **26** (1904), 308–309.

Ray, A. M., An Exploratory Study of Automobile Driving Performed under the Influence of Low Levels of Carboxyhemoglobin LTV, Aerospace Corporation (unpublished paper).

Reynolds, A. K. and Randall, L. O., *Morphine and Allied Drugs,* University of Toronto Press, Toronto, 1957.

Rossi, G. V., The Psychotherapeutic Agents, *American Journal of Pharmacology,* **136** (1964), 6–24.

Saures, P. R. and Davenport, S. J., Review of Carbon Monoxide Poisoning, *Public Health Bulletin No. 195,* U.S. Govt. Printing Office, Washington, D.C., 1930.

Selzer, M. L., Payne, C. E., Westervelt, F. H., and Quinn, J., Automobile Accidents as an Expression of Psychopathology in an Alcoholic Population, *Quarterly Journal of Studies on Alcohol,* **28** (1967), 505–515.

Selzer, M. L., and Weiss, S., Alcoholism and Traffic Fatalities: Study in Futility, *American Journal of Psychiatry,* **122** (1966), 762–767.

Schmidt, W. S. and Smart, R. G., Alcoholics, Drinking and Traffic Accidents, *Quarterly Journal of Studies on Alcohol,* **20** (1959), 631–644.

Shupe, L. M. and Pfau, R. O., Who are these drinking drivers? *Proceedings of the 4th International Conference on Alcohol and Traffic Safety,* December 6–10, 1965, Indiana University, Bloomington, Indiana, 1966, 62–82.

The State of the Art of Traffic Safety, Arthur D. Little, Inc., Cambridge, Mass., June 1966.

U.S. Department of Transportation, *Alcohol and Highway Safety,* Washington, D.C., August 1968.

Voas, R. B., *Cars that Drunks Can't Drive,* National Highway Safety Research Center, November 1969.

Waller, J. A., Chronic Medical Conditions and Traffic Safety, *New England Journal of Medicine,* **273** (1965), 1413–1420.

Waller, J. A., Alcohol and Traffic Accidents: Can the Gordian Knot Be Broken?, *Traffic Safety Research Review,* **10** (1966), 14–21. a

Waller, J. A., Traffic Accidents and the Ingestion of Alcohol, in Curran, W. J. and Chayet, N. L., eds., *Trauma and the Automobile,* W. H. Anderson, Cincinnati, Ohio, 1966, 157–169. b

Waller, J. A., Use and Misuse of Alcoholic Beverages as a Factor in Motor Vehicle Accidents, *Public Health Reports,* **81** (1966), 591–597. c

Waller, J. A., Drinking Drivers and Driving Drinkers—The Need for Multiple Approaches to Accidents Involving Alcohol, in Selzer, M. L., Gikas, P. W., and Huelke, D. F., eds., *The Prevention of Highway Injury,* Highway Safety Research Institute, University of Michigan, Ann Arbor, Mich., 1967, 30–37.

Waller, J. A. and Turkel, H. W., Alcoholism and Traffic Deaths, *New England Journal of Medicine,* **275** (1966), 532–536.

Wood, C. D., Kennedy, R. S., and Graybiel, A., Review of Antimotion Sickness and Drugs, 1954–1964, *Aerospace Medicine,* **36** (1965), 1–4.

Zirkle, G. A., King, P. D., and McAtee, O. B., Effects of Chlorpromazine and Alcohol on Coordination and Judgment, *Journal of the American Medical Association,* **171** (1959), 1496–1499.

Zirkle, G. A., McAtee, O. B., King, P. D., Van Dyke, R., Meprobamate and Small Amounts of Alcohol: Effects on Human Ability, Coordination, and Judgment, *Journal of the American Medical Association,* **173** (1960), 1823–1825.

Zivin, I. and Shalowitz, M., Acute Toxic Reaction to Prolonged Glutethimide Administration, *New England Journal of Medicine,* **266** (1962), 496–498.

XIV

PSYCHOSOCIAL FACTORS AND ACCIDENTS IN THE HIGHWAY TRANSPORTATION SYSTEM

James R. Adams

James Ray Adams is Associate Director for Safety Research of the Continental Research Institute, New York City. He obtained his Ph.D. from Columbia University under the interdisciplinary program in social psychology.

Dr. Adams has been a pilot and research psychologist with the U.S. Air Force, an instructor at the University of Colorado, and assistant professor of psychology at Long Island University.

He became associated with the Safety Research and Education Project at Columbia while a doctoral candidate there in 1960. He has worked on rehabilitation of problem drivers, especially drinking drivers. Dr. Adams has also been interested in the development of a simulator to diagnose judgment of hazards by a driver. It was in relation to work on this simulator that he became acquainted with the Medical Department of the Continental Insurance Companies. He became a consultant to the Continental Research Institute in 1966.

He has carried out research on judgment of impending hazards and other driver characteristics and on rehabilitation of problem and drinking drivers. He has developed materials in population studies, safety education, and health education, and has worked in human relations training. He has been a consultant on safety education and research, has many publications and papers in these areas.

A person's behavior is influenced by his interaction with other people; this is the starting point of social-psychological analysis. These interactions are molded into social institutions and customs which in turn are taken up by individuals in the process of personality development. It is well established that personality variations are associated with accident experience. We consider here some of the empirical evidence for the influences of social interactions which are immediately antecedent to highway collisions.

Sometimes it appears as though a problem is openly acknowledged only by those who think they have an answer to it. The ambiguity of an unsolvable difficulty is intolerable, so the difficulty is denied or "explained " into something else, something more manageable. The contribution of society and its cultural ways and standards to the traffic accident toll sometimes appears to be a problem so dealt with. Those who cannot or will not see that social changes would ameliorate the accident rate insist that "you can't change human nature" or "you can't fight City Hall." Such defeatism leads to a view that efforts to prevent accidents are inevitably futile, and that all our resources should therefore be directed to the amelioration of their tragic consequences.

Actually human nature is changed frequently. The process of change is called learning. And social change, while difficult and sometimes excruciatingly slow, is possible.

There is an equally unhappy counterpart to this view—the partisan who is convinced he has an answer (or, *the* answer) and who will acknowledge nothing that does not support his adopted solution. In this chapter we attempt to avoid both the hopelessness of those who would look the other way and the parochialism of those who will look at only one thing. There are many facets to safety.

To effectively counteract the rising toll of traffic collisions, we must deal more creatively with the problems that lead to collisions. This involves the mechanics of the vehicle and the roadway, the traffic system, the physiology and personality of the drivers, and the social context of driving. In addition to the physical properties of the vehicle traffic system, we need to understand the social norms and cultural patterns underlying the development of personality, not only of the driver but of the automobile designer, producer, salesman, the highway builder, the legislator, the judge, the administrator, the policeman, the voter, the taxpayer—all those who contribute to our man-made transportation system.

We need to understand the social processes underlying the design, production, sale and maintenance of vehicles, highways and traffic control systems; the social processes underlying half a century of largely punitive approaches to control of the driver; reactions to stress in the interpersonal relations of drivers; and the immediate interaction of drivers on the highway. In relation to the magnitude of the need, the published studies of these social processes are few.

The present chapter does not attempt to cover the possible range of psychosocial theories of highway safety. Instead we concentrate on one facet that has some sound empirical evidence and some implications of great importance for countermeasures. The discussion concludes with a short dialectic on models of accident countermeasures.

SOCIAL NORMS, INTERPERSONAL STRESS, AND TRAFFIC COLLISIONS

Regional Differences in Accidents and Other Social Pathologies

Are there influences in the general "social climate" of a community or region which affect the accident rate of people in the area? What is the nature of these influences? By what means do they affect highway safety? How could pernicious influences be changed for the better? In this section we review the following theories and supportive evidence:

1. There are regional differences in accidents which are positively correlated with differences in other forms of social pathology—alcoholism, suicide, and homicide.
2. Accidents may accomplish physical disablement which serves to protect the ego ("save face") in compensation for failure to cope with unacceptable personal disabilities.
3. Stress in the lives of drivers, particularly threats to emotional stability or financial security, often precedes a collision. Stress is more debilitating in drivers with histories of personality disturbance.
4. Alcohol is often the mediator between stress and collisions. Again, this is particularly true for drivers with personality disorder.
5. The combination of personality disturbance and precipitating stress affects highway behavior apparently through inattentiveness (especially when intoxicated) and through half-intended initiatives toward disablement or destruction of self and others.
6. Regional differences in rates of highway accidents and other pathologies reflect differences in amounts of precipitating stresses and in the prominence of misuse of alcohol and motor vehicles in coping with these stresses.

Porterfield (1960) has studied the association between highway accidents and other forms of social pathology. Using rates of homicide and suicide as an index of "regard for life," he has found a significant correlation between age-adjusted rates of death by motor vehicle accidents and homicide and suicide rates in large metropolitan areas. (Correlations are notably higher for males than for females.) Using states rather than cities as the unit of analysis, he found a positive relationship between the passenger-mile traffic death rate and the suicide-homicide rate among the male white population. Furthermore, there was a positive relationship between the passenger-mile death index and a mean of the indexes of six criminal offenses (murder, burglary, aggravated assault, robbery, larceny, and auto theft).

Porterfield argues that a motor vehicle may be seen as a "deadly weapon" and that if the populations of given areas have higher proportions of persons who do not value life, these populations would be expected to have higher rates of motor vehicle fatalities as well as homicides and suicides. His data are congruent with that assumption. Since the suicides, homicides, and traffic fatalities represent different sets of people, it would be unreasonable to argue that any of these "caused" the others; rather it must be that the association reflects something common to the larger population—something about the communities from which they all come. Porterfield interprets this common antecedent as low regard for life; with those becoming involved in suicides, homicides, and traffic accidents having "little regard for their own lives or the lives of others or both . . . ."

This common antecedent might be spelled out more specifically as (1) valuing certain *qualities* of living, (2) holding these values with greater or lesser *intensity*, and (3) having available *differing prominent modes of coping* when these values are violated. The quality of living which is prominent in studies of suicide is the integrity of love relationships. Suicide often follows the loss of a loved person by death or desertion. Homicide is often found related to ego ideals of "masculinity," particularly the physically strong, dominant, virile image of the male which has been transmitted from our agrarian past. (It is no accident that late adolescent males have driving records among the worst.) Both of these qualities are relevant to highway accidents.

When we consider the strength of the fear of bodily injury, it is evident that risk-taking behavior must result from values of great intensity. This intensity is in part a function of the singularity of the value system. To the person with several loves, the loss of one is not so devastating as to the person who is dependent on just one other. The man who envisions several aspects to his manhood is not so caught up in the social obsession with dominance as is the man lacking in this flexibility. A community may be "healthy" only to the extent that it enables sufficient variation of values to allow compensations for every person so that each can stay alive emotionally.

When a person is frustrated in his seeking to attain desired qualities of living, he will have several modes of coping with this frustration. These coping modes are "psychologically available" by virtue of their frequent use by other people in the society—they are literally "modes." The two coping modes that are of greatest significance to highway safety are intoxication and ego-expressive driving. Ego-expressive driving is exemplified in the great emphasis on power, speed, and appearance in the design and purchase of automobiles, to the neglect of safety features.

Another study suggests an association between misuse of alcohol as a prominent coping mode and the correlation between accidents and suicide noted by Porterfield. Porterfield used census data from the years 1949 to 1951. His work has been replicated in part with data from the year 1960. An additional variable, cirrhosis of the liver, has been added to the matrix as an indicator of the prevalence of alcoholism. Table 1

Table 1 Rank Order Correlations for Fatality Rates for Indicated Causes for 30 Cities

	Motor Vehicle Accidents	Suicide	Homicide	Cirrhosis of Liver
Motor vehicle accidents	—			
Suicide	.86[a]	—		
Homicide	.42[b]	.25	—	
Cirrhosis of liver	.53[a]	.63[a]	.01	—

[a] $P < .01$.
[b] $P < .05$.
From Adams and Rosenblatt, 1966.

gives rank order correlations for the four indicated variables. The high correlation between motor vehicle accidents and suicide rates corroborates Porterfield's findings. The correlations between cirrhosis of the liver and both motor vehicle accidents and suicide supports the argument that alcoholism is significant to both of these. (Alcoholism is often referred to as "slow suicide." With the aid of an automobile, it need not be slow.)

Social Norms and the Motivation to Incaution: Acceptable and Unacceptable Disability

A provocative and potentially rich contribution to the conceptualization of the accident process comes from the work of Imboden, Canter, and Cluff (1961) and Hirschfield and Behan (1966). Imboden and his associates were primarily concerned with the chronic persistence of symptoms in certain patients beyond the normal period of recovery. Patients were victims of the infectious diseases brucellosis and influenza. It has been common observation that of patients contracting acute brucellosis, a large minority persist in a chronic illness beyond the subsidence of the acute phase of the disease. Some of these chronic patients have physical symptoms, but many show a subjective syndrome that resembles neurasthenia: fatigue, lassitude, headache, nervousness, depression, backache, and vague general aches and pains.

These investigators report a study of 24 patients who had accidentally incurred cases of acute brucellosis. Of the 24 patients, 8 recovered within two or three months (the acute-recovered group), but the remaining 16 patients retained symptoms well beyond one year (the chronic patients). Evidence of seriously traumatic events or circumstances in the early lives of the patients was found for 11 of the 16 chronic patients and in 2 of the 8 acute-recovered patients. Similarly, there was evidence of disturbed or stressful life situations existing at the time of or within a year preceding the acute infection in 11 of the 16 chronic patients and in none of the acute-recovered ones.

With these chronic symptomatic patients, psychiatric interviews and objective psychological testing supported the observation that preoccupation with the somatic symptoms by these patients served a "face-saving" function—preserving self-esteem by permitting the patient to deny personal disability and rationalize his difficulties as resulting from a persisting organic disease (". . . not my fault") rather than from personal incapacity to cope with emotional maladaptation. These authors concluded that ". . . symptomatic recovery following this acute infection depended critically on the emotional state of the person, particularly the presence or absence of *depression*, at the time of the acute infection or in the convalescent period" (Imboden, et al., p. 1183). The results of this study were supported by pro-active investigations of an influenza epidemic (Imboden, Canter, and Cluff, 1961) and reactions of a group of soldiers to physical insults (Canter, Imboden, and Cluff, 1965).

Hirschfeld and Behan (1966) have carried this conceptualization into the field of accidents with their studies of industrial accidents. They describe an accident as an event that is "captured" by the personality for the purpose of solving the person's problems of living. They see it as an aspect of an ongoing process which they diagram this way (p. 86):

(a) Personality difficulties	+	(b) Troubled life situation	=	(c) Unacceptable disability
(c) Unacceptable disability	+	(d) Accidents, illnesses, alcoholism, etc.	=	(e) Acceptable disability

The critical element in this formulation is the concept of "acceptability." These authors define it this way (p. 87):

"(This points to) the primary characteristic that makes a disability acceptable. It is *apparently* directly related to an external force. It may be a bullet from the enemy, an inconsiderate or incautious employer, an oppressive government or social situation beyond the influence of the person, or a bacterial disease of any kind. In contrast, almost all limitations which are due to intrinsic problems of people themselves are more or less unacceptable."

Venereal disease is cited as an instance of an unacceptable disability.

The significance of social standards in this process is obvious, but to keep the theme of this chapter clearly before us, let us note that the prime motivation operating here is the person's desire to maintain a place of respectability in the eyes of his associates ("saving face") and in his own conscience or self-regard (which is, in turn, the learned and accepted norms of one's society).

We may employ the concept of internal and external groups to portray graphically the social element in this accident process. "Internal" groups are the face-to-face groups that directly and significantly influence one's personality and behavior (family, school class, neighborhood friendship gangs, etc.). "External" groups are the larger, more distant units of society of which a given internal group is a part (extended family, church, school, city, nation, civilization). Figure 1 is meant to emphasize three points: (1) that the norms of each of the elements is influenced by the others, but may not be identical with them, (2) that the result is not a "suicidal" or "*self*-destruction" motive but rather a motive to preserve the "self" (defined to include self-image or "face"), and (3) that while protecting his self, the "accident victim" is at the same time protecting and preserving the group and cultural norms of acceptability.

A second facet of the "accident process" as described by Hirschfield and Behan is also firmly ensconced in our cultural ways. It is also a form of compensation which follows after an accident, but rather than the *psychological* compensatory mechanism described above, it is simply the

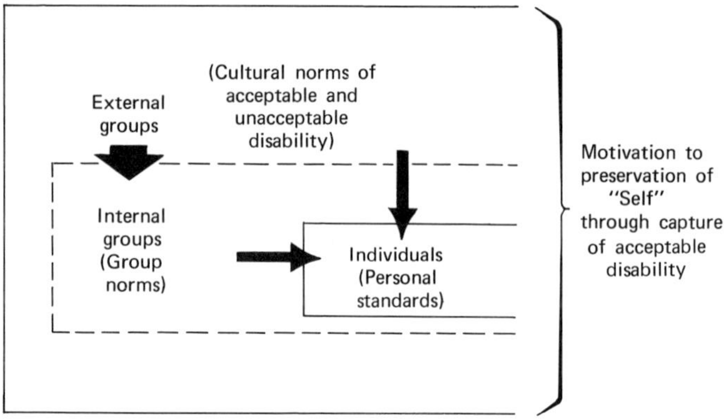

Figure 1. Group-individual influences affecting propensity to half-intentional accident involvement.

monetary compensation of insurance—chiefly workmen's compensation. Hirschfield and Behan (1963 a) tell of one case, among others, of an accident victim who ". . . told that he had worked in an unpleasant city for a number of years and that he felt that the company owed him an early retirement. He had picked out the home that he wanted in another city, priced it, and knew exactly how much it would take (in winning the suit) to finance this plan." While the money is paid only after the fact of the mishap, the awareness that compensation is available may precede it and may thus materially contribute to the acceptability of injury.

Social Stress Antecedent to Highway Collisions

Thorndike (1951) noted after his study of aircraft accidents that an accident often occurred at a time when the pilot was subject to some type of personal crisis. From the instances cited—illness in the family, marital quarreling, gambling debts—it appears that such crises are usually of a social nature. They arise in the course of interpersonal relations and reflect feelings people have toward one another and their internalized social norms of selfhood. No controlled studies were known when Thorndike made his observations but since that time several have been published which are highly pertinent in elucidation of the relationship between social stress and highway collisions.

Selzer, Rogers, and Kern (1968) did in-depth studies of 96 male and female drivers responsible for fatal collisions over a three-year period in Washtenaw County, Michigan. Drivers who survived the collisions and persons close to these drivers were interviewed, and in other cases, persons who had been close to the deceased driver were interviewed. Evidence of the personality and the stressful situations experienced by the fatality drivers before the collision was sought. A control sample of 96 drivers matched for age, sex, and home county were interviewed as were persons close to the control drivers. With regard to personality differences, 40 (42 percent) of the fatality drivers, against 16 (17 percent) of the control drivers were diagnosed as having paranoid thinking, suicidal thoughts or acts, depression, or violent behavior. (In view of the consistent finding by all studies of *depression* as an antecedent to accidents, we should note that 20 (21 percent) of the fatality drivers versus 7 (7 percent) of the control drivers were considered as depressed.)

Social stress for these two groups of drivers was inferred from evidence of interpersonal crises or vocational-financial difficulties. Crises were counted which arose during the 12-month period preceding the fatal accident or the interview of the control driver, and which were judged to be *still affecting the driver* at the time of the fatal crash or interview. The finding that the fatality drivers were significantly more frequently suffering from social stress is pictured in the data abstracted in Figure 2.

Brown and Bohnert (1968) led an intensive case study effort on 25 fatal crashes with male drivers. They employed structured interviews conducted by two clinical psychiatrists to identify and evaluate personal stresses in the pre-crash and pre-interview lives of the fatality group of drivers and 25 control drivers. Wives, other family members, and friends of the dead drivers were interviewed in depth regarding the social and driving history, personality, and the alcohol involvement of the driver. A similar indirect interview was conducted with relatives and friends of the control drivers while a third member of the investigating team interviewed the control driver himself. In no case was there conflict between the evaluations by the direct and indirect evaluations of the control drivers.

Personality evaluations of the two sets of drivers showed marked discrepancies between them. Twenty (80 percent) of the fatality drivers evidenced severe impairment of personality functioning, while three (12 percent) of the controls were so diagnosed. Of these 20, 16 (60 percent) were diagnosed as alcoholics.

The structured interviews were designed to identify and evaluate the significance of any major stresses in the pre-crash and pre-interview lives of the drivers. Proportions of drivers who had suffered such personal stresses within the 6 months preceding the fatal collision or the interview are also presented in Figure 2. (Note that these two sets of data rep-

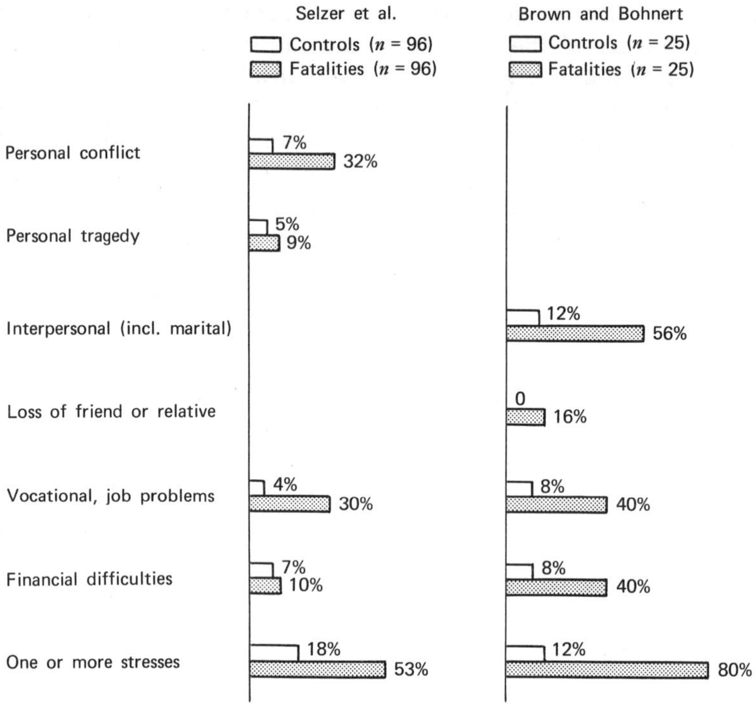

Figure 2. Percentages of fatality drivers and control drivers experiencing social stresses before accident or interview. [Abstracted from Selzer et al. (1968), Table 3, and from Brown and Bohnert (1968), Table 2.]

resent different time intervals. The Selzer et al. data are derived from the full year preceding, while the Brown and Bohnert data come from the 6 months preceding, including their figures for the 24-hour period preceding fatal crashes.)

The most critical period for accident involvement following on stress would seem to be the hours immediately following the onset of an acutely stressful episode. Both these studies find evidence for this. Selzer et al. write (p. 1032):

"One unsought and yet perhaps vital set of data turned up unexpectedly in our interview summaries. No less than 19 (20 percent) of the 96 fatality drivers were found to have been acutely upset by events that occurred during the six-hour period immediately preceding the fatal accident. Most of the 19 drivers had had violent quarrels, for the most part with women: wives, girl friends, barmaids, and female drinking companions. A few had physical fights with other men."

Brown and Bohnert corroborate this finding by comparing the incidence of stress during the 24-hour pre-crash period of their fatality drivers with the 1-week pre-interview period of their control drivers. They found that 56 percent of their fatality drivers were influenced by stress in interpersonal relations, while 12 percent of their control drivers were so troubled. Financial difficulties characterized 36 percent of fatalities versus 8 percent of controls; job problems troubled 24 percent of fatalities versus 8 percent of controls. In all, 80 percent of the fatality drivers versus 12 percent of the controls experienced precipitating stresses in the hours immediately before their collision.

The findings of Tabachnick and his associates (1966) are relevant to our present inquiry although their procedures were designed for the specific purpose of comparing accident cases with overt suicide cases. Their accident subjects were 15 males from one-car fatalities in which the driver was the victim. These 15 drivers were selected so as to be matched with 15 male suicides from self-inflicted gunshot wounds. The extent to which this sample is comparable to those we have just reviewed cannot be ascertained. Persons close to the deceased subjects were interviewed, a process those authors termed a "psychological autopsy." They refer to personality maladjustment and to environmental stress as "disequilibrium in the patient's life," and cite the following results of their investigation (from Table 1):

Upsetting Situation Just Prior To Death

Vehicle Fatalities ($n = 15$)	Suicide Cases ($n = 15$)
1. Nothing strikingly clear just prior to death (12 of 15)	1. Loss of or estrangement from a significant other person, feeling of failure, or feeling unloved (14 of 15)
2. Recent move into situation of greater responsibility (9 of 15)	
3. Loss of or anger toward a significant other person (3 of 15)	

The incidence of 3 out of 15 drivers with stress "just prior to death" is 20 percent of the sample, which happens to match exactly the proportion found by Selzer et al. for the 6-hour period immediately preceding the fatal accidents of their subjects. The finding by Brown and Bohnert that 80 percent of their fatality drivers were experiencing stress situations within the 24-hour pre-crash period is somewhat at variance with these two reports. In considering this, we must allow for the differences in investigative approach, particularly the fact that Brown and Bohnert were aware of the Selzer et al. findings and were alerted to look carefully at the time immediately preceding the fatal accidents. It is to be expected that something will be more apparent to one diligently searching for it. It is a shortcoming of "psychological autopsy" studies that the high degree of subjective judgment involved will inevitably lead to variations in definitions of entities, standards of presence or absence of an entity, and emphasis in search for one or another set of entities. Their great value in the study of accident influences should lead us to seek ways of achieving more precise definitions and more comparable reporting.

Two recurrent themes in the findings of these studies are depression and alcohol intoxication. Selzer et al. found 20 (21 percent) of their 96 fatality drivers to be "clinically depressed," versus 7 (7 percent) of 96 controls. The difference is statistically stable. Brown and Bohnert found 10 (40 percent) of their fatality drivers in a "pre-crash state" of depression, versus 1 (4 percent) driver in the control group. Tabachnick and his associates found 5 (33 percent) of their accident fatalities to be characterized by "depression or self-punishment." (Twelve of the 15 gunshot suicides were so diagnosed.)

Seventy-two percent of the fatality drivers in the Brown and Bohnert study were intoxicated at the time of their fatal crash. All showed blood alcohol levels greater than .15 percent. Tabachnick et al. report that 8 of the 15 fatality drivers had been drinking. Selzer et al. do not report on drinking by their subjects but do note that (p. 52): ". . . alcohol-addicted drivers were heavily over-represented in the 96-driver F group and among F drivers with psychopathology and social stress."

The findings cited here lend consistent and compelling weight to the view that interaction between people is a significant element in the etiology of accidents, and that this interaction is influential especially in the formation of disturbed personalities and in the inducement of precipitating stresses. The personality disturbance is often alcoholism and the socially prevalent practice of drinking often mediates between the stress and the collision. When we ask what the implications of this view are for accident countermeasures, the most general implication seems to be the recognition that accidents are among the symptoms of social pathology and that safety must be a part of the mental health and social improvement concerns of society. As people become healthier, they will attain greater safety; as they become safer, they will be healthier. Health and safety are integral—each must help or each will hinder the other.

A suggestion more specific to the problem of precipitating stress might be that a system be established in each community for intervening with the driver at the time of his crisis. The intervention could serve to warn the driver of his increased vulnerability and to provide comfort and reassurance. Such interventions could be made by designated persons who would be likely to have contact with a driver at the inception of his stress—persons such as physicians and admitting secretaries of hospitals, policemen, personnel officers, ministers, priests and rabbis, psychologists, or ambulance drivers. A word of caution and sympathy at a time when a driver is distraught might be a good preventive for automobile collisions.

SOCIAL ANTECEDENTS TO ACCIDENT COUNTERMEASURE MODELS

Engineering and Economic Sanctions: The First Success

The problem of accidents as we know the problem today had its inception with the introduction of machinery during the time of the industrial revolution. The nineteenth century saw excruciating tolls of accidental injury and death; tolls which saw no significant decline until legislative action imposed upon employers the cost of accidents to the employee, regardless of "fault." The passage of workmen's compensation laws made it advantageous for insurance companies to send inspectors to check for hazardous conditions. Plant owners followed the advice of these inspectors in reducing the physical hazards to which workers were exposed and constructing mechanical safeguards for hazards that could not be eliminated. This "safety engineering" approach, initiated for economic reasons based in legislative fiat, has become a "model" of countermeasures to accidents which has wide popular and professional support. The dramatic reductions in accident rates achieved through this approach in the early years of the twentieth century assure a high regard for the approach in the thinking of people familiar with it.

Traffic Violations: Folk Crime or Legal Fiction?

Our social history provides bases for two other "popular" models of accident countermeasures—with their attendant assumptions as to human nature and accident causation. One may be termed the "criminality" model, the other the "education" model. Criminal behavior violates the requirements or prohibitions of social norms codified in legal statutes. Early in this century traffic rule violations were defined as criminal and subjected to punishments under the police power of the state.

It may be more accurate to recognize, however, that to most people a traffic violation is not a "crime" at all. The small loss of time caused by a driver usurping priority is so petty, and so universal, that it is generally considered nothing more than discourtesy. As for a traffic violation being crime because it creates a hazard, this lacks the essential characteristics of criminal acts: (1) The criminal brandishment of a weapon poses no hazard to the one holding the weapon; only the victim is in danger. A driver, on the other hand, is himself in as much danger from a collision as the "victim." (2) A criminal act is intended to benefit the criminal, to the detriment of his victim. Burglary secures wealth; assault secures hegemony or revenge. A collision secures nothing—the perpetrator is also a victim, also subject to expense, injury, and death. (3) Many if not most traffic collisions involve contributions by both parties to the collision. It is rare for a thief to rob a man who is simultaneously robbing the thief. (4) Events that are statistically predictable resultants of normal, acceptable activities are not considered criminal. Bank robbery is not a frequent accompaniment to check cashing. Yet traffic collisions occur to people who are trying to do something else. They are trying to go somewhere. *More than just being unintentional, collisions occur in spite of intentions to prevent them.*

These differences are so fundamental that there is little popular support for the notion that traffic violations are "crime." Two exceptions here are racing on public highways and driving while intoxicated. Drinking and driving, while the more dangerous of these two, is so universally practiced that it is widely condoned and protected, and probably best qualifies for Ross' definition of a "folk crime" (Ross, 1960–61). Other traffic violations qualify better as nuisances or impoliteness. Their designation as "crimes" is merely by statutory definition; their "criminality" is a legal fiction, not a social reality.

A not uncommon response to the ineffectiveness of the "crime" approach is an effort to intensify the effects of fear of punishment by "cracking down" on enforcement—that is, by increasing surveillance and making punishments more severe. In appraising this, we should consider the words of an address at the Georgetown University Law Center on March 21, 1967, by Howard Leary, the Police Commissioner of New York City,* who noted that "in any event, the causes of the increased criminality of our cities will not be removed by simplistic reliance upon

* Quoted in Y. Kasimar, Some Reflections on the War Theory of Crime Control, *Civil Liberties in New York*, New York Civil Liberties Union, **XVI**, 4 (April 1968), 12.

increased use of force." Commissioner Leary's reference was not specifically to traffic violations, but his point is relevant nevertheless. Simplistic reliance upon increased use of force does not get at the root causes of the problems.

What is the effect of a society's reliance on the present approach to social control of traffic? Are drivers "kept safe in spite of themselves"? Or is the legal fiction a token solution that impedes the development of more effective systems? Would there be promise in an expanded research effort on these questions?

Education and Rehabilitation

The educational model of accident countermeasures has been patterned variously on the information teaching methods of the public schools and the military services, the admonitory practices of churches and the courts, the scare tactics of the mass communications media and, most recently, the emotional and insight evocative techniques of so-called "psychotherapy." The fitful applications and controversial results of the educational approach are dealt with at length elsewhere in this volume, so let us here merely mention some implications derived from the present topic. The prevailing tendency to apply educational methods from other spheres of endeavor to the problem of counteracting accidents—and to do so uncritically and with little concern for objective evaluation of results, may have led us into numerous dead-end roads. It is obvious and supported by the findings we have just reviewed, that the emotional stability and self-control of the driver are crucial elements in driving safety. It is equally obvious that driving is a task requiring knowledge, perceptiveness, and motor skill, and that the driver functions in this task almost entirely alone and on his own. It well may be that educational methods adopted unrevised from other spheres of activity are not adequate to these peculiarities of the driving task. It may be that the somewhat unique challenge of a task requiring, on the one hand, sufficient emotional self-control to enable attentiveness and, on the other hand, the cognitive awareness and motor skill requisite for vehicle guidance, is not well served by the simple transposition of educational techniques developed for other things. To deal with vehicle drivers, we may need a revised curriculum of learning experiences which can achieve a new and fitting integration of the emotional, the cognitive, and the motor components of the driving task.

Systems Analysis: The Wave of the Future

One further conceptual model of the accident problem must be mentioned, not because it derives from our social history but because it is likely to have markedly increasing impact in the coming years. This is the model referred to as the "Systems Analysis" approach. This model is based in scientific methodology, particularly the epidemiological methods of medical research and the mathematical techniques of decision theory. Systems analysis takes account of the interactions of multiple influencing variables and generally employs the relationship of cost to benefit as the criterion measure. All the variables considered in the three models mentioned above, and more, can be incorporated into the development and analysis of traffic systems. Systems analysis is uniquely well suited to capitalize on computer technology.

A vehicle collision may be conceived as a failure of the traffic system. The failure of a specific subunit of the system can be related to the more general components that influence the behavior of the specific units of the system. The elements of psychosocial influences leading to stress on drivers antecedent to accidents might be conceptualized as follows:

General System Failures (social, external groups).

1. Perpetuation of a highway traffic environment with a hazard level chronically above the threshold of adjustment capacity of a portion of the drivers.
2. Maintenance of a competitive social and economic system without adequate compensatory provisions for those who lose out.
3. Persevering social norms of physical strength, emotional suppression, and interpersonal domination as male ego ideals without healthy alternatives adequate to sustain those—especially the young—who cannot meet such norms.
4. Production and sale of alcoholic beverages without adequate preparation to control intake or protection for persons faced with serious stress.

Local System Failures (personal, internal groups).

1. Hostility, quarreling, and fighting.
2. Breakup of friendships and love relationships.
3. Depression, anxiety, anger.
4. Ego-expressive driving.
5. Intoxication.
6. ACCIDENTS—HIGHWAY COLLISIONS.

This outline obviously touches only briefly on some of the social-psychological influences that must be dealt with in analyses of the traffic system. The pioneering investigators we have studied have taken the first steps where many more must follow. We will not reduce the failures of our traffic system by repeating endlessly the inadequacies and errors of the past. The application of scientific methods has brought benefit in many fields of human activity; it may be our best hope for alleviating the tragic highway accident toll.

REFERENCES

Adams, J. R. and Rosenblatt, S., *Traffic Accidents and Other Symptoms of Social Pathology,* Safety Research and Education Project, Columbia University, New York, 1966.

Brown, S. L. and Bohnert, P. J., Alcohol Safety Study: "Drivers Who Die," Baylor University College of Medicine, Houston, Texas, Final Report, Contract #FH-11-6603, National Highway Safety Bureau, 1968.

Canter, A., Imboden, J., and Cluff, L., The Frequency of Physical Illness as a Function of Prior Psychological Vulnerability and Contemporary Stress. Read before the annual meeting of the American Psychosomatic Society, Philadelphia, Pa., May 1, 1965.

Hirschfeld, A. H. and Behan, R. C., The Accident Process: I. Etiological Considerations of Industrial Injuries, *Journal of the American Medical Association,* **186** (1963), 193–199.

Hirschfeld, A. H. and Behan, R. C., The Accident Process. III. Disability: Acceptable and Unacceptable, *Journal of the American Medical Association,* **197** (1966), 85–89.

Imboden, J., Canter, A. and Cluff, L., Symptomatic Recovery from Medical Disorders: Influence of Psychological Factors, *Journal of the American Medical Association,* **178** (1961), 1182–1184.

Porterfield, A. L., Traffic Fatalities, Suicide and Homicide, *American Sociological Review,* **25** (1960), 897–901.

Ross, H. L., Traffic Law Violation: A Folk Crime, *Social Problems,* **8** (1960–61), 231–241.

Selzer, M., Rogers, J. E., and Kern, Sue, Fatal Accidents: The Role of Psychopathology, Social Stress and Acute Disturbance, *American Journal of Psychiatry,* **124** (1968), 46–54.

Tabachnick, N., Litman, R. E., Osman, M., Jones, W. L., Cohn, J., Kasper, A., and Moffat, J., Comparative Psychiatric Study of Accidental and Suicidal Death, *Archives of General Psychiatry,* **14** (1966), 60–68.

Thorndike, R. L., *The Human Factor in Accidents with Special Reference to Aircraft Accidents,* Project #21-30-001, Report #1, USAF School of Aviation Medicine, Randolph Field, Texas, 1951.

XV
HUMAN ABILITIES AND DRIVER IMPROVEMENT

Noel Kaestner

Noel Kaestner is a consultant to the Oregon Traffic Safety Commission and professor of psychology at Willamette University, Salem, Oregon. He received his Ph.D. from the University of Wisconsin specializing in fields of human learning and experimental design.

He began his teaching career at Willamette University. In addition to his academic duties there, he served as a statistical consultant to the Oregon State Highway Division for five years. He later transferred to the Oregon Motor Vehicles Division as a consulting psychologist. In the latter position he conducted research in driver education, driver characteristics, and driver improvement leading to twenty publications in these areas.

He is presently undertaking studies of drivers with suspended licenses and drivers convicted of driving under the influence of intoxicating liquor. Specifically the impact of license suspension as a driver improvement device and the value of diagnosis and treatment of problem drinkers who drive are under investigation, respectively.

THE DOMAIN OF DRIVER IMPROVEMENT

Driver improvement and driver education are conveniently contrasted in terms of the stage in the driver's history in which each occurs. Thus, driver education most typically refers to various educational and training procedures initiated at some time very early in the individual's driving career and usually before receiving his operator's license. Consistent with this distinction is the observation that driver education occurs primarily within high schools and, to a much lesser extent, in commercial driving schools. Driver improvement programs typically arc focused on already licensed drivers with varying degrees of driving experience. Although certain selected driver improvement programs solicit participation of anyone who feels the need for a refresher or retraining course, the thrust of driver improvement programs is directed toward those individuals whose driving records include "too many" traffic citations and/or traffic collisions. The expressed goal of most driver improvement programs is simply to intervene in a manner that will cause the individual driver contacted by the program to drive with greater care, and thus incur fewer traffic citations and accidents.

Driver improvement procedures may be administered by law enforcement agencies, traffic courts, industry, and community service organizations, but by far the bulk of the driver improvement efforts in this country are under the aegis of motor vehicle and driver licensing agencies. It is the role of driver improvement within driver licensing that is the chief concern of this chapter. The American Association of Motor Vehicle Administrators (1965) has assembled the best single description of the rationale, mechanics, and legal aspects of driver improvement presently available.

Very basically driver improvement programs involve variations of the following components. Either through a manual operation or a computer system, driver records are screened to identify individuals who are accumulating frequent traffic violations and/or collisions. The review unit of the program may assess the culpability factor of traffic collisions. As a consequence of the record review, drivers with deviant records are sent warning letters (advisory letters) that tell the recipient that the department has evidence of "unsafe driving acts" and further states that the licensing agency holds him accountable for his errant driving. Beyond this the content of the letter varies widely from state to state. Positive hints and encouragement, veiled (and direct) threats, and other forms of coercion abound. The warning letter action is duly recorded on the individual's permanent driving record. Should the recipient of such a letter continue to accumulate traffic entries on his record (within a prespecified interval after the receipt of the letter), the interview stage of the program is implemented. At this level the driver is invited to appear in person for a review of his record. This step may take the form of a hearing, wherein a decision is made regarding the further disposition of the case, or it may represent a further effort at cajoling, coercing, or motivating and educating the driver in the face-to-face confrontation afforded. Continued traffic entries on the driver's record lead to suspension of the driving privilege and occasionally revocation. The exact prescription of actions through this progression of driver improvement steps may be dictated either by an inflexible point system or by more loosely formulated departmental policies. Regardless of which approach is taken, the essence of most programs involves the application of increasingly restrictive admonitions beginning with the warning letter, followed by the interview or hearing, and culminating in suspension or revocation. Some of the variations in the programs are described in the following sections on the historical aspects of driver improvement and contemporary developments.

Plan of this Chapter

The remainder of this chapter is divided into two major sections. In the first, present and past programs are described. The premises and deficiencies of these programs are considered, and the strengths and weaknesses of contemporary programs are estimated.

In the second part of the chapter, we point to more global and innovative approaches to driver improvement wherein the fuller potential of countermeasures may be realized. After opening with a brief section on problem analysis and redefinition of the goal of driver improvement, a systems approach is attempted.

PAST AND PRESENT PROGRAMS

Early Beginnings in Driver Improvement

In tracing the history of driver improvement programs in this country there has been a progression from procedures requiring individualized in-depth studies of a few errant drivers to semi-automated processing of masses of drivers at more superficial levels. Thus, the early work of the Psychopathic Clinic of the Recorder's Court in Detroit (1936), the Harvard Traffic Bureau and clinics (late 1930's), as well as the early programs of the Pennsylvania State Police, California's Driver Clinic, and New York's Driver Research Clinic, all emphasized the importance of individual diagnosis and treatment. (For a review of earlier programs, see Heath, 1962.)

Clinical assessment of personality, psychophysical testing, and medical diagnosis were frequently integral parts of these early programs. More emphasis on psychological evaluation by professionally competent psychologists characterized these embryonic efforts (Selling, 1937; De Silva, 1938; De Silva and Forbes, 1938; De Silva, Robinson, and Forbes, 1939). In the three decades since these pioneer beginnings, motor vehicle registrations have increased 244 percent. The survival of driver improvement programs in this interval depended on developing semi-automated, impersonal measures such as warning letters (generally form letters), point systems, and group hearings to accommodate the proportional increase in "problem drivers."

A comparison of the earliest programs with the usual contemporary approach described in the next section reveals that, if anything, recent "progress" in driver improvement has moved away from procedures that had greater potential for human factors analysis. The older programs were more prone to view the driver as a whole, including medical, psychological, psychophysical, and educational factors. Today, by contrast, the stress is more exclusively confined to changing driver attitudes, with only desultory reference to the other aspects of driver behavior.

Current Procedures in Driver Improvement

As mentioned in the Introduction, driver improvement countermeasures for the most part involve three steps: the advisory letter, the personal contact, and the suspension (or revocation). Of these stages the personal contact with the driver is the core of the program. Not only is it the most expensive part of the total operation, but also its potential rehabilitative value is the greatest. For this reason this phase of the program is given the greatest attention in this section devoted to current driver improvement programs.

Variants of Driver Improvement. No attempt is made here to provide an exhaustive survey of various driver improvement measures and procedures in effect today throughout the nation. For a more extensive review of the literature see the National Highway Safety Bureau Report 224, *Driver Licensing and Performance* [Vol. I, Chap. 4., pp. 10–85 (Miller and Dimling, 1969)]. The programs described here are regarded as fairly typical of on-going programs in many states. The various types of programs to be considered include: individual interviews, group meetings, court schools, and National Safety Council programs.

In Oregon an individual who is convicted of a moving traffic violation and/or chargeable accident within 6 months of receiving an advisory letter is called in for a personal interview. Failure to appear at the interview results in suspension of the operator's license. The interview itself is conducted by former driver license examiners who are in the process of advancing to supervisory positions in driver licensing. Because of the nonprofessional background of these individuals, they are given brief in-service training in the administration of a standardized interview technique. The present interview format involves five parts: the introduction, a brief review of traffic laws, an inquiry of the circumstances of the recent traffic involvements, a comparison of the driver's record with other individuals in his own age group, and a summary. The advantages of the standardized format involve not only the guarantee that certain topics will be covered for all interviewees, but also that interviewers will not get into certain areas that might antagonize and alienate the interviewees. The general approach of the Oregon interview is broadly motivationally and educationally oriented. The law review represents an abbreviated refresher course on Oregon's traffic laws. The inquiry on the nature of the traffic involvements attempts to uncover any consistent faulty patterns in the interviewee's driving behavior. The presentation of data regarding other drivers is a direct attempt to give the interviewee a greater appreciation that he is in fact experiencing more traffic violations and accidents than typical drivers. Interviewers are strongly urged to refrain from referring to the gruesome aspects of traffic accidents, avoid adopting "holier than thou" attitudes, and desist in "preaching about the evil affects of alcohol" even when strong signs of problem drinking appear. (In regard to the latter, the interviewer may urge that the driver involved seek medical attention.) For most states, the individual personal interview represents some variation of the procedure described here. Note that in Oregon, as in most other states, no attempt is made to actually observe the driving performance of the driver appearing for the individual personal interview. Beyond the routine administration of a vision check, no diagnostic tests are employed.

Primarily because of the cost of conducting individual interviews, a number of states have developed group interview procedures. It is not surprising that these programs were first developed in two of our most populous states, New York and California. In New York, habitual violators are requested to appear at group sessions and are given lectures on safe driving techniques, shown films that demonstrate the outcome of hazardous driving, given information on state driving laws and, if time allows, they are given the opportunity to discuss their grievances. The emphasis here is informally educational, and there is a definite attempt to avoid the more punitive aspects of the individual formal hearings. Over 100 individuals may be invited to a single group session.

In California a one-shot group session involving 10 to 15 persons has been tried. In these sessions each driver is provided with a copy of a driver attitude test, which he completes and scores himself. The driver improvement analyst who led the group session attempted to "sell" the group members on the importance of safe driving habits. General problems arising from home and job pressures are related to driving habits. The group leader also informs the drivers of the legal consequences of continued faulty driving. The group session closes with the presentation to each individual of his own driving record over the past 36 months.

They then have an opportunity to discuss the entries on their records and ask questions and discuss any problems. The session lasts approximately one hour. The purpose of these single-session group meetings is broadly educational and motivational. Neither time nor facilities permit detailed analysis and diagnosis of individual driver problems.

An extension of the single-appearance group driver improvement meetings involves the multiple-group sessions, usually three or four two-hour meetings spaced at weekly intervals. These approaches are variously referred to as driver improvement clinics, mass communication method, or group dynamics sessions. New Jersey has employed these group interaction procedures with the hope that group discussions might modify and change driver attitudes and behavior. Fifteen to twenty accident repeaters are invited to view films, take custom-made psychological tests, and discuss topics on carefully elaborated plans incorporating the theme referred to as the Strategy and Tactics of Driving (Henderson and Kole, 1967a).

The state of Washington was involved in a three-session group dynamics program patterned after a plan developed at George Washington University. The first session involves relatively unstructured discussions of the group participants' feelings toward various parts of the traffic system. The second session is concerned primarily with the underlying motivation of people when they are driving a car. The third session is devoted to discussing specific problems which the class members have encountered. The discussion leader in this format is rather nondirective and permissive, and his primary function is to encourage discussion that is relevant to the topic of the evening. Generally this approach is much less fact-oriented and more concerned with emotional and motivational involvement of the class participants.

The driver improvement course of the National Safety Council is a variation of the multiple-session group meetings. It is much more highly structured and has clear and detailed topical organization for each of the eight sessions presented over four consecutive weekly meetings. The broad theme of the sessions is structured around the concept of defensive driving. Although the National Safety Council supplies guidance and materials for this approach, the actual sponsorship of specific programs is either local government or private industry. The most noteworthy aspect of this program is that it tries to attract all groups of drivers who are in need of a refresher course and does not confine itself to errant drivers only.

The efforts of various court schools for driver improvement roughly parallel those outlined in the paragraph above. These programs often involve an arrangement between the courts and local insurance companies, public schools, police, or other interested community groups. One of the best examples of this approach has been developed by Judge Finesilver in Denver (1962). He has developed special programs for the youthful driver, the military driver, senior citizens, and various handicapped drivers including the deaf. As in the National Safety Council programs, the emphasis is educational and it is the exceptional court program that involves harshly punitive measures.

Evaluation in Current Programs. Over three decades ago Forbes (1938) compared subsequent driving records of accident repeaters and volunteers to a driver improvement clinic. This represented a pioneer effort to objectively evaluate driver improvement influence. Shortly after, Johnson and Cobb (1938) and Johnson (1939) argued persuasively for the need to develop equivalent control groups to offset regression effects as early as 1938. It was not, however, until the early 1960's that this dictum was honored in the application. Chalfant (1960), Chalfant and King (1960), Barmack and Payne (1961), Coppin et al. (1965), Kaestner et al. (1965), Kastelle and Le Sueur (1966), Schuster (1967), and Henderson and Kole (1967) represent some of the more prominent research investigators employing controls in their designs.

Probably the most serious deficiency in the majority of programs is perpetuation and expansion of programs without incorporating provisions for program evaluation at an early stage of their developments. Typically driver improvement procedures are implemented and maintained for a decade or more before the efficacy of the measures is determined. In most cases, no plans for program assessment are ever initiated because the value of assessment goes unrecognized, or if recognized, it is readily dismissed as an unnecessary frill because of the "obvious face validity" of the procedures. The real misfortune of the general status of driver improvement is that there may exist programs that definitely benefit drivers, but there is presently no evidence to establish the value of the procedures involved. Even to this day, highly innovative procedures are being planned without allowing opportunities for evaluation from the outset.

There have been scattered research projects that have clearly established certain principles regarding program assessment. These have conclusively demonstrated precautions in the interpretation of data purportedly displaying the impact of rehabilitative measures. The first of these has been described as the "Hawthorne effect." In this context, the application of this principle implies that conclusions about the impact of court contacts, for example, cannot be regarded as valid unless those attending court school perform better subsequently than those invited but not attending. The fact that the driver has come to the attention of the court program, rather than the content of the program itself, may be responsible for the apparent improvement. Unfortunately, court schools rarely avail themselves of local research manpower to assist in evaluating their traffic schools.

A second limitation on the interpretation of post-treatment effects involves the restrictions imposed by *ex post facto* research designs. This factor has been cogently elaborated elsewhere (Campbell, 1959). Briefly it involves the accommodation of interpretations to the statistical phenomenon known as regression toward the mean. In other words, before-after studies of traffic records preclude definitive conclusions because drivers selected for treatment are at or near a peak in terms of driving errors and would be statistically less likely to maintain such a high level without any intervention whatsoever. This well-documented artifact is compounded by the emphasis of driver improvement programs on younger recalcitrant drivers. The factor of increasing maturity with time would enhance the effect of the regression trend. The employment of matched no-treatment control groups is, therefore, the *sine qua non* of acceptable research in driver improvement.

Finally, attitude changes as revealed by questionnaires administered before and after driver improvement courses constitute a dubious source of evidence for program effectiveness. Changes in a positive direction regarding such things as law enforcement, rights of other drivers, and greater appreciation for the injury potential of careless driving, have been offered as support for the beneficial effects of the educative program. Even when these attitudes shifts are evaluated for statistical significance relative to matched control group attitude shifts, program impact is suspect unless commensurate driving performance reflects (through fewer and less severe accidents and traffic citations) the commendable alteration in attitudes. Much of driver improvement course content is verbal. Attitude surveys (a verbal criterion) readily mirror content exposure. However, driving is largely a nonverbal task and should not be expected to be as responsive to predominantly verbal manipulation of the classroom.

A few examples of carefully designed research studies of the effects of driver improvement procedures follow. Again no attempt is made to develop an exhaustive enumeration of scientifically conducted evaluations, but rather some representative studies and the results are included.

Promising Directions in Driver Improvement. A number of contemporary programs are incorporating measures to identify the specific needs and problems of individual drivers. These diagnostic embryos constitute recognition of the diversity of the driver component (individual difference) as a crucial element in the selection of appropriate treatment programs. In addition to the study by Henderson and Kole (1967), Adams has developed a Driver Vocabulary Test, an invaluable aid in prescribing communication media and levels in the rehabilitation process. Kole and Henderson (1966) have devised a Cartoon Reaction Scale to classify types of problem drivers. The Wisconsin Motor Vehicle Department classifies drivers as lacking in skills or appropriate attitudes (1967). These researchers have shown a proper appreciation for the need to identify sources of strength and weakness on an individual basis rather than uniformly processing nearly all drivers with extensive traffic entries on their records as having "bad attitudes."

The driver improvement studies just listed, as the authors would agree, represent first approximations to effective driver diagnosis. Adams and Kole (1969) have returned to a more refined approach to diagnosis and relevant treatment. In their project, each driver will be individually diagnosed via: (1) public records, (2) standardized test instruments, (3) observation, (4) behind-the-wheel testing and simulation, and (5) medical examinations. As a consequence of the diagnostic procedures, drivers will be assigned to one of three rehabilitative curricula: (1) driving problems, (2) attitude problems, or (3) alcohol problems. No definitive data on the effectiveness of this approach are available at this writing but the project looks very promising indeed. To the extent that personal inadequacy accounts for the excessive difficulties of a hard-core group of high-frequency accident drivers, this approach is essential and deserves continued inquiry and support.

Another welcome approach that is beginning to appear is the application of the principles of behavior modification to the driving situation. Adams (1961) has effectively discussed possible sources of reinforcement schedule control. No direct research applications to drivers, however, have been actually employed with the exception of a project developed in the state of Washington. In it two groups of problem drivers were given restricted operator's licenses. For the experimental group these restrictions were eased progressively every two weeks, contingent on violation- and accident-free driving; while the restrictions for the control group were eased without regard for driving performance. There was a third nonrestricted control group also included in the design.

"Preliminary data showed a significant delay in time to failure for experimental subjects over the restricted control group and the nonrestricted control group during the retraining period. Although in the predicted direction, the number of violations and accidents during the retraining period did not differ significantly" (Kleinhnecht, 1968).

The less than complete success of this program was probably a result of the inability of the researcher to experimentally control all of the contingencies in the non-laboratory driving environment. Additionally, the limited impact of this single effort may also be traceable to incomplete specification of exactly which behavior components are to be rewarded, which extinguished, and which subjected to aversive training. Thus, the development of an enlightened reinforcement schedule presumes the existence of a detailed behavior model that clearly identifies essential components and eliminates unnecessary acts. Again shades of Frederick Taylor and the Gilbreths' job analysis, forerunners of systems engineering.

The need for productive and relevant theoretical and/or behavioral models of the driving task is at last being recognized (Miller and Dimling, 1969). Until the driver's task is conceptually clarified in considerably more explicit detail than it is now, all driver improvement work will involve devising and applying patch-up measures. Until the critical elements of the task are understood, and training and testing for them is perfected, no major breakthrough in accident reduction should be realistically expected. One suggested application of the identification, training, and criterion testing of a particular model (Gibson and Crooks, 1938) is detailed by Schlesinger (1967). As he points out, large segments of the proposed program had little research existence at the time of the writing. (It is also interesting that the model that was subjected to analysis was 1938 vintage, despite the fact that space-age technology has provided more complete models of the astronaut's tasks.)

Summary of Present Programs

Philosophy of Driver Improvement. The underlying philosophy of traditional approaches to driver improvement is reflected in the statement of specific objectives as they appear in the *Driver License Administrator's Guide to Driver Improvement* (American Association of Motor Vehicles Administrators, 1965):

"The ultimate objective of Driver Improvement is to assure the safety of the licensee and of other persons using the highways. To achieve this purpose the program must attain these specific objectives:

1. To improve the attitudes and driving performances of drivers who, because of traffic violations and/or accident involvement, are known to constitute a hazard on the highways; and to instill in those drivers the will to better their driving practices.
2. To determine whether problem drivers suffer from physical and mental deficiencies, and the ways they affect the safe operation of motor vehicles.

3. To apply appropriate restrictions, or to use the device of "deferred action," when drivers suffer from physical or mental conditions that do not appear to preclude safe driving.
4. To eliminate from the highways the unsafe, incompetent, and physically or mentally unqualified driver by refusing to license him or by withdrawing his driving privilege."

These statements embody the essence of the prevailing sentiment regarding the role of driver improvement functions within the driver licensing programs of the nation. Underlying explicit and implicit assumptions include the following:

1. Driver failure is the primary, if not exclusive, cause of traffic accidents and/or violations. (A corollary is the equally prevalent notion that errant drivers have frequent mishaps because of defective "attitudes" and the absence of the "will" to drive better.)

2. Removal of a small segment of the most recalcitrant drivers from the highways would drastically reduce the highway accident toll.

3. Punitive actions, or threats thereof, against operators via license restrictions, suspensions, or revocations will markedly assist licensing agencies "to improve attitudes" and "to instill . . . the will to better driving practices."

The predominant philosophy of driver improvement is defensible to the extent that these assumptions are tenable. It is the contention of the writer that none of these assumptions withstands careful and objective scrutiny, thus calling into question the traditional philosophy of driver improvement. In support of this position, exceptions to each of the above assumptions are cited.

To begin with, the first assumption neglects the view of the driver as but one component in the man-machine-environment system. Its corollary, with the emphasis on attitudes and will, overlooks the multiple-factor aspects of most traffic collisions (Blumenthal, 1968). Similarly, the second assumption disregards evidence to the effect that accident involvement of individual drivers is not a highly stable characteristic (Schulzinger, 1956; Coppin, McBride, and Peck, 1965). Consequently programs aimed at the small segment of drivers with high accident experience over relatively short intervals will have a negligible effect on the total accident picture. Finally, the largely punitive orientations of formal driver improvement procedures reflect ignorance of the research evidence regarding punishment as a motivational device (Solomon, 1964). (For a more extended account of this variable see Miller and Dimling (1969, Vol. I, Chap. 6, pp. 20–26).

In summary, one of the problems in applying a human factors approach to driver improvement would appear to consist of the prevailing philosophy, the assumptions of which tend to run counter to the human factors approach to problem analysis. There is a need for well-designed control experiments that permit testing traditional hypotheses (e.g., the effectiveness of punishment) against alternative human factors interpretations.

The Pragmatics of Driver Improvement. Just as it is possible to be right for the wrong reasons, it is conceivable that current driver improvement is in fact productive despite erroneous assumptions and inconsistencies in its philosophy. As in the Hawthorne Western Electric studies, production levels often went up, not as a consequence of physical or procedural changes, but rather represented artifactual increments resulting from the mere presence of the evaluative study of production (Roethlisberger and Dickson, 1946). Is it not possible, or even likely, that the impact of driver improvement is another example of what has come to be known as the "Hawthorne effect"? Accordingly, benefits, when they are found, may well result from the publicized presence of a statewide driver improvement program, however ill-conceived. Studies in California (Coppin, Marsh, and Peck, 1965) and Washington (Toms, 1966) revealed that drivers invited to driver improvement meetings, but not actually attending the meetings, showed subsequent driving records significantly better than uninvited control group drivers.

Beyond the possibilities of artifact, there are additional practices that are inconsistent with human factors approaches to driver improvement. Because the systems approach to traffic problems is not generally incorporated in driver licensing philosophy, such basic systems principles as selection and special training of the operator in the man-machine-environment system are neglected. As Goldstein has clearly argued, driver licensing as currently encountered has no industrial equivalent as a selection procedure (Goldstein, 1963). Furthermore, there is no counterpart to the usual industrial sequence of selection followed by special training within the system. If driver training exists at all, it typically precedes licensing and most generally no provisions for the analogue of followup training exists for the job of driving. (Repeated rejection by 28 state legislatures of driver reexamination programs implicitly condones the sentiment that "once licensed, forever competent" and regards the need for periodic in-service evaluation and training as superfluous.)

Along this line, the only reservations existing concerning unlimited extension of licenses (with the exception of medical referrals) occurs in response to the accumulation of traffic accidents and/or convictions by individual drivers. These isolated incidents are end-results of system breakdown and, in their form, have limited diagnostic significance. Their continued recurrence typically triggers license suspension. At the termination of the suspension interval the license is automatically returned to the driver, again with no provision made for evaluation and training. Presumably something magical is assumed to occur to improve the driver's performance in the 30-, 60-, or 90-day suspension period (an interval during which driving is expressly forbidden). It is somewhat paradoxical to expect improvement in a highly skilled task that is explicitly prohibited from practice. We need definitive data on the rehabilitative aspects of license suspensions.

Finally, the industrial analogy of professionally qualified specialists is conspicuously absent in the area of driver improvement. The training officer in industry not only understands the implications of the systems approach to a man's job, but also has professional training in psychology, engineering, sociology, or some combination thereof. It should not be presumed that this degree of proficiency is irrelevant to the role of driver improvement personnel because of the "obvious" and "simple" nature of the motor vehicle operator's task. The lamentable absence of an acceptable theoretical model of the driver's task attests to the complexity of the problem. This intrinsic complexity is further confounded by the additional component of the driver's attitudes as they relate to the social aspects of driving, the concepts of vigilance, risk-taking, and so forth. In response to the technical demands of the retraining task, motor vehicle agencies assign driver improvement analysts from the ranks of driver examiners, a job that ill prepares them for meeting the complex needs of an adequate retraining program.

In summary, driver improvement needs to pay greater attention to elementary principles of selection and training of the operator in the total system. Although strict selection processing may not be a realistic or even a desirable expectation, the greater regard for the training phase is central. Future programs should be characterized by more adequate initial training at the time of original licensing, regularly scheduled on-the-job training (to accommodate to evolving systems changes such as increased traffic density, vehicle performance changes, and modifications in design and signing of highways), and effective "crisis intervention" therapy for acute driver failures. These needs must be reflected in a policy that designates appropriately prepared personnel to conduct the selection-training and retraining functions.

To conclude this statement of the problem facing driver improvement planners, it appears that future driver improvement programs must come to represent, both in philosophy and in practice, a serious application of a human factors approach to the problem of upgrading the competence of the nation's drivers. A strong case could be made that present policies and procedures are markedly antithetical to the more scientific application of systems analysis and behavior modification. A radical departure from ingrained thinking and practices is essential before appreciable improvement in driver improvement may be reasonably anticipated.

Research Studies of Driver Improvement Effectiveness

Nearly all of the studies on driver improvement impact include the interview phase of the program or its equivalent. There have been very few studies on the influence of warning letters and no really well controlled study of driver improvement suspensions. Research evaluations of the face-to-face confrontations of driver improvement have taken two basic forms. In one case the data consist primarily of pre- and post-interview attitude measures (either with or without no-treatment control group data). The second research design format involves pre- and post-treatment comparisons of driving records in terms of traffic citations and accidents. Because of both space limitations and the fact that even those studies that have demonstrated significantly large attitude shifts have typically shown no effect whatsoever on actual driving performance, this review of evaluative studies is restricted to the research efforts that have been primarily concerned with measuring actual changes in driving behavior as revealed by traffic citations and collisions. Again only a sampling of the available studies is included and those chosen are regarded as representative of efforts to evaluate the variants of driver improvement discussed above.

Two studies are cited on the effectiveness of individual interview techniques. Coppin, Peck, and Marsh (1965) applying a design with matched control group subjects found:

1. significantly fewer traffic citations in the first post-treatment year;
2. no accident differences;
3. differences in violation rates could not be attributed to the face-to-face contact.

As the authors insightfully point out, the presence of the interview as a step in the total driver improvement program has an effect but its impact was not a direct consequence of the actual appearance of the driver at the interview.

Henderson and Kole (1967 b) evaluated a highly individualized personal contact experience with problem drivers which included background information interview forms, law knowledge examinations, written psychological tests and scales, psychophysical testing and terminal counseling. Post-treatment records of interviewees were significantly better than those for control groups. (The emphasis on individualizing face-to-face individual contacts was corroborated by a study by Kaestner and Syring (1966).)

The effectiveness of single-meeting group driver improvement sessions has been evaluated in both California and New York. In the second of two California studies on this phase of their driver improvement program, Coppin, Marsh, and Peck (1965) employing more effectively matched control groups found significant reductions in traffic violations whereas accidents were not reliably reduced for the treatment group. In New York, Scott (1966) found that there was no significant effect whatsoever on post-meeting driving records. On the basis of data presently available, it would seem that single-appearance group procedures have negligible effects on subsequent driving records.

Multiple-session group meetings have been evaluated in Washington and New Jersey. In the Washington study Toms (1966) cited impressive reductions in traffic involvements for individuals invited to the group meetings, but detailed analysis showed that these improvements could not be attributed to the driver's actual presence at the group sessions, but rather resulted from notices of invitation to these meetings. The New Jersey study by Henderson and Kole (1967a) did in fact demonstrate a significant reduction in post-treatment traffic violations that could be related to actual attendance at the group meetings. Unfortunately, no significant reduction in traffic accidents was observed. This finding reinforces the trend often observed in research evaluations of driver improvement to the effect that it is much easier to demonstrate reductions in traffic citations as contrasted to traffic accidents. This is probably attributable, at least in part, to the lower reliability of traffic accident data and the relative infrequency of traffic accidents as contrasted to traffic citations.

It is our understanding that the National Safety Council's Driver Improvement Program (D.I.P.) is presently undergoing control group research evaluation. Definitive assessment data on this widely employed and highly publicized defensive driving course will be most welcome.

Very few court school evaluations have been undertaken and these have typically not employed the research designs standards commensurate with those described above. If the National Safety Council D.I.P. should prove effective, it would be a suitable program for ready adoption in the courts.

In summary there is very little research support for the effectiveness of driver improvement considering its very extensive implementation throughout the country. Hopefully, the little sound evidence that exists will point to ways to modify current programs and stimulate further research on other innovative driver improvement techniques.

THE POTENTIAL OF DRIVER IMPROVEMENT

Problem Analysis

Systems, Subsystems, and Microsystems. Chapanis (1966) in a chapter entitled "Man in Man-Machine Systems," states, "Systems may be virtually any size, and any given system usually exists as a part of the other systems." The relevance of this pronouncement is considerable for the problem analysis of driver improvement. There are at least three levels in the hierarchy of systems in which the driver interacts. First, there is the global or cultural system within which subordinate systems exist. Thus, an individual in this country drives in a highly industrialized and mobile society. Economic, social, and legal forces within the contemporary societal system impinge upon the driver, directly and indirectly. At the second level in the hierarchy is the transportation system, including highways, traffic enforcement, and licensing agencies. The relative efficacy of this subsystem is critically a function of how well it meets the demands of the larger societal system. Finally, there is the individual driver in his vehicle at a particular time and place within the transportation subsystem. His immediate interaction with his machine and environment constitutes a microsystem. The effectiveness of various driver rehabilitative devices is a product of how well these measures relate to the needs of the higher order system and subsystem.

Progress in driver improvement may well depend on the ability to recognize the driver's problem in these larger contexts. Even relatively sophisticated analytical approaches to the driver's task often tend to be restricted to the lowest order level, that is, man-machine-environment in the narrow or localized sense. For this reason an abbreviated review of some of the implications of these larger system components follows.

Society as the Global System. The societal system level was divided into economic, social, and legal forces. Each of these as related to driver improvement is outlined below.

Economic Factors. First, the health of our economy literally depends on the ready availability of our mobile resources. Not only is the auto industry one of the largest economic forces in the nation, but also there are numerous occupations wherein a very direct equivalence of time and money exist. Preservation of the ease and speed of this mobility is directly translatable into financial gains. Cost-benefit equations for alternate highway routes incorporate time-saving monetary weightings. Because the auto industry (to say nothing of the oil industry) is unlikely to wholeheartedly support extensive development of mass transportation systems, and because economic gain is so often equated with time, we should not be surprised to find counterforces opposing efforts to reduce collision frequency indirectly through decreasing traffic density. Similarly, the amelioration of personal injury severity by means of lessening the rate of locomotion is obstructed by the pervasive pressures of earning a livelihood.

Social Aspects. Various social customs and mores also exert their influence on the individual driver. Societal norms embody inculcated needs for independence and nearly complete autonomy of nearly every individual. An expression of this freedom is readily implemented through the sole possession and control of one's own vehicle, thus constituting another counterforce to the acceptance of mass transportation resources that would alleviate traffic congestion. In addition, certain subpopulations react to further pressures. Thus, the value systems of youthful drivers are heavily weighted in the direction of peer approval as contrasted to traditional forms of acceptance by adults. Attainment of peer approval is often contingent upon behavior associated with unfortunate risk-taking responses contraindicated by safe driving practices. Another subgroup consists of the problem drinkers who drive. A recent Oregon study revealed that more than seven in nine convicted of driving while intoxicated indicated they had been drinking away from their homes before arrest (nearly 60 percent listed a public drinking establishment) (Kaestner, Howard, and Warmoth, 1969). Thus, excessive drinking leading to arrest under probable cause statutes is not primarily a sedentary domestic activity. Societal norms involve "logic-tight compartments" wherein simultaneously dwell acceptance of extensively available distribution points of intoxicants, accessible primarily via private automobiles, together with self-righteous condemnation of driving home after partaking the intoxicating beverages. (For a more detailed account of the social customs of driving, drinking, and the combination thereof, see Bacon (1968).)

Legislative and Judicial Practices. The last of the societal thrusts considered here is the legislative and judicial system. Freedom has been interpreted as freedom of movement. The pendulum reversals between driving as a right and driving as a privilege testify to the lack of unanimity and inconsistency on this issue. Also, implied consent laws have serious implications for freedom from self-incrimination. Legislation comparable to that recently enacted in the United Kingdom is precluded by existing legislation protecting individual rights. The general availability of a jury trial for drunk-driving cases and the social attitude of "There save the grace of God, go I" contribute additional complications. Point systems based on conviction dates rather than arrest dates lead to the propagation of trial delays to prevent point accumulations from exceeding critical levels during designated intervals. The judicial disposition of license suspensions is invoked with reluctance because of its harsh economic consequences, thus fostering case dismissals (and no rehabilitative measure or entry of the citation on the driving record results). It is within this legislative and judicial maze that movement toward driver improvement goals must proceed.

The Nation's Transportation System as a Subsystem. It is within the cultural global system of contemporary society with its economic, social, and legal institutions that the efficiency of the nation's transportation system is judged. Highway components of the system must serve economic needs. For example, highways must provide direct and easy trucking routes between major supply and distribution points. Enforcement and licensing agencies walk a narrow line between legislative fiat and social acceptance of laws relating to control and movement of private means of transportation. Thus, the transportation system and its components form a subsystem of the larger societal system and its impact on the individual local man-machine-environment microsystem should not be viewed as an isolated one.

The Nation's Highways. The highway component of the transportation system has a number of obvious implications for the individual driver. The proportional increase in freeway miles and its concomitant increase in average vehicle velocity definitely serves the economic goals of the society. However, the speed-posting of these highway sections is intended for ideal weather and traffic conditions, and thus, the discrepancy between velocities under optimal conditions and seriously deteriorated conditions for the same sections is drastically increased relative to roadways with lower speed limits. This relationship shifts even more of the driving load on the driver capabilities, that is, to perceive extenuating conditions, evaluate them, and react. Not only is there greater need for occasional drastic adjustment to suddenly changing conditions, but the relative infrequency of these overload conditions contributes to the vigilance strain on the operator. Beyond this emergency component of high-speed roadways, directional and destination signing leave much to be desired. To even casual observers, many signing efforts give the impression that signs were designed and placed by highway personnel who were thoroughly familiar with the area in question. Consequently they needed no help themselves and this precisely is what they provided for others. If a driver is confused and commits a traffic violation or is involved in a collision, is it necessary to presume it is he who needs improvement?

Traffic Regulation and Enforcement. The traffic law-enforcement component of the transportation subsystem also has implications for the goals for a broad-spectrum driver improvement program. The existence of quota systems for issuing traffic citations, the frequent total disregard for traffic regulations by enforcement officials in their own driving, the emphasis on traffic violations that lead to easy prosecutions as contrasted to those demonstrated to be directly accident-producing, are merely a few of the aspects that must be considered in devising driver improvement measures that may have a reasonable beneficial effect.

Licensing Agencies. The final segment of the transportation system considered here concerns the driver licensing agencies. It is within this bailiwick that the traditional driver improvement programs are found as indicated earlier in this chapter. In addition to the philosophical and pragmatic inconsistencies of these programs as outlined above, there are several procedural discrepancies that require reexamination before considering the potential of these programs for real rehabilitative value. Whether it be at the warning letter stage, the hearing (interview), the suspension, or the revocation, the primary triggering events are traffic citations (not violations) as contrasted to traffic collisions. This practice would appear defensible if: (1) citation data records were complete; (2) citation data were themselves reliable indices of all traffic violation behavior; and (3) a strong predictive relationship existed between recorded traffic citations and traffic accidents. Actually each of these preconditions is questionable. Miller and Dimling (1969) discussed the impressions created concerning the completeness of typical records with researchers on driver behavior and concluded, "most of the violations and a large percentage of the minor accidents that occur do not get reported." Sheehe (no date) developed data showing that approximately one in 7600 speed violations, ten miles in excess of the posted speed limit, result in apprehension and conviction. Finally, the value of traffic citations as a predictive index of traffic accidents, while statistically significant (.08 for males), is negligible from a practical standpoint (Coppin, McBride, and Peck, 1965). Despite these inadequacies in the usefulness of traffic citation data, motor vehicle agency policy regarding control procedures continue to exploit this type of traffic entry for case disposition. Virtually no concern for the empirical relationship between particular conviction types and accidents enters these procedural decisions. Myrick and Schlesinger (1964) have discussed the implications of other misconceptions and malpractices in state driver improvement programs in an aptly entitled article, "Driver Improvement or System Improvement?" Real progress in meaningful improvement of drivers is predicated upon upgrading the policies and procedures of motor vehicle agency components of the transportation subsystem.

In summary, the approach taken here rejects the notion that the thrust of driver improvement efforts should be restricted to the driver within his automobile on a particular stretch of highway. Although this aspect of the problem cannot be dismissed, it only involves a micro-system within the transportation sub-system which, in turn, is part of the more global environmental system referred to here as society. Attempts to confine driver improvement measures to the microsystem cannot achieve total success. The role of the driver in the transportation subsystem and the larger societal setting must be appreciated before an integrated and insightful attack on the microsystem can be effectively implemented.

The "Improvables" of Driver Improvement

Before embarking upon suggestions to upgrade driver improvement programs following the problem analysis outlined above, some comments about the traditional concepts of driver improvement itself appear in order.

Improvable Concepts of "Driver Improvement." "Driver improvement" is a double concept—"driver" and "improvement." What drivers? Only the ones with two traffic citations in 6 months, or one year? Only the ones in the upper 1 percent of the driving population in terms of traffic accidents over a relatively short time? Traditional programs tend to limit their concerns to drivers fitting these descriptions. But should they? Even if it were possible to remove from the highways all drivers who come to the attention of driver improvement sections in a particular year, the total number of traffic accidents would not diminish appreciably. Therefore, why should driver improvement, if its goal is accident reduction, be limited to these very few "problem drivers"? Driver improvement via refresher courses, periodic reexamination, and so forth, should be for all drivers. Therefore, the concept of "driver" in "driver improvement" needs extension.

Next consider the concept "improvement." Is it possible to adequately administer improvement programs without clearly defining what is to be improved? Task definition is a necessary prerequisite. What constitutes "good driving"? (In the more global sense, at what point will we regard the efforts of the National Highway Safety Bureau as successful? The United States already has the lowest accident rate of any industrialized nation in the world.) There is a need for a clear standard of acceptable behind-the-wheel performance.

Once having decided on a workable standard of safe and efficient motor vehicle operation, what criteria will be invoked to decide when a particular operator has become a "problem driver"? The vast majority of "problem driver" call-ins and suspensions today are the result of traffic citations only. The popularity of this criterion derives from its ease of administration. Culpability has already been established, either through bail forfeiture or court adjudication. Traffic accidents, unaccompanied by citations for faulty driving, are not as readily processed. Accident reports, unless including an officer's account, are subject to alternative interpretations, and the concept of culpability is shaky indeed. As a consequence, criteria of "problem driving" are disproportionately weighted by traffic violations rather than actual collisions, even though reduction of collisions is more justifiably the purpose of driver improvement.

Summarizing, it appears that the very concept of driver improvement requires clarification and probably redefinition. What are its goals? Its targets? Its criteria? Clear enunciation of answers to these questions should attend the systematic analyses recommended below.

Improvables of the Total (Societal) System. It would be inappropriate and presumptuous to attempt to devise a Utopian society that provides a favorable atmosphere for driver improvement. Suffice it to indicate that to the extent that social advances approach a more perfect and ideal state, it may be possible to ameliorate the social ills that generate excessive frustration and consequent hostility that often filters down as aggressiveness in the individual driver. Rather than consider the broadly humanitarian forces, relevant aspects of the economic, social, and legal system components will be considered as they concern driver behavior. Obviously the compendium treatment permitted here is not meant to be exhaustive.

(a) Economic Factors. Let us begin by assuming economic motives will continue to persist at the present levels for the foreseeable future. How can these needs be structured to serve the cause of traffic safety rather than contribute, as they presently do, to extensive accident experience? The enlightened use of economic motives would involve more extensive application of cost-benefit ratios. The cost and benefits of economic pressures to drive too fast for road conditions, to neglect needed automobile repairs, to design cars for appearance rather than safety, should be subjected to intensive scrutiny. How much is being saved? What is the sum of direct and indirect costs of traffic accidents?

(b) Social Forces. The social norms of our society have evolved as a result of subtle reinforcements delivered largely through peer groups. Social customs reflect these norms via circumscribed behavioral responses. Two customs of special interest are: (1) driving, and (2) drinking. The intersection of these habits involve values not necessarily inherent in either custom viewed separately. Thus, our societal attitudes toward driving (usually neutral) and toward drinking (positive in drinkers, neutral or negative in nondrinkers) are not indicative of the consensus regarding drunk driving (usually strongly negative). As emphasized by Bacon (1968), we need to know more about each custom in isolation. There is an associated need to better understand the life styles of problem drinkers who do not have traffic accidents. Support for continued research in the rehabilitation of alcoholics and problem drinkers is necessary. However, until such time that the recidivisim rate is drastically reduced from its present high level, it will be more expedient to study ways of separating these social customs.

The role of peer pressures is nowhere more pervasive than in the youngest members of the driving population. Status and acclaim are often intimately associated with availability of "wheels." Changes in society that lessen the various pressures on young people and provide acceptable alternatives to the exploitation of the motor vehicle to gratify peer-influenced behavior should contribute to accident reduction in this sizeable segment of society. Every effort should be exerted to equate access to a motor vehicle with responsibility and maturity. In these efforts success will depend upon enlisting the force of peer group pressures from within the young people themselves.

(c) The Law. The legal and judicial segment of the social enterprise also requires some reexamination. The tone of the laws of the land is basically punitive in orientation, as contrasted to therapeutic. In a nation where mobility is so closely bound up with economic survival (of the individual and society as a whole), it is debatable that driving should be regarded as a privilege rather than a right. Prohibition of driving (for months, years, and occasionally a decade or longer) is tantamount to expulsion from the jurisdiction (and with expanding reciprocity arrangements among states, the region, or the country). Consequently this form of prohibition is probably no more effective as a driver improvement device than was the nation's experience with the prohibition of alcohol as a deterrent to drinking.

Another aspect of the punitive nature of the legal system is its self-defeating character. Because of the severity of some mandatory penalties for various infractions of the law, judges and juries are often reluctant to find defendants guilty. (The impact of this policy of the legal system will be extended in the section below on enforcement within the transportation subsystem.) It is axiomatic that unenforceable laws or unenforced laws have dubious functional significance.

Improvables of the Transportation Subsystem. (a) Enforcement and Traffic Laws. Considering the enforcement aspect of the highway system, the excessive severity of certain penalties not only precludes conviction even when strong evidence exists, but it also seriously undermines the law enforcement official's resolve to make arrests except where chances of conviction are near certain. Thus, there evolves a *de facto* enforcement program incorporates low-probability, high-cost convictions. Edwards may or may not be related to accident causation. Furthermore, such a program incorporates low-probability, high-cost convictions. Edwards (1968) has persuasively delineated the role of penalties by ascribing greater effectiveness to high-probability, low-cost negative incentives. Thus, a deterrent system with fairly high probability of apprehension coupled with reasonable penalty features should be most effective. Unfortunately, this optimal system bears little resemblance to current enforcement-penalty procedures.

The law regarding traffic violations incorporates constitutional issues. An example concerns the "probable cause" aspect of arrests for drunken driving. Under existing statutes an officer may stop a drunk-driver suspect only after his driving itself provides a high probability of intoxication on the part of the driver. Only then may he administer such tests as the breathalyzer. Even to one who advocates the maintenance of strong safeguards to protect individual rights, this policy appears to be leaning over backwards and poses serious threats to the individual rights of others on the highway. Changes in the law to circumvent this predicament were recently advocated by Haddon (1969). Further evaluation of implied and expressed consent laws might be relevant.

The procedures for adjudicating traffic offenses also need reexamination. Local courts that largely depend on fines for traffic violations for revenue support cannot be expected to serve the ultimate goals of driver improvement. Blatant inequities abound. Atypically high fines for nonlocal arrested drivers are commonplace. The heaping on of fines in addition to the threat to the driver's life and the cost of vehicle damage in collision-related citations seems not only cruelly redundant but also devised to create ill will toward enforcement and the courts. Disdainful disregard for the plaintiff's account of extenuating circumstances involved in the traffic involvement have the same effect. Court actions and attitudes such as these can only engender justifiable resentment toward traffic law enforcement in general and operate to negate any therapeutic value punitive measures may have. The part of the legal system involving "fine dependent" courts must be replaced by a judicial system that commands, not demands, respect.

Probably one of the most significant improvements of the transportation subsystem might derive from the adoption of nationwide uniform traffic laws (and signing). The mobility of typical drivers involves relatively frequent movement among several jurisdictions. While it is legally incumbent upon the driver to acquaint himself with the vagaries and idiosyncrasies of the several jurisdictions he is driving in, this expectation is inconsistent with the requirements of good human engineering. It would be more consistent with a human factors approach to establish legal standards of traffic movement and control rather than require drivers to acquire and retain knowledge of arbitrary laws regarding traffic maneuvers. Uniformity of highway signing style and placement would be especially welcome so that drivers from distant places would not have confusion created by strange and unfamiliar designations added to the general foreignness of the locale.

(b) Highways. There is relatively little in the training of highway engineers that prepares them for a human engineering approach to highway construction. For this reason, often arbitrary decisions are made regarding sign legibility, placement, uniformity, and so forth. The value of warning signals during hours when construction crews are working is totally negated if signs reading "CAUTION—Men Working," or "SLOW—Heavy Equipment" are left in place during off-hours, on weekends, and occasionally long after completion of the project. Ignorance of psychophysical methods to determine size and distance factors for warning signs and destination guides is apparent. Similar unfamiliarity with the information-processing limits of drivers results in signs bearing too many bits of data and in too close proximity with competing signs. Finally, the vigilance capacity of the operator is often overestimated by the placement of only one (or two widely spaced) critical turn-off destination signs. It is fairly common that faulty alignment or inadequate sight-distance is discovered only after accidents pile up for particular roadway sections. The prevalence of such *ex post facto* redesign measures might possibly be reduced if the human factors approach were more evident in the initial highway design.

A basic tenet of human engineering is that it is easier to change the machine-environment than the human partner in the system. This principle would appear to have many exceptions in highway engineering.

This inflexibility is exemplified by the maintenance of signal lights at intersections in the red-green-amber sequence for all hours and all traffic conditions. The use of flashing red opposite flashing amber for early morning hours when traffic is minimal should become standard policy.

A welcome addition to high-density freeway routes would be the development of an "early warning system" to provide more advance notice of traffic standstill ahead. This would be especially appropriate in areas where inclement weather (fog, ice, etc.) drastically diminishes the effective volume characteristic of an otherwise high average daily traffic (A.D.T.) route within a few hours or minutes.

(c) Driver Licensing. The general role of driver licensing agencies has already been discussed at various places throughout this chapter. In this section, only one aspect of the licensing function will be elaborated—the collection and utilization of accident records.

Chapanis states, "For all their value in the analysis of certain man-machine problems, accident data can be more hindrance than help. Indeed it is probably correct to say that there are more useless than useful accident data" (1966, p. 76). Five minimum requirements of useable accident information follow and their relevance to traffic accidents in particular is discussed.

The first requirement involves the *adequate definition* of an accident. Among the various definitions of an accident is the legal one which is "generally unsatisfactory for human engineering purposes. The reason is that legal definitions are too much concerned with establishing guilt or responsibility. The lawyer is primarily concerned with, 'Who pays for it?' and not with, 'How could we have prevented it?'" The remarks quoted here referred primarily to industrial accidents, but their appropriateness to the field of traffic accidents is apparent.

The second essential to the development of useful accident data is the establishment of an *adequate system for reporting accidents.* Chapanis cites three necessary features of an adequate system: proper personnel (for reporting accidents), a good accident report form, and central-office facilities. Regarding personnel, he states, ". . . if each member of an organization is left to do his own (reporting), many accidents will never get into the files, or if they do, will be incompletely or improperly reported" (p. 77). Now consider the source of most traffic accident reports—the bulk of them are self-reports. Thus, the validity of the majority of traffic accident reports is seriously open to question. Furthermore, they are certainly not a reliable index of all traffic collisions that occur.

The need for uniform accident reports is especially critical in view of the source of accident reports. Also, "good accident reports are of little use unless there is some place where they can be collected, organized, compiled, and stored for future reference" (p. 78). In most traffic accident reporting systems, the emphasis is on collection, compilation, and especially storage. If the data are organized, it is usually by some univariate analysis, that is, by hour of the day, highway route number and mile post, day of the week, age of the driver(s), or type of accident (ran off road, struck fixed object, etc.). Only rarely is provision made for multivariate analysis of the data (i.e., how many ran-off-roadway, single-car, early morning, weekend collisions occurred for males aged 35–44 who have had prior traffic arrests for drunk-driving?). Because multiple determinism, rather than single-factor overdeterminism, is the rule rather than the exception, traffic accident data must be organized so as to facilitate multivariate evaluation that may uncover the realities of the accident circumstances. The increasing availability of computers to motor vehicle agencies should enhance this approach assuming that they are not already too overburdened with menial bookkeeping tasks to permit these analyses.

The third requirement for useful accident data involves provision for *complete coverage of all accidents.* Chapanis stresses that accidents be reported for all persons regardless of occupation or station in life. He continues, "Bias also comes into the data if certain types of accidents are less likely to be reported than other types" (p. 79). Not only are fatal traffic accidents and serious injury and/or damage accidents more likely to be reported, but also state laws specifically condone and encourage incomplete reporting via laws to the effect that non-injury collisions involving less than x dollars loss need not be reported. Thus, it is safe to conclude that accident statistics are based not on accident *occurrence* but on accident *reporting.*

Full and accurate reporting is the fourth requirement in Chapanis' list. Here he enumerates some basic conditions that must be controlled to assure complete and valid records. Distortion of reports made by people involved in the accident is an obvious factor in traffic accidents. False reports of nonexistent accidents is exemplified by Chapanis in the field of traffic accidents.

Finally, good accident *reporting should suggest cures.* Cliches such as "faulty attitude, impulsiveness, irresponsibility, slow reaction" are nonproductive. Chapanis warns that "'pigeon-holing' human actions does not help reduce accidents" (p. 83). (Many driver improvement analysts in today's interview programs would be well-advised to heed this admonition against stereotyping.) A system such as that published by the American Standards Association is recommended as a workable alternative.

In the A.S.A. outline, only the last of six factors involves personal factors of the operator, which is in marked contrast to the heavy emphasis on driver faults in driver improvement.

In summary, Chapanis has cited the basics of a useful accident reporting system. Unfortunately, he has not been as specific in detailing how such requirements could be adapted to traffic accidents that occur under much less controlled circumstances. It is very likely traffic accident records will never prove as useful an index of performance overload on the highways as they can in the more circumscribed industrial setting. Nevertheless, there must be increased efforts to approach standards recommended by Chapanis. In addition, there is need for more study of "near accidents" and "critical incidents" as diagnostic keys to operator and system inadequacies.

Probably the most insightful utilization of available traffic accident data is represented by the 1964 California Driver Record Study. In Part 4 of this project the relationship between concurrent accidents and citations was explored. The correlations between accidents and violations was significantly reduced (.23) when corrections for the inclusion of spurious citations were made. Spurious citations result when citations are issued as a result of an accident investigation. In Part 6 of this extended study the stability of reported accidents and citations was investigated (Coppin, McBride, and Peck, 1965). In this segment of the report accidents and traffic citations do not occur according to a chance (Poisson) distribution. By contrast some individuals have many more than average and others have very few. However, it was noted that drivers involved in accidents in every year of the six-year study constituted only 2.2 percent of the total accident-involved population. The authors note that "if these drivers were removed from the highways, total reported accidents would be reduced only slightly." While this finding contraindicates present procedures that focus on a very small proportion of the driving population, another finding to the effect that traffic citations are more predictive of subsequent traffic accidents, does in fact correspond to current operations that concentrate on traffic violations to the near exclusion of accidents. Part 7 of the report refers to the relationship between types of convictions and accidents (Coppin, Lew, and Peck, 1966). As mentioned earlier more effort should be devoted to establishing the relationship of particular citation types to subsequent traffic accident data, and therefore this type of research should receive more support. Later parts of the California study are concerned with the prediction of accident involvement using concurrent driving record data and the prediction of accident involvement from driver records and biographical data.

The State of Oregon has also attempted to study accident records in greater depth (Kaestner, 1963, 1964, 1967). In these studies baseline data for typical age and sex groups were devised to objectively assess the accident record histories of drivers involved in fatal accidents, drinking drivers, drivers involved in motorcycle accidents, and the subpopulation of driver improvement cases. In the last two references cited, the relationships between specific errors and traffic accidents were investigated, and clearly different qualitative patterns existed from one age group to another. For example, "following too closely" was the prime driver error for the 20–24 age group, whereas the foremost driver error for the 65 and older age group involved drivers who "did not have the right-of-way." Clear age differences also existed with regard to the type of traffic collision involved. Collisions with another vehicle increased almost linearly (by percent) from the teenage years to the post-retirement years, whereas "ran off road" traffic accidents showed a steady decrease with chronological age. Findings such as these were incorporated in the revised Oregon driver improvement interview (Kaestner and Syring, 1967). Both the California and Oregon studies exemplify how traffic records can be usefully employed in developing countermeasures in driver improvement.

Improvables of the Microsystem. In the analysis of the problems associated with driver improvement, we have already considered examples of the global social system and the elements of the transportation subsystem as they relate to driver improvement. In this section, the performance of the individual driver in his vehicle on a given stretch of roadway is discussed. Engineering improvements in the vehicle and the highway design that reduce the task requirements for the driver are relevant here. Again the need for explicit and detailed analyses of the drivers tasks is paramount.

As presently constituted, driver improvement programs react to the quality of the driver's performance within this microsystem. Therefore, whatever factors influence driver failure should concern driver improvement functions. Driver characteristics (Chapter 4), driver judgment and skills (Chapter 7), highway facilities (Chapter 5 and 6), vehicle design (Chapter 9), the driver's training (Chapter 3 and 11), and the influence of alcohol and other drugs (Chapter 13) are significant factors that should enter into an effectively operating driver improvement program. On the basis of direct experience with various driver improvement procedures and the vicarious experience accruing from an exhaustive literature search in the field, it is possible to state that with very few exceptions, none of these factors plays a large role in contemporary driver improvement activities. The parts of the highway facilities, the vehicle, the driver's training, or lack thereof, are either underplayed or omitted altogether. The only driver characteristics that are featured are "poor attitudes." The influence of alcohol, while often emphasized in an unenlightened way, is not typically reacted to by diagnosis and rehabilitation.

SUMMARY STATEMENTS

Table 1 summarizes typical present and idealized future approaches to the driver and his interface within larger social, economic, and legal systems and their subsystems. Driver improvement as outlined in the ideal begins with a larger conception of driver improvement functions that encompasses, in fact begins with, prelicensing driver education (training).

Table 1

Program Features	Present Programs	Ideal Programs
Orientation.	Coercive-punitive.	Instructional-motivational.
Purpose(s).	Improve (attitudes toward) driving.	Reduce personal injury and property damage.
Target population.	Hard-core "intractable" cases.	All eligible drivers.
Initiation stage.	Excessive convictions and/or collisions.	Pre-licensing training.
Relation to other licensing functions.	Little or none.	Diagnostic-remedial initial licensing; routine retesting and re-training.
Relation to prior driving records.	Basis for suspension and revocation.	Violations as critical incidents or near accidents. Individualized rehabilitation.

The reaction to the individual driver by the idealized program presumes the existence of two developments not presently realized. First, the presence of a precise, scientific model of the driver's task that can be employed during prelicensing driver training, for licensing itself, in periodic driver reexamination, and for diagnosis and remedial treatment of stress cases. Such a model should include the social and economic aspects of driving, vigilance, risk-taking, information processing capabilities, as well as the strictly perceptual-motor factors. To date, no such comprehensive model exists. (A timetable for its development appears in Miller and Dimling, 1969, Vol. I, Chap. 7, p. 14.)

The second development is one of orientation which would substitute for the prevailing notion, that driver improvement exert punitive pressures on a small minority of recalcitrant drivers, a view that the distinction between driver licensing and driver improvement is an artificial one. According to this second position, driver improvement begins for everyone just before he or she becomes eligible to drive. The rationale is one of identifying strengths and weaknesses (relative to the perfected model called for above) of drivers at every stage in their driving careers. Driver error identification would trigger remedial retraining followed by training evaluation. Traffic violations and minor accidents would be used as field diagnositic indices much as "near accidents" and "critical incidents."

REFERENCES

Adams, J. R., Reward Incentives in Driver Improvement: Safety Research and Evaluation Project, Teachers College, Columbia University, New York, 1961.

Adams, J. R., Driver Vocabulary Test: Safety Research and Evaluation Project, Teachers College, Columbia University, New York, 1964.

Adams, J. R. and Kole, T., Driver Rehabilitation: An Approach Based on Diagnostic Differentiation and Group Interaction, Continental Research Institute, New York, 1969.

American Association of Motor Vehicle Administrators, *Driver License Administrators' Guide to Driver Improvement,* American Association of Motor Vehicle Administrators, Washington, D.C., 1965, p. 3.

Bacon, S., Alcohol and Highway Safety: The Role of Social Science Research, Driver Behavior: Cause and Effect, Insurance Institute for Highway Safety, Washington, D.C., 1968, pp. 145–164.

Barmack, J. E. and Payne, D. E., The Lackland Accident Countermeasure Experiment, *Highway Research Board Proceedings,* **40** (1961), 513–522.

Blumenthal, M., Dimensions of the Traffic Safety Problem, *Traffic Safety Research Review,* **12**, 1 (1968), 7–12.

Boe, E. E. and Church, R. M., *Punishment: Issues and Experiments,* Appleton, New York, 1968.

California, State of, *The 1964 California Driver Record Study, Part 4—The Relationship Between Concurrent Accidents and Citations,* 1964.

Campbell, B. J., The Effects of Driver Improvement Actions on Driving Behavior, *Traffic Safety Research Review,* **3** (1959), 319–331.

Chalfant, M. W., *An Analysis of the Problem Driver Characteristics and the Differential Effectiveness of the Several Types of Interview Disposition,* Highway Traffic Safety Center, Michigan State University, East Lansing, Mich., 1960.

Chalfant, M. W. and King, G. F., *Reports of Studies on the Effectiveness of Driver Improvement Procedures,* Michigan State University, East Lansing, Mich., 1960.

Chapanis, A., *Man-Machine Engineering,* Wadsworth, Belmont, Cal., 1965.

Chapanis, A., *Research Techniques in Human Engineering,* Johns Hopkins Press, Baltimore, Md., 1966.

Coppin, R. S., Marsh, W. C., and Peck, R. C., *A Re-evaluation of Group Driver Improvement Meetings,* California Department of Motor Vehicles, Sacramento, Cal., 1965.

Coppin, R. S., McBride, R. S., and Peck, R. C., *The 1964 California Driver Record Study, Part 6—The Stability of Reported Accidents and Citations,* California Department of Motor Vehicles, Sacramento, Cal., 1965.

Coppin, R. S., McBride, R. S., and Peck, R. C., *The 1964 California Driver Record Study, Part 7—The Relationship Between Types of Convictions and Accidents,* California Department of Motor Vehicles, Sacramento, Cal., 1966.

Coppin, R. S., Peck, R. C., Lew, A., and Marsh, W. C., *The Effectiveness of Short Individual Driver Improvement Sessions,* California Department of Motor Vehicles, Sacramento, Cal., 1965.

De Silva, H. R., Applications of Driver Clinics, *Journal of Psychology,* **6** (1938), 233–241.

De Silva, H. R. and Forbes, T. W., Improving Bad Drivers, *Safety Engineering,* 1938, 98.

De Silva, H. R., Robinson, P., and Forbes, T. W., Some Psychological Factors in Accident Repeater Drivers, *Journal of Abnormal and Social Psychology,* **34** (1939), 124–128.

Edwards, W., Information Processing, Decision Making and Highway Safety, *Driver Behavior: Cause and Effect,* Insurance Institute for Highway Safety, Washington, D.C., 1968, pp. 165–180.

Finesilver, S. A., Denver Citizens Go to Traffic School, *Traffic Safety,* **61**, 2 (1962), 20.

Forbes, T. W., Age Performance Relationships Among Accident Repeater Automobile Drivers, *Journal of Consulting Psychology,* **2** (1938), 143.

Gibson, J. J. and Crooks, L. E., A Theoretical Field-analysis of Automobile Driving, *American Journal of Psychology,* **2,** 3 (1938).

Goldstein, L. G., Driver Selection—The Logic and Logistics, *Motor Transportation Transactions of the National Safety Congress,* Chicago, Ill., 1963.

Haddon, W., Jr., Keynote address to Governors' Annual Traffic Safety Conference, Sacramento, Cal., 1969.

Heath, E. D., The Driver Improvement Clinic: A Review of the Literature, *American Society of Safety Engineers' Journal,* **7**, 9 (1962), 125–130.

Henderson, H. L. and Kole, T., *Mass Communication and Group Discussion Techniques,* Drivers Safety Service, New York, 1967a.

Henderson, H. L. and Kole, T., *Driver Improvement Clinics in the State of New Jersey,* Drivers Safety Service, New York, 1967b.

Imhoff, C., The Driver Improvement Program, *Traffic Safety,* 1966, 22.

Johnson, H. M., Evidence for the Educational Value in Drivers Clinics, *Psychological Bulletin,* **36** (1939), 674–675.

Johnson, H. M. and Cobb, P. W., The Educational Value of Drivers Clinics, *Psychological Bulletin,* **35** (1938), 758–766.

Kaestner, Noel, *Study of Licensed Drivers in Oregon, Part I—Description of Driver Characteristics,* Oregon Department of Motor Vehicles, Salem, Oregon, 1963.

Kaestner, Noel, *Study of Licensed Drivers in Oregon, Part II—Analyses of Traffic Involvement Records,* Oregon Department of Motor Vehicles, Salem, Oregon, 1964.

Kaestner, Noel, *A Second Look at Licensed Drivers in Oregon,* Oregon Department of Motor Vehicles, Salem, Oregon, 1967.

Kaestner, N., Howard, V., and Warmoth, E., *Oregon Study of Drinking Drivers,* Salem, Oregon, 1969.

Kaestner, N. and Syring, E. M., Accident and Violation Reduction Through Brief Driver Improvement Interviews, *Traffic Safety Research Review,* **11**, 4 (1967), 99.

Kaestner, N., Warmoth, E., and Syring, E. M., Oregon Study of Advisory Letters—The Effectiveness of Warning Letters in Driver Improvement, *Traffic Safety Research Review,* **11**, 3 (1967), 67–72.

Kastell, C. G. and LeSueur, C. M., An Evaluation of the Pierce County Pilot Program In Driver Improvement Utilizing the Group Discussion Method, (mimeograph), Washington State Department of Motor Vehicles, Olympia, Wash., 1965.

Kleinknecht, R., *Program for Behavior Modification of Problem Drivers,* Washington State Department of Motor Vehicles, Olympia, Wash., 1968.

Lewin, K., *Resolving Social Conflicts,* Harper, New York, 1948.

Miller, L. and Dimling, J. A., *Driver Licensing and Performance,* Vol. I, U.S. Department of Transportation, Washington, D.C., 1969.

Myrick, R. and Schlesinger, L. E., Driver Improvement or System Improvement, *Traffic Quarterly,* **18** (1964), 92–104.

Roethlisberger, F. J. and Dickson, W. J., *Management and the Worker,* Harvard University Press, Cambridge, Mass., 1939.

Schlesinger, L. E., Objectives, Methods, and Criterion Tests in Driver Training, *Traffic Safety Research Review,* 1967, 18–24.

Schulzinger, M. S., *The Accident Syndrome,* Charles C. Thomas, Springfield, Ill., 1956.

Schuster, D., A Short Term Evaluation of a Driver Improvement Course for Military Drivers, *Traffic Safety Research Review,* **2**, 1 (1967), 25–26.

Scott, B., Effects of Group Sessions in Changing Driver Attitudes, *Summary of Proceedings Research Conference and Workshop;* Sacramento, Cal., April 1966.

Selling, L. S., The Psychological Approach to the Traffic Problem, *Scientific Monthly,* **XLIV** (1937), 547–554.

Sheehe, G., Informal study conducted at Michigan State University, East Lansing, Mich.

Solomon, R. L., Punishment, *American Psychologist,* **19**, 4 (1964), 239–253.

Toms, D., Pierce County Pilot Study. *Summary of Proceedings.* Research Conference and Workshop, American Association of Motor Vehicle Administrators, Sacramento, Cal., 1966.

Wisconsin Motor Vehicle Department, *Wisconsin's Driver Improvement Program,* Madison, Wisconsin, 1967.

XVI

HUMAN FACTORS IN CONTROL AND MODIFICATION OF DRIVING BEHAVIOR BY THE LEGAL SYSTEM

Murray Blumenthal

Murray Blumenthal is a professor at the University of Denver College of Law. He previously directed the Social Systems Division at Travelers Research Center and was research director at the National Safety Council. He has also served as a consultant to the USPHS, the National Bureau of Standards, the Institute for Educational Development, the CBS-TV News Department, the NHSB in the development of the Traffic Records Manual, the Massachusetts Driver Registry, and the Florida Bureau of Law Enforcement. Dr. Blumenthal is presently directing a study, supported by the NHTSA, of the effect of selected sanctions on two classes of traffic violators. A previous study for the NHTSA provided a standard traffic crash investigation form and investigation and coding manuals. He received a Ph.D. in experimental psychology from the University of Denver in 1959.

When a human factors specialist joins a system design team, he contributes by studying and improving the fit or match between the human and the machine components of the system. In addition to assisting with the design of the hardware, he may formulate rules or directions to guide the behavior of the human operator. As a system increases in complexity and includes other human operators and their machines, the rules or directions that he devises will regulate the interactions *between* man-machine units. However, ambiguous, inappropriate, or unworkable rules can contribute to system inefficiency or malfunction. Thus, the specialist soon learns that it is as necessary to apply human factors criteria to the devising of rules as it is for their application to the physical dimensions of controls or dials.

One definition of a rule is (Webster, 1965) "a prescribed guide for conduct or action." Kelso (1965) defines a rule of law* as "a general statement that is intended to guide conduct, applied by government officials and supported by an authoritative source." The parallel definitions and functions of rules and laws support the usefulness of a human factors analysis of the traffic law conceived as the rules that guide the behavior of the humans indirectly and directly associated with the functioning of the motor vehicle transportation system.

A human factors specialist knows that rules cannot compensate for inherent deficiencies in workplace layout or hardware design. He knows that laws that place unwarranted responsibility on the human operator for successful system functioning are in fundamental conflict with human factors principles. What then does the specialist do when he is called upon to evaluate the laws or rules regulating a system that is inherently faulty?

We faced this question in preparing this chapter evaluating traffic law from a human factors point of view. In an earlier paper (1969), we described the motor vehicle transportation system as "poorly conceived, designed, constructed, managed, monitored and maintained." Figure 1 shows our propositions (1967, 1968) descriptive of the structure and dimensions of the traffic safety problem.

Proposition 2 in Figure 1, concerning system demands and driver capabilities, is illustrated by a U.S. Department of Commerce analysis, quoted by Miller (1966). The analysis concludes that "Drivers are being asked to make judgments that they cannot make well; to make decisions faster than humanly possible; and to make changes in direction and speed more accurately than they can." Stonex (1965), General Motors automotive safety engineer, concludes that the system is "*precisely that which we would have built if our objective had been to kill as many people as possible.*"*

* To laymen, the term "law" generally connotes a statute passed by a legislative body. However, "rules of law" are not made exclusively by legislatures. The "common law" or judge-made law represents a significant part of the body of law. Administrative regulations and decisions constitute another major segment, particularly in the traffic safety area. The federal and state constitutions represent a body of law used to evaluate the acceptability of other laws and legal procedures.

* Emphasis added.

Problem Level	Content	Proposition
I Symptom level	Deaths, injuries, and property damage	1. Traffic accidents and their consequences are symptoms of an underlying sociotechnical problem.
II System level	Man/motor vehicle/ environment	2. There is an imbalance between the technology of the motor vehicle transportation system and the demands upon driver capabilities.
III "Management" level	Decision structure and processes (Laws, rules, etc.)	3. Despite the present inevitability of local system failures (accidents), there is minimum provision for avoiding or reducing the consequences of such failures . . . .
		4. There is inadequate provision for functional coordination between the inputs and components of the motor vehicle transportation system.
IV Values and knowledge level	Support (conceptual, factual, and material)	5. There is inadequate provision for systematically identifying research needs and incorporating research findings.
		6. The knowledge is not presently available that is required to increase the safety of the system to "desirable" levels, given existing resources and constraints.
		7. The value conflicts and tradeoffs underlying the motor vehicle system have not been made explicit.

Figure 1 A proposed macrostructure and associated propositions for describing the traffic safety problem (1967, 1968).

In attempting to resolve the dilemma of evaluating the rules or laws used to regulate human behavior in an inherently faulty system, this chapter outlines briefly the history of traffic law, searching for clues as to the origins of the system and its regulation. The brief history is followed by a discussion of selected criteria used to evaluate traffic law, with the criteria applied to two landmark examples of statutory traffic law. Finally, the application of law is traced through enforcement, adjudication, and penalization and/or correction. The underlying question throughout the chapter concerns the extent that traffic law is cognizant of, and attempts to remedy, the motor vehicle transportation systems' fundamental deficiencies, or in Myrick and Schlesinger's terms (1964) "Driver improvement or system improvement?"

HISTORY OF TRAFFIC LAW

Given an object, such as a chair, reasonable men can be expected to agree as to its color, function, or material. However, given a legal or social problem, reasonable men will often disagree as to the existence of a problem, its nature and magnitude, and the steps for its melioration. Statutory law develops when a situation is perceived as a problem, and this perception or judgment leads to the enactment of legislation. Judge-made or common law develops when a dispute is brought before a court. Administrative rules are made by administrative agencies carrying out the provisions of statutory law. The history of traffic law is the history of anticipated or perceived problems and their effect on the rule-making behavior of legislators, judges, and administrators.

In a comprehensive history of the emergence of motor vehicle traffic law, Fisher (1961) identifies the struggle for the right to share the use of the roads by the automobile as the first problem that stimulated the development of vehicle law. The early laws tried principally to reduce the frightening effect of the noisy and unreliable vehicles on horses, which frequently bolted at their sight or sound. While comics or movies have often pictured a runaway team as humorous, it was far from amusing to the drivers, passengers, and frequently pedestrians who were involved. The outcome of the initial legal struggles was that the horseless carriage won the equal right to the use of the streets.

The next issue was the status of the automobile as a danger or nuisance. Opponents of the vehicle described it as an "inherently dangerous instrumentality" (Fisher, 1961) in the same class as wild animals considered inherently dangerous to human beings, such as lions, tigers, and leopards. The consequence of the application of this position would have been the *strict liability** of the owner for any damage attributable to the vehicle without need to demonstrate fault. However, the opponents of a strict liability doctrine won out. Automobiles per se were not to be feared, but rather "the ferocity of those who drive them"

* Defined in *Black's Law Dictionary* (1968) as "Liability without fault. Case is one of 'strict liability' when neither care nor negligence, neither good nor bad faith, neither knowledge nor ignorance will save defendant."

(*Lewis v. Amorous*, 1907). The attempt to have the automobile classed as a nuisance won a limited victory with the enactment of regulations prohibiting the vehicle's use in ways that interfered with the rights of others to use the streets. Examples cited include parking a vehicle in public streets in a way that denied the use of the street to others or operating a vehicle while under the influence of an intoxicating liquor.

With the increase in the number of vehicles and the corresponding increase in casualties resulting from automobile and pedestrian collisions and other mishaps, and with the growth of congestion and parking problems, there was a parallel increase in traffic law. As a latecomer to the highway system, initially the motor vehicle had to adapt to the existing regulations. Davis (1950) reports that "long before motor vehicles were manufactured or used, it was the custom for horse-drawn vehicles approaching from opposite directions to pass each other to the right. Also . . . it was a matter of custom . . . to overtake and pass on the left . . . ."

Thus, our initial thinking about the regulation of the motor vehicle was based on the performance of horses, moving at a maximum speed of 10 miles per hour, with response characteristics not dissimilar from their human driver. At a more subtle level, the regulation of vehicle, highway, and operators reflected the prevailing moralistic view of social systems —with the system accepted without question and the responsibility of the system users to display "good" behavior and adapt to the system, lest they be punished by the authorities for their departure from the "good" and, therefore, only morally acceptable behavior.

This brief history has traced the roots of present traffic law to the regulation of horse-drawn vehicles. It would not be inappropriate to speculate that such regulation grew, in turn, out of folkways regulating foot traffic on widened animal paths. In light of this conjecture, it is wryly amusing to consider Chapanis' (1970) warning that "[i]f human factors engineering is to have an impact on the systems design process, the behavioral scientist must be called in at the beginning, while it is still possible to influence major design decisions."

TWO TRAFFIC LEGISLATION LANDMARKS

The Uniform Vehicle Code

As traffic laws developed out of the social matrix of problem, custom, and conflict, they tended to reflect local tradition and values. A motorist crossing a city, county, or state line could be met by bewildering changes in laws or regulations. A right turn on a red signal would be permitted in one state but not in another. In one jurisdiction, vehicles were required to stop when a pedestrian merely entered a crosswalk; in another, vehicles were not required to stop.

In response to the mushrooming varieties of often conflicting and inconsistent traffic laws, national efforts to develop model traffic and motor vehicle law that could serve as a basis for uniformity began during World War I and eventuated in the first edition of the *Uniform Vehicle Code* (UVC) in 1926, which was approved by the National Conference of Commissioners on Uniform State Laws. A model municipal traffic ordinance was first published in 1928. Both of these documents were based on a selection from what was believed to be the best of existing legislation. In 1947, following a study by the President's Highway Safety Conference of the extent to which the states had adopted the UVC, the National Committee on Uniform Traffic Laws and Ordinances (NCUTLO) was created. The Committee revised and published subsequent editions of the UVC and Model Traffic Ordinance, with the latest full publication in 1969.

The Foreword to the UVC (1962) describes it as "a concise statement of significant principles of traffic law in the form of essential legislation; not in the form of administrative details best left to administrative regulation and handling." The Code is periodically reviewed and "changes made when warranted by new developments in state laws and by practical experience."

The importance of the Code and its influence on the enactment of traffic legislation in this country is highlighted by the remarks of Economos (1967), the director of the Traffic Court Program of the American Bar Association, who referred to the Code as embodying "the best current thinking of those who have been dealing with the traffic problem, . . . the best of state traffic laws and other experience considered valid for this purpose" and as "the best available tool today to create the important features of the legal environment for travel on our highways and streets." It is significant as a landmark among the attempts to systematize or codify the experiences of the American legal system in regulating the development of motor vehicle transportation. The Federal Role in Highway Safety (1959), a report from the Secretary of Commerce to the Speaker of the House of Representatives, described the UVC as "the yardstick against which the legislative achievement of a State is commonly measured." The federal document reported further, that "[a] recent survey by the NCUTLO showed that the legislatures of 38 States have enacted, verbatim or in substantial conformance with the Code, the basic 'Rules of the Road' . . . Uniform requirements for driver licensing, as prescribed in the Code, have been enacted in 34 States . . . ."

Motor Vehicle and Highway Safety Acts of 1966

In 1966, the President of the United States, in a message to Congress (H. R. Report, 1966) evaluated existing highway safety efforts, stating that "[t]he toll of Americans killed in this way since the introduction of the automobile is truly unbelievable. It is 1.5 million."

The message continues with the observation that:

"Our knowledge of causes is grossly inadequate. Expert opinion is frequently contradictory and confusing.

"Existing safety programs are widely dispersed. Government and private efforts proceed separately, without effective coordination.

"There is no clear assignment of responsibility at the Federal level.

"The allocation of our resources to highway safety is inadequate.

"Neither private industry nor Government officials concerned with automotive transportation have made safety among their priorities. Yet we know that expensive freeways, powerful engines, and smooth exteriors will not stop the massacre on our roads. . . ."

These are harsh criticisms and a case can be made for the application of several of these criticisms to the UVC as it exemplified the ideal legal regulation of the automotive transportation system up to the time of the President's message.

Enacted in response to the President's message, the second landmark in the development of traffic law was the Highway Safety and Motor Vehicle Safety Acts of 1966. An intention of these acts was to enlarge and strengthen the role of the federal government in highway safety, compensating for failure of the states to coordinate their programs and for the deficiencies of previous legislation which was predominately enacted by state legislatures.

The Motor Vehicle Safety Act (1966) provides for safety standards for motor vehicles and equipment in interstate commerce and for the support of safety research and development. The act represents a major shift in policy, with the federal government moving into an area that had previously been left to the states. With the regulation of the motor vehicle left to state government, this in practice meant that little or no regulation would occur, since individual states did not have the resources for developing, testing, or enforcing vehicle standards, nor could states agree upon desired policies.

The Highway Safety Act (1966) was set up to "provide for a coordinated national highway safety program through financial assistance to the States to accelerate highway traffic safety programs. . . ." Heretofore, national efforts were undertaken by private safety organizations, such as the National Safety Council, the Automotive Safety Foundation, and Insurance Institute for Highway Safety, organizations without regulatory power whose funds were derived principally or totally from private business sources and which supported a policy of state responsibility for highway safety. This approach left major industries, such as motor vehicle and tire manufacturers, free from safety regulation and unaccountable to government for performance of their products.

HUMAN FACTORS CRITERIA AND TRAFFIC LAW

If we think of law as a specialized type of rule and if we agree with the assignment of responsibility for evaluating system rules to human factors specialists, then we can apply human factors criteria to traffic law and the automotive transportation system as it reflects the ways the law works.

Starting with the premise that the motor vehicle transportation system is inherently faulty and makes unrealistic demands upon the human operator which result in a failure rate and a social cost that is societally unacceptable, then the first criterion for traffic law is that it be cognizant of the system's innate faults and provide for their correction. This means that the behavior which the law must change in order to correct the fundamental faults of the system is that of system, subsystem, and support system managements. It is essential that the decision-making behavior of the various management levels be modified, so that they make those *changes in the system* and its components that reduce or eliminate the unrealistic demands made upon the human operator and the destructive consequences of inevitable human failure.

Next, a set of rules should be *comprehensive.* It should include all relevant behaviors and subsystems. In highway safety, this includes, in addition to the driver and his behaviors, support systems, such as vehicle maintenance and repair, manufacture of replacement parts, and emergency medical care.

Rules should also be *uniform* in concept and application, where uniformity is desirable. (Uniformity in some instances may be undesirable, such as in vehicle registration, plate color, or where diversity is encouraged in order to evaluate alternatives.) Ambiguity and generality tend to decrease the uniformity of rules, since they increase the need for interpretation. Nonuniformity can also arise out of a set of rules that are internally inconsistent, again increasing the exercise of interpretation and discretion.

Without provision for *feedback*, ineffective rules are often tenaciously applied for generations. Even initially effective rules may become ineffective as the conditions for which they were originally designed change.

The criteria discussed above—system modification, comprehensiveness, uniformity, and feedback—are not exhaustive. For example, a set of rules should also be internally consistent, be based on empirical research (Reese, 1970), and include the smallest number necessary to achieve a given set of behaviors. However, the study of these additional criteria is beyond the scope of this chapter.

In this analysis, the selected criteria are applied to the UVC and the Highway Safety and Motor Vehicle Safety Acts of 1966, selected as prototypes of traffic law. The Code (1962 revision) is regarded here as representing the type of legal thinking that accompanied the traditional development of the motor vehicle transportation system. The federal legislation is interpreted as representing dissatisfaction with the traditional regulation of the system, while attempting to apply new concepts of system regulation and sets of performance standards.

SYSTEM MODIFICATION

The 1962 edition of the UVC shows a limited awareness of the need to modify the unrealistic demands made upon the human operator. The Code's emphasis on uniformity reflects a desire to help the public in interstate travel to "understand, remember, and observe" the rules as they move from state to state. The Code provides power to the department of motor vehicles to refuse registration or certificate of title if "a vehicle is mechanically unfit or unsafe to be operated or moved upon the highways."

There is no indication of the need to modify highway design or signing or to coordinate the various elements in order to bring about a match or fit of system demands with operator capabilities. Instead, the emphasis is on restricting access to vehicle operator's status to selected groups. Licenses are denied (with stated exceptions) to those under 16 years of age; to that person "adjudged to be afflicted with or suffering from any mental disability or disease and who has not at the time of application been restored to competency by the methods provided by law"; and "to any person when the commissioner has good cause to believe that such person by reason of physical or mental disability would not be able to operate a motor vehicle with safety upon the highways" and where "such persons would be inimical to public safety or welfare."

The examination of applicants for a license, according to the Code "shall include a test of applicant's eyesight, his ability to read and understand highway signs . . . his knowledge of traffic laws of this State, and shall include an actual demonstration of ability to exercise ordinary and reasonable control in the operation of a motor vehicle." Furthermore, there are restricted licenses for those requiring special vehicles or special mechanical control devices. There is also provision for the mandatory revocation of licenses when a driver is convicted of reckless driving within a period of 12 months; when a driver refuses to submit to a chemical test; and when a "law enforcement officer has reasonable grounds to believe the person to have been driving . . . while under the influence of intoxicating liquor." The motor vehicle department is also empowered under the Code to reexamine drivers or suspend their licenses, under special circumstances relating to their driving capabilities.

In contrast with the UVC, the federal legislation makes explicit the need to modify the system in its reference to "highway design and maintenance (including lighting, markings, and surface treatment), traffic control, vehicle codes and laws, surveillance of traffic for detection and correction of high or potentially high accident locations, and emergency services."

The federal legislation defines "motor vehicle safety" as "the performance of motor vehicles or motor vehicle equipment in such a manner that the public is protected against unreasonable risk of accidents occurring *as a result of the design, construction, or performance of motor vehicles** and is also protected against unreasonable risk of death or injury to persons in the event accidents do occur, and includes nonoperational safety of such vehicles." These provisions indicate a significant change from the orientation of the UVC, indicating the law's acceptance of the responsibility for the nature of the environment in which the operator must function. In the extension of legal responsibility to the managements of the vehicle and highway subsystems for selected aspects of system safety, it represents a modification of the moralistic approach that characterized the Code.

COMPREHENSIVENESS

The criterion of comprehensiveness looks for the inclusion in the set of rules of those components having a potential influence on the safety of the system. For example, the functioning of the system is influenced by the behavior of vehicle operators, managers of support systems (such as vehicle manufacturers, repair shops, etc.) and managers of subsystems

* Emphasis added.

(such as state motor vehicle and highway departments). The criterion of comprehensiveness also includes the regulation by subsystem and support system managers of all of the relevant physical components and services required by the system, including the vehicle and the related components of the environment.

Applying this criterion to the Code, it appears that the Code omits an explicit reference to the educational, medical, debris removal, and research support systems. A reference to driver education is limited to the statement "driver education program . . . which is approved by the department . . . ," without elsewhere specifying the conditions of approval or the nature of such a program. Research is referred to only once, as one of the few "proper" areas of federal involvement in highway safety.

On the other hand, the federal legislation and standards include the support systems missing from the Code and make explicit functions such as highway design and maintenance and research. There is also recognition of the national character of the problem with the expansion of the National Driver Register.

UNIFORMITY

Applying the criterion of uniformity to the UVC, the first indication of a departure from the criterion is found in the fourth paragraph of the Foreword, which describes the Code as representing "a concise statement of significant principles of traffic law in the form of essential legislation; *not in the form of administrative details best left to administrative regulation and handling.*"* This statement is indicative of a failure to recognize that functional uniformity is achieved or not achieved through precisely that "administrative regulation and handling" which the Code does not specify. Reese (1970) concludes, in the case of driver licensing, "[t]hat it is the administrative agency which creates the effective driver licensing law, rather than the legislative body which adopted the statute under which the agency operates."

The Rules of the Road Section of the Code is replete with examples of phrases which, while often found in law, require a degree of interpretation by the citizen, the police, and the courts or administrative agencies that inevitably result in variability rather than in the desired uniformity. A sampling of these terms and phrases is: "endanger life and property . . . , due regard for the safety of all persons . . ." (11-106)†, "sufficiently legible to be seen by an ordinarily observant person . . ."

* Emphasis added.

† These numbers refer to sections of the UVC.

(11-201), "Green, Red and Yellow shall be used . . ." (11-202), "rapid intermittent flashes . . ." (11-204), "normal speed of traffic . . ." (11-301), "at a safe distance . . . until safely clear . . ." (11-303), "unless such left side is clearly visible and is free of oncoming traffic for a sufficient distance ahead . . ." (11-305), "within such distance as to create a hazard . . ." (11-306), "shall not follow another vehicle more closely than is reasonable and prudent, having due regard for the speed of such vehicles and the traffic upon and the condition of the highway . . . whenever conditions permit, leave sufficient space so that an overtaking vehicle may enter and occupy such space without danger . . ." (11-310), "speed reasonable for the existing conditions . . ." (11-403), "making use of an audible signal only . . ." (11-405), "exercise due care . . . exercise proper precaution . . ." (11-504), "at a speed greater than is reasonable and prudent under the conditions and having regard to the actual and potential hazards . . ." (11-801), "reckless driving . . . willful or wanton disregard for the safety of persons or property . . ." (11-901), and so forth.

While a given jury or sample of police officers would tend to agree in applying these phrases to extreme examples of the behavior denoted by the law, this nevertheless leaves a wide range of possible disagreement. What is meant by "sufficiently legible to be seen by an ordinarily observant person," or "shall not follow another vehicle more closely than is reasonable and prudent"? In practice, this type of vague statute tends to be ignored by enforcement personnel until a crash or mishap occurs and then the statute is cited after the fact as the basis for charging violations that have "caused" the crash.

The federal legislation, in referring to required state safety programs, specifies that they "shall be in accordance with uniform standards promulgated by the Secretary." Reese (1970) in an analysis of the Driver Licensing Standard concludes that "its components are, in general, not sufficiently precise to achieve more than a modicum of uniformity in state driver licensing programs. Because of the vagueness of the component expressions, state licensing programs may be widely different and yet comply with the literal expression of the standard."

Similar vagueness and ambiguity can be found throughout the other standards. For example, the Periodic Motor Vehicle Inspection Standard (1969) refers to "competent personnel," without specifying the criteria for competence and also to "systems, subsystems and components having substantial relation to safe vehicle performance," without indicating what these subsystems are. The Highway Safety Program Standard for Codes and Laws (1969), which has as its stated purpose "to eliminate all major variations in traffic codes, laws and ordinances on given aspects of highway safety among political subdivisions in a State . . ." recommends doing this by having ". . . each State undertake and maintain continuing comparisons of all State and local laws, statutes and ordinances with the comparable provisions of the Rules of the Road section of the Uniform Vehicle Code." However, the preceding analysis has suggested that this section of the UVC with its vagueness and the attendant necessity for a high degree of interpretation by drivers, police, courts, and administrators will almost certainly lead to variability rather than uniformity.

PROVISION FOR FEEDBACK

Unless a rule or a law is based on previously gathered empirical data or has been empirically tested after its promulgation, it can be considered as an *hypothesis* as to how people should function in accord with system objectives. There are, of course, many situations when law-making cannot wait for the data or when the consequences of a faulty rule involve less cost than empirically testing the rule. However, there is a fundamental difference between a set of rules that admits exceptions to a need for validation and a set of rules relying largely on common sense, folklore, and informal experience. Testing and validation can keep a set of rules responsive to change. The conservatism and limited flexibility of common sense and informal experience tend to lead to a system's increasing rigidity and decreasing effectiveness.

The Code, in its Foreword, indicates that it is based "not on theory but on actual experience under various state laws throughout the nation." What does this mean? Is it sufficient for a rule of law to have been adopted by a number of states for it to be eligible for inclusion in the Code? Considering how raw experience for centuries supported belief in a flat earth, in a demoniacal explanation for disease, and in spontaneous generation of living things, to what extent can it be trusted as a source of standards for human behavior in the motor vehicle transportation system? "Theory," which the Code rejects, at least implies a recognition of the uncertain state of knowledge. "Experience," as used in the Code's Foreword, implies an unwarranted certainty.

The Code recognizes the need for change and articulates its criteria for change as "only on a clear preponderance of evidence of need and practicality." The judgment of "clear preponderance of evidence," in turn, is based on the judgments of

"more than 100 representatives of federal, state, and local governmental units (legislators, police officers, highway and traffic engineers, motor vehicle administrators, judges, prosecutors, educators, mayors, county officials, and attorney generals), motor vehicle equipment manufacturers and dealers, insurance companies, motor clubs, safety councils, trade associations, national transportation associations, and other individuals and groups having an interest in achieving sound, uniform motor vehicle laws and regulations . . . ."

Note that there is no reference to scientific method, research, or researchers. The limitations of this approach can be more readily appreciated if we could imagine an analogous body voting on the efficacy of one medical treatment versus another, rather than the use of adequately controlled research to provide the required evidence.

A consequence of this orientation has been the ritualistic dependence upon untested measures, such as the use of license suspension or revocation when, according to one empirically based estimate by Coppin and Oldenbeek (1965) that up to 33 percent of the drivers with suspended licenses and 68 percent whose licenses have been revoked continue to operate their vehicles. Another consequence has been the allocation of resources to traditional driver education and vehicle inspection programs, where the evidence for their effectiveness is at best moot (A. D. Little, 1966).

In contrast with the Code, the federal highway safety legislation specifically provides for research funds, facilities, and training. The Highway Safety Act also takes a highly unusual step and encourages the *provisional* application of standards, pending an assessment of their effectiveness. The law states that "the Secretary shall be authorized to amend or waive standards on a temporary basis for the purpose of evaluating new or different highway safety programs instituted on an experimental, pilot, or demonstration basis by one or more States. . . ." This section recognizes the experimental nature of rules and provides the means for feedback although it does not specifically require feedback nor its use as a basis for change.

APPLICATION OF TRAFFIC LAW

Language is, at best, an imperfect carrier of the intended meaning of the source. This is particularly true of law, when a rule arrived at following a number of legislative compromises may be applied by those who misunderstood or disagree with the law's original intention to situations not conceived of by the law's originators under social conditions far removed in time and place from those that existed at the time of the law's enactment.

In traffic law, the sequence of applications and interpretations of the law begins with the police, motor vehicle highway departments, or other governmental agencies. Because of the general nature of statutory law, governmental agencies are generally forced to develop new law in the form of administrative regulations to guide their functioning.

The next step in the application of traffic law may be the courts. Here, too, interpretation of the language of the law is not an option but a necessity that may result in judge-made or common law. The violator may end this particular contact at the judicial level or move on to a penal or rehabilitation program and its administrative laws. The violator, continuing in or returning to society, will also interpret his sequence of experiences in various ways. Some of the violator's interpretations may reflect the intentions of the legislative, administrative, or judicial sources of the law. On the other hand, other interpretations and the behaviors that follow may be in direct conflict with the official intentions. Thus, the application of traffic law involves its shaping and possible misshaping by a sequence of institutions and individuals, with the outcome always uncertain. This section of the chapter examines selected phases of the sequence of interpretations and applications of traffic law in greater detail in the light of experience, conjecture, and empirical research.

ENFORCEMENT

Enforcement can be evaluated according to some of the same criteria that are applied to the rules of law: comprehensiveness, uniformity, effectiveness, and provision for feedback.

Under the UVC, the *comprehensiveness* of the enforcement provisions reflect directly that of the substantive sections of the Code. Since vehicle or highway design, for example, are not meaningfully regulated by the Code, there will be no enforcement in relation to these components. However, with the passage of the federal safety legislation, the concepts of "policing" and "enforcement" have been broadened to cover the quality of the vehicle and parts manufactured for use in the automobile. During the four years of the Act's application, the newer enforcement has been responsible for the call-back of literally millions of defective vehicles and tires.

The *uniformity* of enforcement was studied by Gardiner (1969) in four Massachusetts cities. Gardiner perceives traffic law as a "'gray area' . . . an area of regulation in which neither the police department nor individual officers are given clear instructions by the public or its law-making institutions." As a result, the police have to decide how much of their limited time and resources to devote to traffic, "whether to enforce laws strictly or loosely, or which sanction to be applied in what situation . . . ." He observes that "variations in traffic-enforcement policies can be explained only to a limited extent by such environmental variables as political pressures, demographic characteristics, or court conviction and accident rates." He identifies the most significant variables accounting for variations in enforcement "within the departments—specialization of the traffic enforcement function, demands by the chief and commanding officers that ticket writing or courtesy to motorists be stressed . . . ." Gardiner concludes that "[w]here the norms of the department reward active ticket writers, the police will respond with tickets; where norms are neutral or openly hostile toward traffic enforcement, ticketing will be low and only serious offenders will be cited."

Further evidence concerning the lack of uniformity of enforcement can be found in a study by Zylman and Bacon (1968) of the police handling of drinking and driving offenses. The authors conclude that:

"A lack of uniformity in definition of a reportable accident and of an alcohol-involved accident was observed. State legislation was often obscured by local policies; the basis for inclusion or exclusion of cases in local records and in subsequent reporting to state and national agencies was drastically changed by local procedures. Variations among the departments in the interpretation and description of alcohol involvement in the officer's reports and subsequent translation in department reports made it impossible to measure extent of alcohol involvement. No uniformity of reporting the presence of alcohol was found. Compatibility in data gathering was almost nonexistent."

The *effectiveness* of traffic enforcement has long been a matter of concern. The results of the various studies do not generally support the enthusiasm that the safety and police groups have shown for traditional enforcement practices through the years. In December of 1955, the State of Connecticut began to suspend licenses for speeding convictions. This was followed by a decrease in fatalities by the end of the following year. Traffic safety authorities generally related the decline to the changed enforcement policy. However, Campbell and Ross (1968) analyzed the data using a "quasi-experimental analysis" and concluded that there was "no unequivocal proof" that the reduction in fatalities was due to the crackdown.

Fennessy and Joksch (1967) conclude, following a critical evaluation of "the studies that have scientifically attempted to measure the relationship of police services to highway safety and accident reduction . . ." that "only one quantitative research study (Operation 101) on the relationship of police traffic services to highway safety was found that showed a statistically significant reduction of accidents and a sufficient control of other factors that influence accidents. . . . This reduction must, however, be considered in light of the fact that police manpower, on an already well patrolled road, was doubled." Gardiner (1969) reports that ". . . no evidence was found to support the theory either that high ticketing will produce a low accident rate (thus yielding a strong *negative* correlation) or that high accident rates will cause the police to adopt a strict ticketing policy (thus yielding a strong *positive* correlation); little correlation was found in either direction." Borkenstein and Joscelyn (1968) of the Indiana University Department of Police Administration in their study of the "State of the Art Report of Police Traffic Services" concluded that "[w]e were unable to identify within single jurisdictions effective practices. The agencies do not measure the level of the problem faced nor the effect of the services performed. . . . We were also unable to compare police traffic services performed by different jurisdictions because of incompatibility and unreliability of basic data."

Two studies of the effect of enforcement on pedestrian behavior are of interest. A study by Dunlap and Associates (1969) reports that "the results show an absence of any consistently significant enforcement or post-enforcement effects on the level of pedestrian compliance." Weiner's study (1968) of the effect of an enforcement campaign directed at the elderly pedestrian concluded that "there was a dramatic increase in legal crossings during the campaign, but four months after the campaign the percentage of legal crossings was the same as before the campaign, unless a police officer was present on the corner."

Cramton (1968) concludes that "there is basis for skepticism on two grounds concerning the performance of the present system of traffic justice: (1) the extremely low apprehension rates and enforcement levels may dilute the possible deterrent effect; and (2) the relationship of behavior that results in violations to the causation of accidents has not been clearly established."

Supporting Cramton's first point was a study in the *New Yorker* magazine (1968) that described a Long Island Parkway police campaign for higher wages:

"Scorning the banality of a strike, the policemen have devised a strategy that is marked by the simplicity of genius and the iridescence of madness. They are working at their jobs. They are doing what they are paid to do. When they see a motorist violating the law, they give him a ticket. In five days, they have issued about thirteen hundred summonses (their previous rate being about forty a day) . . . . A Long Island lawyer has obtained a court order challenging the move, and the troopers' lawyer has answered, with impeccable logic and a perfectly straight face, 'I can't see how the Long Island State Park Commission can ask its police authority not to enforce the law.' "

A limited response to the enforcement question may involve automated surveillance. Harris (1970) describes a photographic system that automatically identifies a car, license number, driver involved in a violation, vehicle speed, date, and time of day of the violation.

In an experimentally uncontrolled study of the effect of the British Road Safety Act of 1967, which attempted to remove drunken drivers from the roads, Ross, Campbell, and Glass (1970) concluded that "the crackdown, with its attendant publicity, did save lives and prevent injuries, and that it continues to have an important beneficial effect on British highways." Their suggestion that the British Act, properly modified, would be likely to have a "similarly beneficial effect in this country," is open to question, considering the considerable differences in traffic volume, police resource allocation priorities, American attitudes toward law enforcement and drinking and driving.

ADJUDICATION

The effectiveness of the traffic courts is limited, in part, by the nature of the traffic law. If the laws regulating an inherently faulty system ignore the system's faults and concentrate instead on the symptoms, then to this extent the courts are irrelevant. For example, Cheshire (1965) has pointed out that "the automobile manufacturers are developing vehicles designed to travel 100 mph or more, the highway engineers are designing highways for maximum design speed of perhaps 70 or 80 mph, and the people who design the laws are thinking in terms of 65 and 70 mph." Freed (1965), Westchester County Traffic Engineer, found that "the automobile designers . . . seemed intent upon making the silhouette of the car lower and lower, the driver eye height lower and lower . . . ." with the consequence of making "all the existing markings for 'No Passing Zones' obsolete." The judge who passes judgment upon an operator charged with speeding and causing an accident while passing does not have an opportunity to rule upon the management of a system that does not coordinate highway and vehicle design characteristics, even though this lack of coordination increased the probability of the drivers making a faulty passing decision. To this extent, the courts also are limited in their *comprehensiveness* and *effectiveness.*

Economos (1968) studied 65 courts as part of a broader study of police traffic services. A lack of *uniformity* was the most consistent finding, particularly in regard to the organization of the courts, the age limits set for juvenile court jurisdiction for offenders, the presence of written rules of procedure, policies as to personal appearance of violators in court, the opportunity for violators to plead guilty and pay a fine by mail, and so on. He also found variability in the collection, organization, and dissemination of data collected by the courts. He concluded that "sufficient data does not exist to allow the formulation of objective criteria for operational decisions."

This brief overview of the traffic courts suggests that they are in a prescientific state. When their objectives have been articulated, they often reflect moralistic-legalistic assumptions rather than an awareness of the need to match system demands and operator capabilities. Justice Thomas Gallagher of the Supreme Court of Minnesota (1965) distinguishes between the "intentional" and "non-intentional violators." He stated that "[t]he basic objective of penalties in traffic violation cases is to punish the offender, to deter him and others from future violations, where necessary to change his mental attitude so as to create within him a respect for traffic regulations, to effectuate the removal of improperly equipped motor vehicles from the highways, and to terminate driving privileges of incompetent drivers." (Note that there is no awareness of or reference to vehicle or highway design or to the need to coordinate the system components.) Justice Gallagher goes on to state that "[w]hile the nonintentional violators do not merit the same condemnation as do the deliberate violators, since the danger caused by them often exceeds that caused by intentional violators, obviously some severe penalty for their violations is required."

Economos (1957), Director of the Traffic Court Program of the American Bar Association, estimates that a 5 to 10 percent maximum reduction in accidents would result "if the latest engineering techniques were applied to make each highway as safe as the safest highway." On the other hand, he suggests that "through educational means and adequate enforcement there appears to be an opportunity to secure a maximum reduction of eighty to ninety percent in traffic accidents." He concludes that "[w]hile there is need for highway and vehicle improvements, there are greater opportunities for numerically greater reductions through improvement of the driver and the pedestrian." Economos presents this conclusion based on an unstated rationale and recommends that the courts be "used as a classroom" and that all operators charged with moving violations be required to appear before a judge, rather than having an opportunity to plead guilty to a clerk of the court and pay a fine, either in person or by mail.

In contrast, Judge Lyle H. Truax (1970) states that "[w]hen a driver charged with failing to stop at a stop sign stands before me, I like to think that by appearing in my court his driving will improve. But does it? Other than satisfying my own ego, there is no proof that his appearance benefits anyone. There is no evidence that the violator who comes to court is going to be a better driver than the one who forfeits bail."

Despite the absence of evidence supporting the usefulness of a required appearance in court of all operators charged with a moving violation, the National Highway Safety Bureau (1968) incorporated this recommendation, modified to include only "moving hazardous violations," as part of its program standard for traffic courts. A study by Blumenthal and Ross (1971) of the "Efficacy of Certain Types of Penal Actions for Two Classes of Traffic Violators" and supported by the National Highway Safety Bureau* is presently underway. The study compares the effect on driver records of court appearance as compared with selected alternative methods of handling such violators. The results are due in 1971.

If the present NHTSA standard remains in effect, the presently overtaxed courts will either have to increase their caseload using existing facilities, thus reducing the time and consideration allowed each individual case, or the courts will have to expand their facilities at considerable cost—estimated by the NHSB (1968) at almost $1 billion—over the next ten years.

PENALIZATION AND/OR CORRECTION

The outcome of the adjudicatory process for convicted violators may be a suspended sentence, jail, fine, required attendance at a driver improvement school, license suspension or revocation, or any logical combination of these alternatives. If the penalization or correction occurs as a result of administrative action by a driver licensing agency, there may be a sequence of actions following the operators being brought to the agency's attention, such as a warning letter, interview, and assignment to driving school or clinic, reexamination, imposition of license restrictions, or license suspension or revocation.

The American Association of Motor Vehicle Administrators' "Driver License Administrators" Guide to Driver Improvement (1965) is intended to act as a guide for improvement programs. While the Guide states in its Introduction that a driver improvement program "works with Engineering in attempting to match the capabilities of drivers to the demands of highways, and in providing a concept of the average driver to whom road construction must be fitted," an examination of the Guide

* Now the National Highway Traffic Safety Administration.

fails to reveal any indication of such coordination. The section of the manual dealing with relations with other agencies refers to the courts, the attorney general's office, the departments of public health and instruction, and other states and provinces but not to highway or engineering departments. And while the Guide calls for research on its suggestions, there is no indication that available research was used in the formulation and selection of the recommended programs and techniques.

After reviewing the evidence concerning the lack of uniformity in the statutory, adjudicatory, and enforcement stages of the legal process, it would not require a soothsayer to predict a similar lack of uniformity in driver improvement procedures. However, the lack of uniformity can hardly be considered a fault in the absence of evidence supporting the effectiveness and superiority of a given pattern of correctional activities. The findings to date (A. D. Little, 1966; Owens, 1967; Kaestner, 1968; Kaestner and Syring, 1968; Marsh, 1969) are of the severely limited and decreasing effects of present programs. From a human factors point of view this is hardly surprising, since such programs have reflected a combination of legalistic, educational, and clinically or socially oriented psychological points of view. The behavior of a vehicle operator can be thought of as the interaction and resultant of social, personality, attitudinal, and skill or psychophysical components. Improvement programs, under the influence of personality and social psychologists, have tended to stress adjustment and attitudes to the neglect of skills. The AAMVA Guide places principal emphasis on the individual interview with suggested reexamination in special cases. However, it is unlikely that reexamination would include driving at night or on high-speed highways or evaluate the ability to cope with emergency conditions. The ineffectiveness of this approach becomes clear if we can imagine its application to the correction of pilots' or astronauts' deficiencies in the handling of their vehicles.

It is also possible that most operators are driving near their optimum and further training of almost any kind would have a minimum effect. Netherton (1954) observed that "Today, one may drive with almost the same degree of detachment from conscious attention to what he is doing as when he is walking along a street. Psychologically, therefore, driving practices are largely beyond the reach of statutory standards of conduct, which at best affect only the part of human behavior arising from deliberate and conscious response to the stimulus of environment and events." Stonex (1965) suggests that "With our present system of complete definition of traffic practice, we still have people who are slightly unreliable. I do not believe that we can legislate human reliability . . .

I do not think we can reduce our rates significantly by additional regulations or improved enforcement or court procedures."

CONCLUSION

The evaluation of traffic law from a human factors point of view has revealed a major shift in the law's orientation. The 1962 revision of the UVC, representative of a traditional approach to system regulation, placed the major responsibility on the driver for avoiding crashes. There is little recognition in the Code of the need to provide the operator with a vehicle and an environment that fit or match his capabilities. There are provisions covering registration, responsibility, and insurance but none requiring rational vehicle design. There is no attempt to regulate highway design, no recognition of the inherent deficiencies of the total system.

In contrast, the National Traffic and Motor Vehicle and Highway Safety Acts of 1966 explicitly recognize the role of vehicle and highway design. There is a reference to "the risk of accidents, occurring as a result of the design, construction, or performance of motor vehicles . . . ." The legislation requires standards for "highway design and maintenance . . . traffic control, . . . surveillance of traffic for detection and correction of high or potentially high accident locations . . . ." After decades of moralistic safety propaganda emphasizing the role of the driver, the shift to a broader view of the problem is all the more significant as the managements of subsystems and support systems are brought under the law's regulation.

When the other human factors criteria discussed in the chapter—comprehensiveness, uniformity and provision for feedback—are applied, the Code comes off poorly. In its piecemeal view of motor vehicle transportation and safety, significant elements, such as education, research, and emergency medical care, are absent. Those components that are present, such as the vehicle and dealers, are treated largely as *economic* units, rather than as functional components of a system. Perhaps the Code's greatest omission is its failure to manage the managers of the subsystems and support systems. Its view of the system's regulation as principally a state rather than a national responsibility ignores the actual nature of the system.

Despite the Code's emphasis on uniformity, its general approach—leaving details to administrative agencies—and the use of vague terminology could only lead to variability. The Code's conception of feedback is based on informal experience rather than on empirical research, thus failing to provide an objective and systematic means of self-correction.

The criteria applied to the federal legislation provide mixed results. Uniformity suffers because of broad terminology, particularly in the standards. The comprehensiveness of the legislation far exceeds that of the Code. There is recognition of the status of "new law as hypothesis" in the provision for temporary standards and the deviation by individual states for evaluation purposes. The emphasis on research throughout the acts provides hope for a factual basis for ongoing change.

When the application of law to the modification of operator behavior through enforcement, adjudication, and penalization and/or rehabilitation is analyzed, the results are not encouraging. The police, the courts, and the correction agencies reflect and magnify the limitations of the Code in their moralistic-legalistic view of the problem. There is little evidence of uniformity or appreciation of the need for feedback. Given the degree of discretion available to these institutions, a generation could pass before discernible changes occur, unless their discretion is drastically reduced.

There appears to be little basis for major changes in the short run through legislation. Highway safety is linked to other social concerns, such as the use of alcohol and drugs, poverty, the allocation of limited resources to the military, and the organization of medical services. In the past twenty years, the patterns of community growth have made many more people dependent on the automobile. Recreation often involves the use of a motor vehicle. There are innumerable institutions and industries that have a vested interest in maintaining the transportation status quo. It appears that there is an implicit willingness to accept traffic fatalities and injuries as the inevitable cost of the American romance with the automobile.

It is more likely that a reduction of the social cost of the system will come about following crises and through the development of more convenient and economical modes of travel. If multiple-vehicle accidents begin to exact a catastrophic and generally visible social cost; if measures to reduce the motor vehicles' emissions are ineffective; if delays and congestion lead to extended and chronic system breakdowns; then the public and government will become more receptive to major modifications and to the possibilities of alternative modes of transportation.

A human factors specialist must first of all be a realist about the capabilities of the human being. The field has traditionally limited this realism to the assessment of physical, psychophysical, and cognitive capabilities. Perhaps it is time to consider also the capability of a society to make and implement rational decisions in the management of its communities, rather than merely attempting to make "microadjustments on faulty macrosystems."

REFERENCES*

Black's Law Dictionary, Rev. 4th ed., West Publishing Company, St. Paul, Minn., 1968.

Blumenthal, Murray, Knowledge for Action, *Traffic Safety: Strategies for Research and Action,* H. J. Miser, ed., Travelers Research Center, Inc., 1967, 54–63.

Blumenthal, Murray, Dimensions of the Traffic Safety Problem, *Traffic Safety Research Review,* **12** (1968), 7–12.

Blumenthal, Murray, Alternative Approaches to the Drinking-Driving Problem, presented at the Third Triennial Congress on Medical and Related Aspects of Motor Vehicle Accidents, New York, May 30, 1969.

Blumenthal, Murray and Ross, H. L., Determination of Efficacy of Certain Types of Penal Actions for Two Classes of Traffic Violators, Contract No. FH-11-6923, U.S. Department of Transportation, NHSB, The Center for the Environment and Man and the University of Denver, College of Law, Denver, Colo., (in process 1968–1971).

Borkenstein, R. F. and Joscelyn, K. B., Police Traffic Services: "A State of the Art Report," Interim Report No. 2, Vol. 1, Department of Transportation, NHSB Contract No. FH-11-6604, Subcontract with the Travelers Research Center, Inc., Hartford, Conn., 1968.

Campbell, D. T. and Ross, H. L., The Connecticut Crackdown on Speeding, *Law and Society Review,* 3 (1968), 33–53.

Chapanis, Alphonse, Human Factors in Systems Engineering, in *Systems Psychology,* K. B. De Greene, ed., McGraw-Hill, New York, 1970.

Cheshire, Harry V., Discussant, A Colloquy on Motor Vehicle and Traffic Law, Highway Research Board, Special Report 86, NAS, NRC, Pub. 1315, 1965, 78–83.

Coppin, R. S. and Van Oldenbeek, G., Driving Under Suspension and Revocation, State of California, Department of Motor Vehicles, Division of Administration, January 1965.

Cramton, Roger C., Driver Behavior and Legal Sanctions: A Study of Deterrence in Driver Behavior, *Cause and Effect, Proceedings of the Second Annual Traffic Safety Research Symposium of the Automobile Insurance Industry,* James O'Day, ed., Insurance Institute for Highway Safety, Washington, D.C., 1968, 181–216.

Davis, J. Allen, Problems in Drafting Traffic Laws, *Traffic Review,* Winter, 1950.

Driver License Administrator's Guide to Driver Improvement, American Association of Motor Vehicle Administrators, Washington, D.C., 1965.

Dunlap and Associates, Inc., Pedestrian Regulation Enforcement and the Incidence of Pedestrian Accidents, Department of Transportation, NHSB Contract No. FH-11-6968, 1969.

* For other views of the problem, *Law and Contemporary Problems* 33 (Summer 1968), Duke University School of Law, is recommended.

Economos, James P., The Traffic Problem, Traffic Laws, and Traffic Courts; Standing Committee on Traffic Court Program of the American Bar Association, Chicago, Ill., 1957.

Economos, James P., The Legal Environment and Traffic Safety, in *Traffic Safety, A National Problem,* The Eno Foundation for Highway Traffic Control, Saugatuck, Conn., 1967, 15–24.

Economos, James P., The Judicial System, in R. F. Borkenstein, and K. B. Joscelyn, Police Traffic Services: "A State of the Art Report," Interim Report No. 2, Volume 1, Department of Transportation, NHSB Contract No. FH-11-6604, Subcontract with the Travelers Research Center, Inc., Hartford, Conn., 1968.

Estimate of the Cost of Carrying Out the Provisions of the Highway Safety Act of 1966, A Report to the Congress from the Secretary of Transportation, U.S. Department of Transportation, Washington, D.C., October 1968.

The Federal Role in Highway Safety, Secretary of Commerce, U.S. Government Printing Office, Washington, D.C., 1959.

Fennessy, E. F. and Joksch, H. C., Police Traffic Services and Road Safety: An Evaluation of the Literature, U.S. Department of Transportation, NHSB Contract FH-11-6604, Travelers Research Center, Inc., Hartford, Conn., 1967.

Fisher, Edward C., *Vehicle Traffic Law,* The Traffic Institute, Northwestern University, Evanston, Ill., 1961.

Freed, Arthur, Discussant, *A Colloquy on Motor Vehicle and Traffic Law,* Highway Research Board, Special Report 86, NAS, NRC, Pub. 1315, 1965, 85–86.

Gallagher, Thomas, Law, Traffic Regulation and the Administration of Justice, in *A Colloquy on Motor Vehicle and Traffic Law,* Highway Research Board, Special Report 86, NAS, NRC, Pub. 1315, 1965, 93–99.

Gardiner, John A., *Traffic and Police—Variations in Law-Enforcement Policy,* Harvard University Press, Cambridge, Mass., 1969.

H.R. Report No. 1700, 89 Cong., 2d Sess. 8 (1966) (Highway Safety Act of 1966).

Harris, F., The Long Eye of the Law, *Sports Car Graphic,* May 1970, 54.

Highway Safety Act of 1966, Public Law 89-564; 80 Stat. 731.

Highway Safety Program Standard for Codes and Laws, Standard 6, Highway Safety Program Standards, U.S. Department of Transportation, Federal Highway Administration, NHSB, February 1969.

Highway Safety Program Standard for Traffic Courts, Standard 7, Highway Safety Program Standards, U.S. Department of Transportation, Federal Highway Administration, NHSB, February 1969.

Kaestner, Noel, Research in Driver Improvement—The State of the Art, *Traffic Quarterly,* October 1968, 497–520.

Kaestner, Noel and Syring, E. M., Follow-Up of Brief Driver Improvement Interviews in Oregon, *Traffic Safety Research Review,* December 1968, 111–117.

Kelso, Charles D., *A Programmed Introduction to the Study of Law,* Bobbs-Merrill, New York, 1965.

Lewis v. Amorous, 3 Ga. App. 50, 59 S.E. 338, 340 (1907).

A. D. Little, Inc., *The State of the Art of Traffic Safety,* Cambridge, Mass., 1966.

Marsh, William C., Modifying Negligent Driving Behavior: A Preliminary Evaluation of Selected Driver Improvement Techniques, State of California Transportation Agency, Department of Motor Vehicles, August 1969.

Miller, J. N., Traffic Turbulence, *Traffic Safety,* **66** (1966), 18–20, 34–35.

Myrick, Richard and Schlesinger, L. E., Driver Improvement or System Improvement?, *Traffic Quarterly,* **18**, 1 (1964), 92–104.

National Traffic and Motor Vehicle Safety Act of 1966, Public Law 89-563; 80 STAT. 718.

Netherton, Ross D., Highway Safety Under Differing Types of Liability Legislation, *Ohio State Law Review,* **15** (1954), 110–133.

New Yorker (November 30, 1968), Talk of the Town, New York.

Owens, Claude M., Report on a Three Year Controlled Study of the Effectiveness of the Anaheim-Fullerton Municipal Court Drivers Improvement School, *The Municipal Court Review,* **7** (1967), 7–14.

Periodic Motor Vehicle Inspection Standard, Highway Safety Program Standard 1, Highway Safety Program Standards, U.S. Department of Transportation, Federal Highway Administration, NHSB, February 1969.

Reese, J., The Federal Highway Safety Act of 1966: NHSB Driver Licensing Standard—Power Not Used, (1970), 408–450.

Ross, H. L., Campbell, D. T., and Glass, G. V., Determining the Social Effects of a Legal Reform, *American Behavioral Scientist,* **13**, 4 (1970), 493–509.

Stonex, K. A., Law, Traffic and Engineering Technology, in *A Colloquy on Motor Vehicle and Traffic Law,* Highway Research Board, Special Report 86, NAS, NRC, Pub. 1315 (1965), 71–78.

Truax, Lyle H., Let's Abolish Traffic Courts, *Court,* **9** (1970), 6–7.

Uniform Vehicle Code, National Committee on Uniform Traffic Laws and Ordinances, Washington, D.C., revised 1962.

Webster's Seventh New Collegiate Dictionary, G & C Merriam Co., Springfield, Ill., 1965.

Wiener, Earl L., The Elderly Pedestrian: Response to an Enforcement Campaign, *Traffic Safety Research Review,* December 1968, 100–110.

Zylman, Richard and Bacon, S. D., Police Records and Accidents Involving Alcohol, *Quarterly Journal of Studies on Alcohol,* Supplement No. 4 (May 1968), 178–211.

XVII
CONCLUDING COMMENTS

T. W. Forbes

It is almost impossible to summarize the wide range of information in the various technical areas covered in the preceding chapters. These concluding comments, therefore, simply note a significant trend in human factors research development in the highway traffic and safety areas discussed in this book.

Early studies in the 1929 to 1931 period measured driver abilities by means of psychological driving tests devised and applied, for the most part, by individual investigators. The first objective was to look for those few drivers whose characteristics might cause most of the accidents. It was hoped that retraining them might solve the traffic safety problem. This proved to be a false hope. Analyses of accident data for two 3-year periods showed that 96 percent of the accidents occurring in the second period were experienced by normal drivers, that is, nonrepeaters who had had zero or one accident only. Similar findings have been reported from more recent studies.

Although there is a small group of drivers with consistently poor records who must be given special treatment, they represent only a small part of the problem. Designing the highway transportation system task requirements to fit the abilities and limitations of most drivers—the human factors approach—therefore becomes highly important. This is a positive rather than a negative approach.

The human factors method was first applied to such problems as the designing of more visible, legible, and effective highway signs at Iowa State University and the Yale Traffic Bureau between 1932 and 1939. This was the beginning of a system designed to fit human abilities, which was later developed into the human factors or engineering psychology approach. This slightly preceded the great development of human factors research in aviation areas during World War II.

These human factors methods, begun with the measurement of simple driving behavior, later developed into studies of more complex judgments and responses on the highway and used part task simulation. More recently there has been development of higher-fidelity simulation, larger-scale research on driver characteristics, sophisticated instrumentation for studying drivers in traffic, and studies of driving in relation to the highway transportation system.

In general, the chapter describing each area of traffic safety research starts with some of the earlier, simpler measurements of drivers' abilities and moves toward the more complex systems approach that uses human factors methods. This is true for the studies of driver characteristics, of drivers on the highway in traffic, of sign legibility and visibility, and of information transmission to the driver directly from the road itself and from special markings, signs, and warnings on high-speed freeways. Studies of human factors in vehicle design included consideration of complex interrelationships of visibility control characteristics and vehicle dynamics, factors that may lead to driver-operating errors.

In military driving, development of test batteries for selecting military drivers was an important contribution, but the questionable value of selection tests for civilian driver licensing was pointed out together with the need for a human factors systems research approach to highway safety.

The need for better driver education and some of the shortcomings of past efforts were noted. To achieve improvement, a human factors task analysis of automobile driving, as required by the highway transportation system, was outlined.

The pedestrian's needs were described, and studies of his individual characteristics were reported. But longer-range solutions of pedestrian traffic problems were shown to require new design of streets, highways, buildings, and pedestrian walks, thus involving changes in design of the system to fit needs and characteristics of people, in this case their needs as foot travelers.

Effects of fatigue on driver behavior were analyzed, but later studies of trip planning, facilities for rest stops, and the like were included. Similarly, effects on individual driver behavior of both medicinal and other drug use were surveyed. However, it was pointed out that drug effects on driver behavior are related to traffic system requirements as well as habits, attitudes, and other factors. Again, psychosocial reactions of people and effects of their driving performance were viewed both for individuals and in terms of their relation to the larger traffic and social system.

The important treatment of problem drivers by driver improvement procedures of motor vehicle departments has dealt largely with motivation and reeducation of the driver. A more effective, much needed approach was suggested involving examination of the characteristics of the highway traffic and enforcement systems. Such examination should consider, it was suggested, possible redesign of features that impose requirements on the driver that are excessive or that he considers unfair or unnecessary.

Discussion of legal and enforcement areas noted that the older basis was the motor vehicle code. This code was designed to achieve desirable uniformity and standardization but was largely the result of past experience without provision for change based on human factors and other considerations. A newer and more desirable approach included in the 1966 Congressional Highway Safety Acts provides for the development of new standards followed by evaluation and, where needed, modification. The need for human factors information and research on sytems requirements for drivers was stressed in this procedure.

In summary, human behavior characteristics and limitations must be considered in designing highway traffic system requirements. Man, whether driver, pedestrian, traffic engineer, or police officer, can respond amazingly well, but when the task overloads his abilities to sense and process the information, make decisions, and respond appropriately, his responses become less accurate and less well adapted to the situation.

The largest part of the traffic accident problem has been shown to involve lapses by normal drivers rather than errors by just a few problem cases. For this reason, designing the system to fit driver abilities and limitations based on human factors research provides a most important positive and hopeful approach.

INDEX